NATURAL SYSTEMS

and human responses

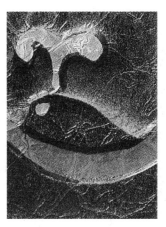

Robert Prosser

Nelson

To Wendy, Simon and Samantha

Thomas Nelson and Sons Ltd
Nelson House Mayfield Road
Walton-on-Thames Surrey
KT12 5PL UK

Thomas Nelson Australia
102 Dodds Street
South Melbourne
Victoria 3205 Australia

Nelson Canada
1120 Birchmount Road
Scarborough Ontario
M1K 5G4 Canada

First published by Thomas Nelson and Sons Ltd 1992

I(T)P Thomas Nelson is an International
Thomson Publishing Company
I(T)P is used under licence

ISBN 0-17-444069-3
NPN 9 8 7 6 5 4

Printed in China

CONTENTS

SECTION FOUR: THE BIOSPHERE AT WORK 190–246

Making good use of this book

This book is a collection of case studies stretching across the field of 'physical geography' or 'natural environments'. Further, as there is no natural environment on planet earth which is not affected in some way by human activities, most of the examples include this 'human' dimension, and ask you to think critically about the relationships. The aim of the materials is to add breadth and depth to your understanding of topics on coasts, rivers, ecosystems, tropical weather, etc by applying the general principles and processes covered in classes or textbooks to specific examples.

Each case study is free-standing and so you can select the materials in any sequence to fit your syllabus. Most of the case studies are made up of four elements:

1 A background element sets the example within the broader context, e.g., if the case study is illustrating aspects of discharge along a specific river, then this background links it to the general topic of river flow. It sets the scene and jogs your memory.

2 The key understandings are those essential understandings which you should gain from working through the case study.

3 The case study element is the core of the book and makes up the bulk of the materials. A range of resources are presented to give opportunities for you to become practised in the use of varied data and written material. Many of the case studies are adapted from articles in geographical periodicals. Using them should improve your confidence to seek out and   use such academic sources for yourself.

4 The activity element is intended to first, allow you to check and review your understanding, second, to give you exam practice, and third, suggest ideas for coursework assignments and projects.

The use you make of the activities may depend upon the type of coursework and examination questions you are preparing for.

The best way, then, to use these case studies, is in conjunction with class notes, textbooks and other reference materials, to enrich and vary your learning.

(Please note: where case studies have been adapted from American publications, measurements such as feet, yards and miles have been retained.)

CHAPTER 1

Plate tectonics theory and the impacts of vulcanicity and earthquakes

Introduction

For hundreds of years, one of the great questions scientists have asked has been: 'What causes earthquakes and volcanic eruptions and why do they occur where they do?' Today, the scientists have their answer, through the general acceptance of plate tectonics theory, and most physical geography and geology textbooks devote a chapter to it.

The explanation is part of a broader understanding: that the earth's crust consists of a number of segmented plates which move slowly across the upper boundary of the aesthenosphere (plastic layer of the upper mantle). The colossal energy for this movement is provided by slow-moving convection currents in the earth's mantle. If we compare two world maps – one of the plates of the earth's crust, and the other of occurrences of earthquakes and volcanoes – the importance of plate margins becomes clear. At least 90 per cent of all significant earthquakes and eruptions occur along the junction zones between plates moving in different directions. The case studies in this chapter help you to extend your understanding of the processes, the impacts, the effects on people's lives and how people respond to these tectonic hazards.

◗ *You should check your understanding of these terms before working through the case studies:*

magma	**pyroclast**
tephra	**pluton**
shear	**slurry**
dacite	**andesite**
basalt	**subduction**
Benioff zone	

Key understandings

◆ The earth's structure and the way plate tectonics work

◆ the main types of plate margin (constructive, destructive, conservative)

◆ types of volcano, e.g. effusive; explosive

◆ seismology and *p* and *s* waves

◆ strain and stress release in rocks

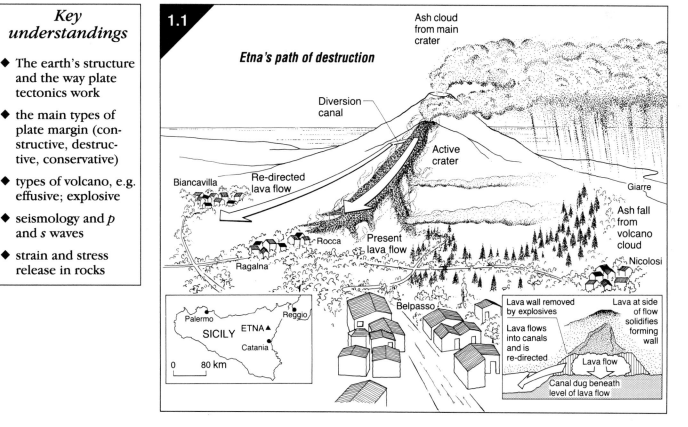

1.1

Etna's path of destruction

Ash cloud from main crater
Diversion canal
Active crater
Re-directed lava flow
Biancavilla
Rocca
Present lava flow
Ragalna
Belpasso
Giarre
Ash fall from volcano cloud
Nicolosi

SICILY ETNA ▲
Palermo
Reggio
Catania
0   80 km

Lava wall removed by explosives
Lava flows into canals and is re-directed
Lava at side of flow solidifies forming wall
Lava flow
Canal dug beneath level of lava flow

CASE STUDY 1.1 *Finding out about volcanoes*

Background

Television and the press feed us with rapid and vivid news of major eruptions, especially when there are hazards to human life and property (resource 1.1). Obtaining objective data and learning about the many less catastrophic events is not as easy. Usually we have to wait for magazines and textbooks – and these are selective in their materials. The standard source of information for geologists, geographers, etc., is the Bulletin of Volcanic Eruptions, published each December by the Volcanological Society of Japan. Even this has a two year time-lag, i.e. the record of world volcanic eruptions for 1982 was published in December 1984. The materials below are extracted from this excellent database. (Many university and polytechnic libraries or geology departments hold this publication.)

Activities

1 a Use resource 1.2 to plot the 1982 eruptions on a world outline map. (You may wish to use graded symbols to indicate the scale of the eruption. You could also devise ways of showing other characteristics, but beware – make your map large enough, so that it does not become overcrowded.)

b Add the crustal plate boundaries to your map.

2 Resource 1.3 shows the location of 1980 and 1981 eruptions. By comparison of the two maps, identify the two main regions of volcanic activity. Use references on plate tectonics to explain the location of these regions.

Key to resource 1.2

○ eruption in the central crater	▲ extrusion of a spine
∞ eruption in a parasitic crater	⇑ phreatic explosions, mud eruptions
⊶ eruption in a fissure	→ mud flows
= eruption in a regional fissure	⋔ subglacial erutions
↑ normal explosions	⌅ submarine eruptions
→ eruptions producing nuées ardentes*	⇌ islets formed by submarine eruptions
⇒ lava flows	∞ tidal waves (tsunamis)
▽ eruptions in crater lake	⑅ solfatara fields, vapours
▼ eruptions in lava lake	⊠ destruction of arable land
△ extrusion of a lava dome	† casualties

(* including ash flow, pumice flow etc.)

The intensity of eruption is classified into three categories: little (*l*), medium (*m*) and great (*g*) according to the volume of erupted material.

1.2 *World volcanic eruptions for 1982*

Name of Volcano	Lat	Long	Main Activity
Stromboli	39°N	15°E	○ ↑ (l)
Etna	38°N	15°E	○ ↑ (m)
Nyamulagira	1°S	29°E	⊶ ↑ ⇒ (g)
Nyiragonga	2°S	29°E	○ ⇒▼ (g)
Mount Cameroon	4°N	9°E	⊶ ↑ (m) ⇒ (g) ▼ →
White Island	38°S	177°E	○ ⇑ or ↑ (l) † ⑅
Ruapehu	39°S	176°E	○ ▽ ↑ (l)
Manam	4°S	145°E	○ ↑ (m)
Langila	6°S	148°E	○ ↑ (m) ⇒ (m), ⊶ ⇒ (l)
Bagana	6°S	155°E	○ △ ⇒ (m)
Kovachi	9°S	158°E	⌅
Gaua	14°S	168°E	○ ⇑ or ↑ (l)
Lopevi	17°S	168°E	○ ↑ (m)
Marapi	0°S	100°E	○ ↑ (l)
Galunggung	7°S	108°E	○ ↑ (g) → (m) ⇒⊠ †>20 killed, 3 missing (or 27 deaths)
Merapi	8°S	110°E	○ △ (m) → (m)
Semeru	8°S	113°E	○ ↑△ (l) → (l) →⊠
Raung	8°S	114°E	○ ↑ (m)
Ili Boleng	8°S	123°E	○ ⇑ or ↑ (l)
Soputan	1°N	125°E	○ ↑ (m)
Suwanose-Zima	30°N	130°E	○ ↑ (l, m)
Sakura-Zima	32°N	139°E	○ ↑ (l, m) ⊠ †
Asama	36°N	139°E	○ ↑ (m) → (l) ⊠
Kusatu-Sirane	37°N	139°E	○ ▽ ⇑ (l), ○ ⇑ (l),

Name of Volcano	Lat	Long	Main Activity
Iwo-Zima	25°N	141°E	○ ⇑ (l)
North Pagan	18°N	146°E	○ ↑ (l) ⑅
Usu	43°N	141°E	⑅ growth of new dome
Karymsky	50°N	159°E	○ ↑ △ (m)
Bezymianny	56°N	161°E	○ ↑ △ → (m) ⇒ (m)
Klyuchevskoy	57°N	161°E	○ ↑ (l)
Gareloi	52°N	179°W	○ ↑ (l)
Pavlof	55°N	162°W	○ ⑅ or ⇑ (l)
Mount St. Helens	46°N	122°W	○ ↑ (m) △ (m) → (m) ⇑ (l)
Kilavea	19°N	155°W	○ ⇒ (m) and magma intrusions
Colima	20°N	103°W	○ △ ⇒ (m) → (l)
Chichōn	17°N	93°W	○ ⇑ ↑ (g) → (g) →⊠ † 187 killed and dozens missing
Santa Maria	15°N	92°W	∞ ↑ △ ⇒ → (l−m)
Volcan de Pacaya	14°N	91°W	○ ↑ ⇒ (m)
Telica	13°N	87°W	○ ↑ (m)
Masaya	12°N	86°W	○ ▼ ⑅ ↑ (l−m)
Cencepcion	12°N	86°W	○ ⇑ (l)
Arenal	10°N	84°W	∞ ⇒ (m) ⑅
Guagua Pichincha	0°N	79°W	○ ⑅ ⇑ (l, m)
Sangai	2°N	78°W	○ ↑ ⇒ (l)
Volcan Wolf	0°N	91°W	⊶ ↑ ⇒ (l) ○ ↑ ⇒ (g)
Erebus	78°S	167°W	○ ▼ ↑ (l)
Macdonaldo Seamount	29°S	149°W	⌅ explosive signals
Teahitia	18°S	149°W	⌅ volcanic tremor

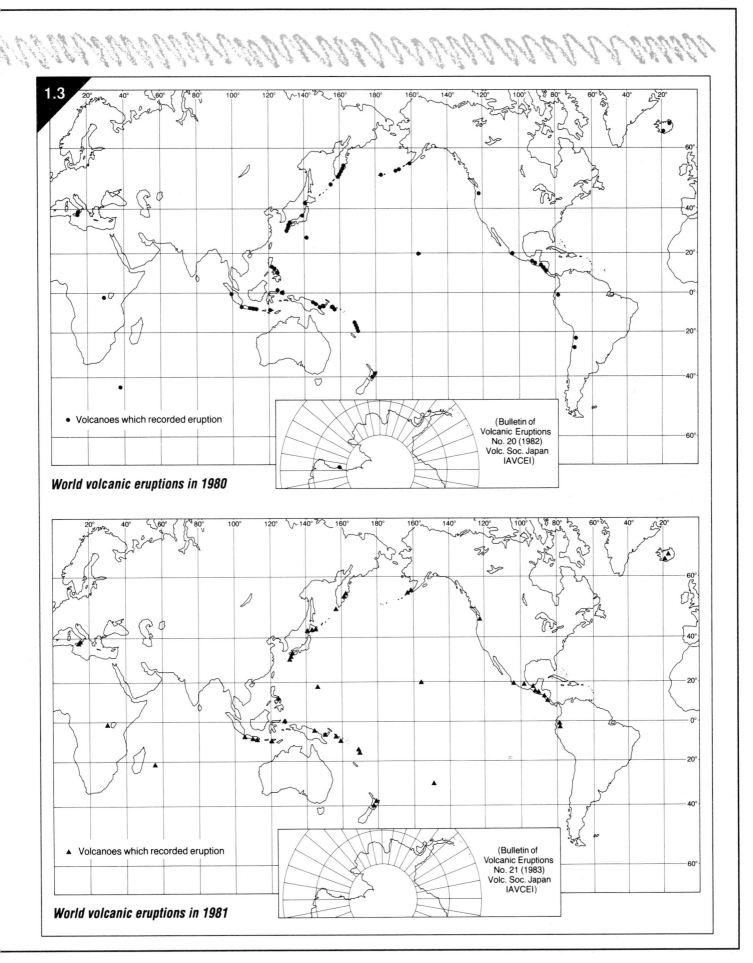

1.3

• Volcanoes which recorded eruption

(Bulletin of Volcanic Eruptions No. 20 (1982) Volc. Soc. Japan IAVCEI)

World volcanic eruptions in 1980

▲ Volcanoes which recorded eruption

(Bulletin of Volcanic Eruptions No. 21 (1983) Volc. Soc. Japan IAVCEI)

World volcanic eruptions in 1981

CASE STUDY 1.2   *Volcanic hazards of the USA*

Background

Resource 1.4 shows the North American and Pacific plates moving differentially, with the latter drifting more quickly. This causes the crustal stresses and **transform faults** of the San Andreas Fault system with which is associated a high risk earthquake zone (case study 1.6). The Pacific Plate is squeezing the remnants of the Juan de Fuca Plate beneath the North American Plate, creating a destructive margin and subduction or Benioff zone which energises active volcanicity (case study 1.3).

The map shows the main line of volcanoes and the hazard zones which surround them. Around these major vents is an inner zone in which clusters of minor vents occur and which suffers the most severe impacts of lava flows and ash falls.

Beyond this is a broad zone which is liable to ash falls at least 5 cm thick. Progressively thinner ash layers may spread across the whole area covered by the map, dependent upon the location and character of the eruption, plus wind direction and speed.

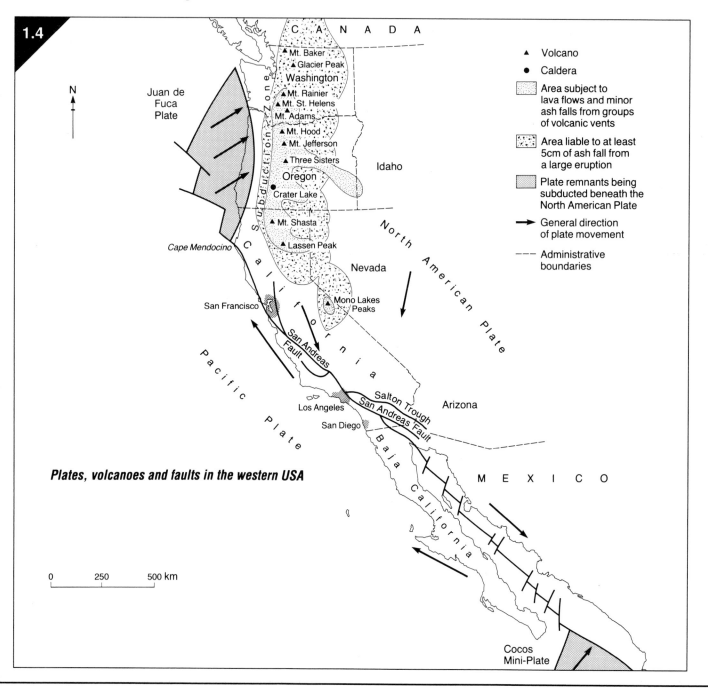

Plates, volcanoes and faults in the western USA

Volcanic hazard zones

The map shows zones that, over a long period of time, are relatively likely to be affected in one or more places by various kinds of hazardous volcanic event. These hazards include lava flows, mudflows, hot rock avalanches, ashfalls and floods.

Severe volcanic hazards are limited to areas in the western United States, principally in the Cascade Mountain Range in California, Oregon and Washington; in Idaho's Snake River Plain; and in parts of Arizona, New Mexico and Utah.

The immediate risk from volcanic hazards is low because eruptions are so infrequent. Severely destructive effects of eruptions, other than extremely rare ones of catastrophic scale, would probably be limited to areas within a few tens of kilometres down-valley or downwind from a volcano. Thus, the area seriously endangered by any one eruption would be only a very small part of the western United States.

Before Mount St. Helens in May 1980, the only explosive volcanic eruption in the coterminous states (i.e. the states excluding Hawaii and Alaska) since the area was settled by Europeans, was 3400 m (10 457 ft) high Mount Lassen in northern California during a series of eruptions in 1914–15. This eruption was moderate compared to major eruptions at other volcanoes in the world during recorded history. No one was killed in the Mount Lassen eruption, and damage was minor.

Eruptions of moderate volume may occur somewhere in the Cascade Range as often as once every 1000 to 2000 years, but very large eruptions may occur no more than once every 10 000 years. A few large cataclysmic eruptions have occurred during the last two million years in and near Yellowstone National Park, at Long Valley, California, and in the Jemez Mountains of New Mexico. These eruptions affected very large regions and deposited ash over much of the western United States. The sites of these eruptions are shown on the map, but are so infrequent that it is not possible to judge whether one might occur during the time for which planning is feasible.

Risk from volcanic hazards decreases as distance from an erupting volcano increases. Lava flows are nearly uniformly destructive to their outer limits. Some other volcanic hazards, especially ashfalls, become less destructive and less frequent with increasing distance. The boundary of such a hazard is indefinite and often dependent on land use. For example, an ashfall 1 cm or so thick might cause little damage to structures, yet destroy crops.

(Source: *Earthquake Information Bulletin,* 12(4), July–August 1980, pp. 162–163.)

Activities

1 Use tracing paper and colours to redraw the map in resource 1.4. Add the following details from resource 1.3 and other sources:

- names of states
- names of main volcanoes
- San Andreas fault system
- names and boundaries of plates, with arrows showing movement
- destructive and conservative margins
- subduction (Benioff) zone

2 Explain the size and shape of the ash fallout in resource 1.4.

3 Explain the location of the main volcanic zones.

4 How does your map illustrate that crustal stresses are not restricted to plate margins?

Background

The great Mount St. Helens volcanic eruption of 18 May 1980 is the world's most closely observed and documented eruption. 'So', you might ask, 'why include it?' Well, precisely because it exhibits all the features of a classic episode we can probe the workings of a volcano, and follow the environmental and human responses in detail. The material here uses less accessible sources and is intended to be used alongside other references to explore several key understandings.

Key understandings

◆ A major eruptive event is always part of a longer episode in the life of a volcano.

◆ Active volcanic areas remain hazard zones because of the sheer power of tectonic forces and because of our continuing inability to predict them accu-

rately. As an American geologist said recently: 'There's no such thing as a dead volcano – they're just asleep!'

◆ Environmental and human responses to hazard and impact are surprisingly rapid.

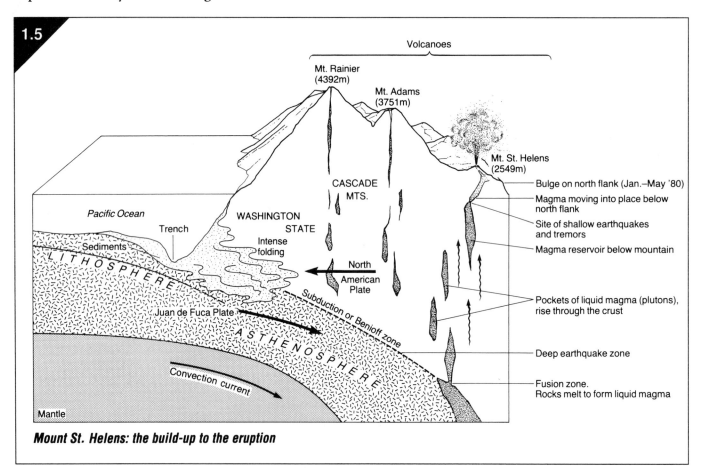

1.5

Mount St. Helens: the build-up to the eruption

Activities

Follow carefully the 'Countdown of an eruption' (resource 1.6) and resources 1.5 and 1.7, then with a partner answer the following questions.

1 What signals did the mountain give before the major eruption?

2 Why were scientists not surprised when the mountain erupted?

3 List the sequence of events triggered by the earthquake on 18 May.

4 Explain the eruption in terms of plate tectonics.

5 How does this example illustrate that an 'eruption' is in fact an episode in three stages, which may last for several years?

Countdown of an eruption

From the records of the USGS (US Geological Survey) and the USFS (US Forest Service)

1969 A geologist of the USGS targets Mount St Helens as 'a young, active and dangerous volcano'.

1972 Seismometers (to measure wave patterns) and a geodimeter network (to measure ground shape) are installed by the USGS to monitor the mountain.

1978 USGS bulletin: 'The volcano's behavior pattern   suggests that the current quiet interval will not last as long as a thousand years; instead, an eruption is more likely to occur within the next hundred years, and perhaps even before the end of this century.'
(Note: The last active episode had lasted from 1800 to 1857.)

1979 USGS scientists suggest: 'It is tempting to predict that Mount St Helens will now follow its normal progression of viscous dacite domes leading to explosive eruptions, releasing tephra and andesite lava flows, followed by more viscous domes in the crater and on the flanks.' They add, prophetically, that the mountain is capable of 'more complex behaviour'.

1980 20 March, 1547 hrs: Earthquake measured at 4.0 on the Richter scale. This ends a dormant period of 123 years for the volcano.

25 March: 47 earthquakes of 3.0+ on the Richter scale. Their centres lie about 2 km below the north flank of the mountain. Such frequent tremors are known as an earthquake swarm. Geologists begin to study the volcano more closely.

26 March: 'Hazard alerts' go out to the local population.

27 March, 1236 hrs: First emissions of steam and a new 70 m crater appear in the summit snows.

28 March: The steam and ash plume is 3 km high. Water level in Swift Reservoir, south of the mountain, is lowered by 8 m. This is a precaution against floodwaters from snowmelt if an eruption occurs.

29 March: A second crater appears and from then the summit gradually collapses.

30 March: Many small eruptions of steam and ash.

3 April: The first harmonic tremors are recorded. (Harmonic tremors are continuous vibrations caused by the movement of magma beneath the volcano.) A dome begins to grow on the north flank of the mountain, swelling by more than a metre a day.

12 April: A bulge in the north flank of the mountain, first seen on 1 April, reaches 2 km in diameter, and protrudes 100 m. It lies directly over the earthquake swarm centre and the source of the harmonic tremors.

29 April: The new summit craters have joined up to become one big crater, 500 m across and 200 m deep.

30 April: A 30 km radius 'red zone' (or danger zone) is put round the mountain to keep out the thousands of sightseers.

7 May: After two weeks with little surface activity, the steam and ash eruptions begin again.

9 May: A USGS geologist assures the residents of the small town of Toutle, 25 km from the volcano; 'Instead of a huge slide where the whole north side of the mountain would come down at once ... a series of smaller landslides is more probable.'

10 May: Several earthquakes of 4.0+ Richter, and the north flank bulge is growing by 1.5 m a day.

15–17 May: A series of earthquakes, and the bulge continues to grow.

The eruption 18 May 0832 hrs: On 18 May, following an earthquake of magnitude 5.0 on the Richter scale, massive failure of this north flank produces one of the largest landslides in recorded history. This avalanche, containing water and ice, as well as debris up to 200 m thick, crashes down the valley of the north fork of the Toutle River for 18 km. The sudden exposure of the volcano's vent produces a simultaneous blast of high temperature steam, gases, pumice and ash directly upwards and outwards in a northerly direction, moving at speeds approaching 300 km/hr. It devastates more than 360 km², killing all vegetation and other life forms in its path.

The heat melts the snow and ice cap of the cone and in the few hours following the initial avalanche and blast, huge mudflows roar down all major river valleys radiating from the mountain. In places 1 km wide and 50 m deep, these flows, moving at perhaps 60 km an hour, first destroy everything in their path before clogging the valleys with a grey amalgam of mud, rock debris and shattered timber up to 50 km from Mount St Helens. In the upper valley of the River Toutle the deposits are 200 m thick.
Meanwhile, a spectacular ash cloud surges to a height of 20 000 m and as it drifts, continues to give heavy ash fallout over extensive areas of the northwestern USA.

25 May: Second substantial ash eruption with pyroclastic flows.

12 June: Third substantial ash eruption, with pyroclastic flows. Lava dome grows in the crater until 19 June.

22 July: Lava dome in the crater destroyed by ash eruption, followed by pyroclastic flows.

7 August: Fifth substantial series of ash eruptions followed by pyroclastic flows. By 10 August, a new lava dome has grown in the crater.

16 October: Lava dome destroyed by an ash eruption series, with pyroclastic flows. By 19 October a new lava dome has grown.

November: USGS scientists conclude: 'The catastrophic slope failure of 18 May, unprecedented in Mount St Helens' history, has removed a 1 km thick mass of pre-existing rock from the top of the magma column. This constitutes a significant change in a system that had probably existed for at least the past 500 years.'

1980/81 27 December 1980–30 October 1981: Spasmodic minor outbursts of ash help to build up the dome in the crater.

1982 19 March–12 April: Dome-growth eruptive phase with minor explosive events and small mudflows, adding two new lobes to the existing dome in the crater.

14–20 May: Minor ash eruptions add lobes to the NW side of the composite dome.

17–23 August: Small lava eruption adds new lobe to SW of the dome.

1983 June: Geologists say the mountain 'is expected to remain relatively quiet, with occasional eruptions of ash and steam and continued lava dome-building activity in its crater'.

Nature uncorked a very powerful bottle

'Mount St Helens was like a champagne bottle.'

University of Oregon geology professor Dr Brian Baker made that analogy in describing the sequence of events that led to the cataclysmic eruption.

The force of the eruption has been estimated to be the equal of the largest hydrogen bomb ever exploded, or 2500 times more powerful than the bomb that destroyed Hiroshima.

In essence, Mount St Helens was like a large bottle of carbonated soda pop or champagne with its cap still on. The earthquakes that shook the mountain were similar to a person shaking the capped bottle. When the cap came off, the 'beverage' – ash, smoke, rocks and the like – spewed out.

Baker explained that the magma which scientists now know was welling up inside the mountain, forming a giant blister on the north side, was dacite, a silica-rich magma common in the Cascades and quite unlike the fast-flowing magmas found in Hawaii.

Baker said that the chemical composition of dacite allows it to hold a great quantity of water vapor, carbon dioxide and sulphur in gaseous suspension.

The heated water and gas form a highly pressurized material that was unable to expand due to the weight of the 'cork' – in this case the blister on Mount St Helens – sitting atop it.

'When the pressure is released on the liquid (the dacite magma) the result is very similar to what happens when you uncork a champagne bottle,' Baker said. 'You can't see the gas before you uncork it – and then it comes out instantaneously.'

Baker said it is plausible that the weight of the blister had been just enough to hold the dacite in place until the earthquake, which scientists say preceded the eruption by a few minutes.

According to Baker, that quake could have upset the

Mount St. Helens eruption

equilibrium in the mountain. Photo sequences of the eruption show geysers of ash and rock blasting out of the upper and lower fringes of the blister as if the cap had moved and the first spurts of explosive dacite were bursting up around it.

While Baker said that it would have been virtually impossible to estimate the force with which Mount St Helens blew, explosive activity in the Cascades – even lateral blasts of the type that leveled 156 square miles of forest – are relatively common.

If Mount St Helens stays

true to form, the next step will be the rebuilding of the cone.

Baker said this was likely to be a slow process as the remaining dacite creeps to the surface.

This material, what Baker referred to as the 'flat champagne' leftover from the big pop, presents very little danger.

'Now that things are uncorked,' he said, 'things should be much quieter for a while.'

(Source: Douglas Gantenbein, *The Columbian*, 25 May, 1980)

CASE STUDY 1.4 *The response – managing the mountain*

Background

The management problems of the area centre around two factors: the scale of the impact and the number of interests involved. Mount St Helens itself lies within the Gifford Pinchot National Forest, but the impact area extends well beyond the US Forest Service boundary. The Forest Service, an agency of the US federal government, is the majority landholder, but considerable areas are owned or leased by the State of Washington, by large lumber companies, e.g. the Weyerhaeuser Corporation, by power generation companies, e.g. Pacific Power and Light Company, and by a variety of smaller companies and private individuals, e.g. farmers, resort developers, families etc. Thus although 'remote' in one sense, the environmental resources are comprehensively allocated for industry, power generation, agriculture, recreation, conservation and domestic living. The events of 1980 not only disrupted the natural environmental system but also dislocated a well-established human activity system.

Key understandings

◆ When disasters occur in populated regions, a wide variety of groups will be affected, all with distinct interests, values and priorities.

◆ If response to hazards and disasters is to be quick and effective, there must exist the right kinds of group, or body, capable of making decisions.

◆ Decisions about environmental management must be based on clearly defined criteria which allow priorities to be identified.

The timescale of the response

In June 1980 the Forest Service set up a planning team which, by February 1981, had published a draft Environmental Impact Statement (EIS) for public discussion and comment. In October 1981 a final EIS and Management Plan were published, setting out eight alternative strategies for a planning area of 100 000 hectares. The alternatives ranged across the spectrum from conservation-dominant to exploitation-dominant, and argued a case for a 'preferred alternative'. Meanwhile, the State of Washington had set up its own 'Mount St Helens Long Range Planning Council', whose purpose was to 'consider a wide range of rehabilitation, access, safety, planning, tourism, and other needs'. This council submitted its own proposals to the State Governor in April 1981.

During this time, the Forest Service was producing a 'Forest Plan', in collaboration with the lumber companies, notably Weyerhaeuser, and the State Department of Natural Resources. This plan was complete by the end of 1982. The various plans were co-ordinated and an overall management strategy came into operation in the summer of 1983. The important points to note are; first, the complexity of the problem; second, the speed of the response; and third, the comprehensiveness of the response.

Key issues and how to resolve them

For all the agencies and interested parties, there were two central questions.

1 What proportion of the impact zone should be left in its natural state and how much should be available for rehabilitation, timber salvage, and other resource uses that would alter the natural character of the area?

2 Who should pay for losses and rehabilitation/restoration programmes?

Ten key issues were identified (resource 1.8) which were to be taken into account in all alternative proposals. The next problem was how to measure or assess each alternative. This was solved by the identification of 12 evaluation criteria (resource 1.8).

It is hardly surprising that the management plan finally agreed attempts to satisfy, in part at least, the demands of all interest groups. It is founded on the twin concepts of **multiple use** and **sustained yield**, and adopts the zoning principle whereby individual criteria are given priority in specific areas. Two examples illustrate this approach to resource management – geologic features and lumber industry demands.

Geological features

For scientists, the eruptive area is a rich and rare 'laboratory' in which to study earth processes, while many thousands of visitors flock in to view the awesome beauty and devastation. Geologists surveyed the impact area and listed 39 geologic features. They then ranked them in order of their 'uniqueness', i.e. how rare and special they are. Eight features have been awarded the highest grade, and so given priority in terms of protection, research and visitor access/interpretation (resources 1.9 and 1.10). This protection priority is ensured by their inclusion in the 34 400 hectare 'Mount. St. Helens National Volcanic Monument', designated in August 1982.

Activities

Group discussion

How does the information illustrate the key understandings set out at the beginning of the case study?

1.8 Key issues

1 How should the lands and resources of the area be managed to protect the unique geologic features?
2 Should unique geologic features on state and private lands be included in the development of the management plan?
3 What action is appropriate to aid the rehabilitation of watersheds and reduce downstream flooding?
4 What level of timber management and timber salvage is appropriate?
5 What public interpretive, educational and recreational facilities should be provided?
6 How should fish and wildlife habitats be managed?
7 Should the geothermal resources of the area be managed and developed?
8 To what extent should the mineral resources be managed and controlled for the benefit of other resource uses?
9 What action is necessary to prevent the spread of insects, disease and fire to lands surrounding the impact area?
10 Should specially protected 'wilderness areas' be designated?

Evaluation criteria

Evaluation according to the degree to which a management alternative ...
1 Provides a spectrum of the effects of past and present volcanic activity.
2 Provides for research opportunities.
3 Reduces soil sediment yield and transport into river systems.
4 Provides for timber salvage.
5 Maintains the annual programmed timber harvest.
6 Provides for safe public access and a wide range of recreational activities.
7 Provides for public education and interpretation of the volcanic events and effects.
8 Provides for development and use of fish and wildlife resources.
9 Provides for use of mineral and geothermal resources.
10 Protects adjacent lands and resources, e.g. from fire, pests etc.
11 Provides for maintenance and/or enhancement of the local and regional economy.
12 Considers the availability, suitability, manageability of, and need for, additional wilderness areas.

1.9

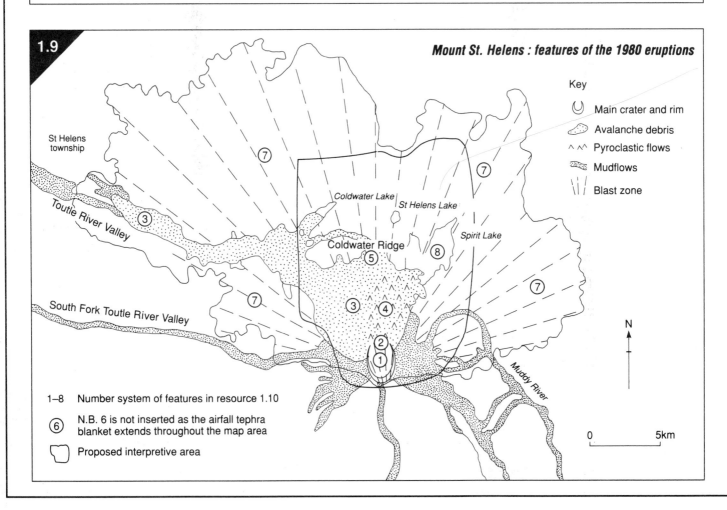

Mount St. Helens : features of the 1980 eruptions

Key
- Main crater and rim
- Avalanche debris
- Pyroclastic flows
- Mudflows
- Blast zone

St Helens township

Toutle River Valley

Coldwater Lake | St Helens Lake

Coldwater Ridge

Spirit Lake

South Fork Toutle River Valley

Muddy River

N

1–8 Number system of features in resource 1.10

⑥ N.B. 6 is not inserted as the airfall tephra blanket extends throughout the map area

Proposed interpretive area

0   5km

1 New Crater	The explosions of May 1980 destroyed approximately 12 per cent of the mass of the volcano, reducing it in height by more than 400 m. A new crater was formed, almost 700 m deep and up to 3 km across, resembling a steep-walled amphitheatre west, south and east, and open to the north. A depositional ramp of pyroclastic flows spills across this northern lip.	**5 Coldwater Ridge**	A segment of the debris avalanche roared across the Spirit Lake and North Toutle basin and on up the flanks of the valley to a height of 350 m before overtopping the Coldwater Ridge and coming to rest in the valley beyond.
2 New lava dome	A succession of domes of viscous dacite lava have been extruded on the floor of the new crater, each being partially destroyed by explosions and then rebuilt. By late 1982 the dome was approximately 600 m wide and 180 m high. It may be a permanent or a temporary feature.	**6 Airfall tephra blanket**	An extensive blanket of ash and pumice up to 1 m thick. Its uniqueness lies in its recent origins, the unvegetated exposure and its stratigraphic record of the eruptive cycle.
3 Debris avalanche	These deposits result from the landslide of the north flank of Mount St Helens triggered by the earthquake of 18 May 1980. The materials are spread across the lower north flank, in Spirit Lake and the valley of the North Fork Toutle River. It is one of the largest debris avalanches of recorded history and exceeds 2 km^3 in volume, although most is now buried by subsequent mudflows and pyroclastic deposits.	**7 Blast zone**	The 30 km^2 zone affected by the lateral explosive release of steam, gases and tephra northwards on 18 May 1980. The particle-laden wind and heat totally devastated an inner zone, grading outwards to areas of decreasing impact. In addition, varying thicknesses of material from sand to boulder-size debris partially smothered the devastated forest.
4 Pyroclastic flows	An overlapping series beginning on 18 May 1980, totalling 0.20 km^3, covered the crater floor, the depositional lip, the north flank of the mountain and part of Spirit Lake. These deposits occur during explosive eruptions and consist of a mixture of tephra and hot gases, moving downslope as a high density current at speeds of up to 140 km/hr.	**8 New Spirit Lake**	The debris avalanche and subsequent pyroclastic flows partially filled Spirit Lake and blocked its outlet, raising the level by more than 100 m. Water displaced by the debris avalanche surged upwards and outwards across the surrounding slopes, removing soil and vegetation and leaving a pronounced scour line.

Note: The extensive mudflows along the valleys of the Muddy River and the North and South Forks of the Toutle River were spectacular and caused much damage, but they are not 'unique' and are being comprehensively moved or modified.

Lumber industry

For many years this has been the largest economic activity in the Mount St Helens area. Infra-red aerial photographs and ground surveys showed that the May 1980 eruptions destroyed or damaged more than 800 million board metres of commercial timber over 35 000 ha. About 60 per cent of this was regarded as salvageable, and the lumber companies wanted to move in as soon as possible, for once dead the wood begins to decay. Within three years the dominant species, douglas fir would have lost at least 20 per cent of its value. By the end of 1982, at least one third had been salvaged, but there was much controversy about this clearance. Scientists, conservationists, water engineers, the recreation/ interpretation sections of the Forest Service all want to restrict the area cleared.

They are concerned:

1 To seize a perhaps unique opportunity to monitor the ecological regeneration and succession.

2 To provide visitors with the experience of the blast zone.
3 To minimise the exposure of the steeply sloping, ash-blanketed terrain, so reducing erosion and subsequent sedimentation and flooding in surrounding rivers.
4 To limit impacts from heavy lumber equipment.

The management plan allows for 75 per cent of useable timber to be salvaged, while leaving about one third of the area for research and visitors, where 'management will protect in a substantially undisturbed condition the significant geologic, ecological and human interest features'.

Management decisions over the next few years will depend upon the outcome of the fascinating competition between the forces of erosion and the stabilising powers of vegetation (resource 1.11). For instance, one might think that timber salvage causes accelerated erosion by exposing the surface and churning it up. This may be true in some areas, e.g. on steep slopes, but in other situations this activity may actually help plant growth. First, reduction of wood fibre to a form usable by plants is a long, slow process and so a dense mat of dead trees may inhibit plant growth. Second, the new ash may form a crust which reduces water infiltration and encourages runoff and the formation of gullies. The logging equipment may break this crust and churn up the ground to bring the pre-eruption organic soil horizon back within reach of young plant roots.

Remember, the forest ecosystem is remarkably resilient. During the 123 year dormant period from 1857, the forest had re-established itself across the flanks of the mountain to a height of 1400 m, and was creeping towards its climax tree line of 2000 m. Some day, the timber harvest may be 80 per cent of pre-1980 levels. Environmental and human resilience are highlighted in the reports of resources 1.11 and 1.12. The newspaper reports from 1980, which document the various dimensions of the environmental impact, are gloomy. Yet only eight years later, the message is so optimistic

The environmental impact of the explosion

1.11

Lung problems up at Moses Lake
A health survey shows lung problems increased at Moses Lake in the two weeks following the Mount St Helens eruption on 18 May, a Center for Disease Control doctor said on Monday. The study shows 'there were increases in pulmonary problems. It is not surprising, but it is one of the first times we have concrete evidence of certain kinds of problems associated with volcanic ash,' said Dr Roy Ing.
(Source: *Associated Press*, 10 June, 1980)

Gritty stuff brings early summer vacation
Ash problems, including the risk of driving schoolbuses on ash-covered roads, caused public school officials to bring an early end to the school year in Eastern Washington and northern Idaho.

School's out early for more than 7000 primary and secondary students in the two states.

About 1 400 students at Washington State University in Pullman have left campus for the rest of the term because of ash-related problems, officials said.

While the rain that fell on much of the region Sunday and Monday has helped, Spokane County officials were quick to point out the emergency has not ended. Suspended particulate readings Monday were 228 micrograms per cubic meter, three times the area's normal reading.
(Source: *Associated Press*, 27 May 1980)

Trail of ash cuts gritty pathway across the nation
Fallout from the Mount St Helens Volcano crossed the Mississippi River today after causing more traffic problems in the Pacific Northwest than any blizzard ever has.

Montana's governor closed state offices and businesses. Residents of Spokane, Washington, were ordered off the streets and airlines curtailed operations as the mountain gone beserk sprinkled some areas with the gritty fine powder up to 7 inches deep.

The National Weather Service said the cloud, wafting at between 25 000 and 41 000 feet, reached western Kentucky and Tennessee this morning and was expected to be over northern Virginia by early tonight.

The ash, spreading with high clouds slowly across western North Dakota blotted out the sun in Williston ND today with a thin layer of dust falling in some areas. Visibility was reduced from the usual 25 miles to 4 miles in the west.

Flights were canceled in and out of Bismarck, Grand Forks, Fargo and Dickinson, ND, because the ash damages airplanes.

Officials in Colorado, where residents with respiratory ailments were urged to stay indoors, said the ash contained sulphur and iron that could taint drinking water.

The ash raised blisters on the paint of cars in Wyoming and some pilots reported having to replace wings and windshields that sustained abrasions while flying through the fine particles.
(Source: *Associated Press*, 20 May 1980)

Ash loss to farmers put at $175 million

Losses to Washington's farmers from the 18 May eruption of Mount St Helens are less than originally forecast, but still enormous, says a State agriculture official.

'Agricultural losses directly linked to the eruption are serious only within a narrow band across Eastern Washington.

'Estimates of volcanic ash damage are now hovering at $175 million, down from earlier forecasts of $213 million.

'The biggest problem growers and commodity groups have now are the negative impressions to buyers of Washington products.'

Crop damage, according to the state Department of Agriculture, compared to 1979 crop values estimated by the Washington State Crop and Livestock Reporting Service are:

- Wheat, $19 million in damage compared to a 1979 crop valued at $460 million.
- Dairy and livestock, $38 million damage, 1979 crop of $575.1 million.
- Alfalfa hay, $35 million damage, 1979 crop of $172 million.
- Peas and lentils, $10 million damage, 1979 crop of $47 million.
- Apples and other tree fruits, $25 million damage, 1979 crop of $289 million.

Also included in the agricultural damages estimates are: machinery repairs, $30 million; bees, $1 million; other crops, $17 million.

(Source: *Associated Press*, 9 July, 1980)

Dust driving Cougar residents out

People have been moving out constantly since Mount St Helens began erupting on 18 May, and especially since Cougar was bathed in ash last week.

When the wind blows, it's impossible to see across the deserted street. If you happen to be under a tree that hasn't broken from the weight of the ash, your head is pelted with pumice stones that have been hung up in the branches since the 12 June eruption. If you rub your face after ash has blown, it feels like tiny glass slivers are being raked across your skin. Without a mask, you are constantly biting down on grit.

The Lewis River Highway is littered with the downed trees. Ash continually blows, coating windows of the locked, closed-for-the-duration stores. Only an occasional dog leaves footprints in the two-inch deep ash along the side of the road.

The post office is shut down.

The Lone Fir Motel is out of business, its swimming pool water a murky gray-green.

(Source: *The Daily News*, Longview, Washington, 18 June 1980)

St Helens eight years later: asleep and approachable

An outing to Spirit Lake, at the heart of Mount St Helens National Volcanic Monument, not far from Interstate 5 in Washington, seems about as difficult and dangerous as a trip to the zoo. A brand new 1 mile hiking trail leads down to the lake, where blue-green waves lap at a pumice beach scattered with driftwood. Beyond it, the gray volcano rises, its crater yawning benignly.

Eight years ago, it was a different scene. The earthquake-triggered avalanche that ripped down the volcano on 18 May 1980, and the subsequent volcanic eruption left, the lake doubled in size and mired with mud and timber, the surrounding forest flattened and blanketed in a thick layer of mud and ash.

Today, the lake appears to have regained most of its clarity: there's even talk of restocking it with trout.

And only at a distance do the hills in the blast zone now look barren: up close you can see fireweed, alder, even young Douglas fir emerging through the ash between downed logs.

Most significantly, the volcano itself seems to have fallen back to sleep (what looks like thick steam in our picture is actually dust blowing off the snowless summit). More than a year has passed with no rumblings save a few small earthquakes. While experts don't consider that St Helens is dormant, they're confident enough to let climbers go clear to the summit and hikers to Spirit Lake, both off-limits until last year.

Part of the monument is still restricted, mostly to protect the ecologically fragile 'new' terrain in the Spirit Lake basin. With the volcano's co-operation, the 'red zone' should disappear by 1991, the same year Spirit Lake Memorial Highway up the Toutle River is due to be completed. If all goes as planned, in only eleven years a natural disaster will have become a fully accessible national monument.

(Source: *Sunset Magazine*, June 1988)

Spirit Lake, showing regeneration of the area

CASE STUDY 1.5 *Details of a major eruptive episode*

Background

The El Chichón eruption of 28 March 1982 is one of the great eruptions of recent years (resource 1.13). As with Mount St Helens (case studies 1.3 and 1.4), this explosive event was part of an episode of activity.

1.13

The El Chichón eruption, 28 March 1982

Activities

1 Produce a diary of the episode similar to that used for Mount St Helens (pages 7 – 8), identifying the three phases: (a) pre-eruption; (b) main eruption; (c) post-eruption activity.

2 Compare and contrast the El Chichón and Mount St Helens active episodes, e.g. characteristics, impacts, responses.

3 From the evidence of the two episodes, what are the main pre-eruption signals given by volcanoes which may help in forecasting eruptions?

Countdown

The chronology and character of the episode are summarised in resource 1.14.

The March–April major eruptions produced a large amount of tephra which is estimated to be as much as 10^8–10^9 m^3 in total volume. An area of 37 000 km was covered by the ash deposit (greater than 0.1 cm thick). The old lava dome which had occupied the shallow floor of the old summit crater has been mostly destroyed, and a new crater, about 1 km across, opened there.

Mudflows occurred occasionally. On 26 May, a destructive mudflow occurred in Magdalena river due to the failure of the natural dams of pyroclastic flow deposits. Most of the villages within a 7 km radius were

Summary of the El Chichón eruption, 1982			**1.14**

Name of volcano in eruption	Location		
	Latitude	Longitude	Country, region
El Chichōn	17° 20'N	93° 12'W	State of Chiapas, Mexico

Duration of the eruption:

	(beginning)			(end)		
	year 1982	month III	date 28	year 1982	month IX	date 11

DATE	SITE	CHARACTER
March-Sept Summary	Summit	○ ⇑ ↑ (g) → (g) ⇒ ⊠ † 187 killed and several dozens missing
March 29	Summit	○ ⇑ ↑ (g) → (g) ⇒ ⊠ † Large phreatomagmatic explosion with an eruption column 18 km high.
30	"	○ ↑ (l) weak explosion
31	"	○ ↑ (l) "
April 2	"	○ ⇑ ↑ (g) → Eruption column 3.5 km high
3	"	○ ↑ (l) →
	"	○ ⇑ ↑ (g) → (g) ⇒ ⊠ † Accompanied by pyroclastic flow
4	"	○ ⇑ ↑ (g) → (g) ⇒ ⊠ † Large explosion with an eruption column 25 km high. Pyroclastic flow extended about 5 km from the summit
5	"	○ ↑ (l)
6	"	○ ↑ (l)
8	"	○ ↑ (l)
9	"	○ ↑ (l) → † Large mudflows caused by breaking of natural dams made of new ash at Magdalena and Ostuacán rivers
May 11	"	○ ⇑ (l) Minor ash emission
September 11	"	○ ⇑ (l) Minor ash emission

N.B. For key to conventional symbols, see page 2

Extract from Bulletin of Volcanic Eruptions, No. 22. December 1984, 69 – 72

completely destroyed or heavily damaged by fallen tephras, pyroclastic flows, and mudflows. The casualties by the eruption were reportedly 187 deaths, several tens of persons missing, and hundreds of persons injured.

The large stratospheric cloud ejected by the 4 April eruption remained dense over lower northern altitudes, but gradually dispersed afterwards. Some brilliant dawns and twilights were seen from many places in the world.

No previous historic eruptions are known from El Chichõn, but geological evidence indicates that the last explosive activity occurred in AD 800–900.

Details of the forerunning phenomena

Felt shocks : occurred

Seismic activity including felt shocks began in November 1981.

Frequency: 15 per day from 1 month before the eruption.

Max. M-M intensity: IV at 30 km from the vent.

Unfelt shocks : recorded

From 4 months before the eruption.

Increase of gas at fumaroles : moderate

Change of ground : occurred

Deformation in the central part of the old dome occurred to form an extrusion like spine.

Details of the eruption

A Vertical explosion : occurred

The explosion was essentially phreatomagmatic (a combination of steam and magma).

Nature of the major ejecta: andesitic ash.

Height of the eruption cloud above the crater: max. 25 km

Area covered by the deposit: 3.7 km x 10^4 km

Volume of the deposit: 10^8 m^3 to 10^9 m^3

B Volcani-clastic flow : occurred

Pyroclastic flow (ash flow, pumice flow) and mudflow.

Area covered: 3 x 10^2 km^2

Mean thickness: 0.5 m

Approx. volume: 1.5 x 10^8 m^3

Temperature of the flow:

400°C measured at 6 km from the source.

C Lava eruption : none

D Notable topographic change : occurred

Destruction of the old lava dome in the old crater (1.8 x 0.9 km in depth)

Formation of a new crater (1 x 1 km in diameter, 150 m in depth, and 108 m^3 in volume) inside of the old crater.

E Damage : occurred

Casualties: 187 persons killed, several tens of persons missing and hundreds injured.

Destruction of arable land: total 300 km^2

150 km^2 by fallen ejecta

150 km^2 by volcani-clastic flow.

(Source: *Bulletin of Volcanic Eruptions*, No. 22, December 1984)

Background

'Transform faults ... are huge, vertical, strike-slip faults cutting down into the lithosphere ... Neither compressional nor tensional forces are associated with the faults; they are simply margins along which two plates slide past each other. The sliding margins smash and abrade each other like two giant strips of sandpaper, so the faults are marked by zones of intensely shattered rocks. Where the faults cut oceanic crust, they make elongated zones of narrow ridges and valleys on the seafloor. When transform faults cut continental crust, they do influence the topography; however, the features are less pronounced than on the seafloor. Transform faults on the land tend to be marked by parallel or nearly parallel faults in a zone that can be as much as 100 km wide.

The sliding movement of transform faults causes a great many shallow-focus earthquakes, some of them of high magnitude. Most transform faults do not have any volcanic activity associated with them. Occasionally, however, a small amount of plate separation does occur and a 'leaky' transform results in a small amount of volcanism. Probably the best-known transform fault in North America is the San Andreas Fault in California. The many earthquakes that disturb California are caused by movement along it. Some of those earthquakes, including the one that devastated San Francisco in 1906, have been particularly destructive. ... As long as the plates continue to move, activity must occur along the San Andreas Fault, and residents of California can expect more earthquakes.' (Resource 1.16.)

(Source: B J Skinner and S C Porter, *Physical Geology*, Wiley 1987, pages 487-8)

Since that last sentence was written, the San Andreas Fault *has* moved again, causing the October 1989 earthquake in San Francisco.

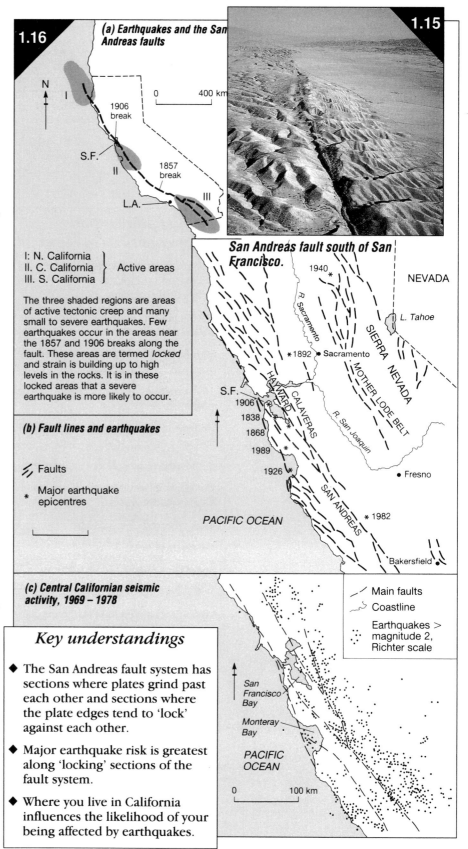

1.16

(a) Earthquakes and the San Andreas faults

1906 break

S.F.

1857 break

L.A.

I: N. California
II. C. California } Active areas
III. S. California

The three shaded regions are areas of active tectonic creep and many small to severe earthquakes. Few earthquakes occur in the areas near the 1857 and 1906 breaks along the fault. These areas are termed *locked* and strain is building up to high levels in the rocks. It is in these locked areas that a severe earthquake is more likely to occur.

(b) Fault lines and earthquakes

⚡ Faults

✳ Major earthquake epicentres

1.15

San Andreas fault south of San Francisco.

1940
NEVADA
L. Tahoe
1892 Sacramento
SIERRA NEVADA
MOTHER LODE BELT
R. Sacramento
R. San Joaquin
S.F.
HAYWARD
CALAVERAS
1906
1838
1868
1989
1926
Fresno
SAN ANDREAS
PACIFIC OCEAN
1982
Bakersfield

↗ Main faults
↶ Coastline
Earthquakes > magnitude 2, Richter scale

(c) Central Californian seismic activity, 1969 – 1978

San Francisco Bay
Monteray Bay
PACIFIC OCEAN
0   100 km

Key understandings

◆ The San Andreas fault system has sections where plates grind past each other and sections where the plate edges tend to 'lock' against each other.

◆ Major earthquake risk is greatest along 'locking' sections of the fault system.

◆ Where you live in California influences the likelihood of your being affected by earthquakes.

The San Andreas system at work

In seismically active zones such as that along the San Andreas Fault, earthquakes are common, as resources 1.16 and 1.17 show. Yet if you live there you are not aware of most of them. Even those you can 'feel', you may mistake for the vibrations caused by a passing heavy lorry or aircraft. Why then, do 'great' earthquakes occur, and why are there fortunately so few?

On page 16 the phrase 'the sliding margins smash and abrade each other like two giant strips of sandpaper', describes vividly the powerful friction along these rough edges. Stress continues to build up until the friction is overcome, and the sections of the two plates jerk forwards, perhaps only millimetres, but the shocks caused by this sudden stress release create a small earthquake. Such frequent shuddering motion is the normal behaviour along these plate margins.

Great earthquakes are caused when sections of a transform fault 'lock', i.e. sections of plates cease to move past each other. This allows enormous stresses to build up, and the longer the fault section stays 'locked', the more severe the earthquake is likely to be when the stress is finally released (resource 1.17). Thus, the strange truth is that if you live near the San Andreas fault you may breathe a sigh of relief if the seismologists' maps tell you there are frequently minor tremors. This means that the two plates are grinding their way past each other. However, if your sector of the fault goes quiet for a number of years you may be in big trouble! The San Fernando Valley experienced a 'break' in 1971 (resource 1.17).

1.17

Approximate relationships between the magnitude and intensity of an earthquake

Richter scale magnitude	Area felt over (square kilometres)	Distance felt (kilometres)	Intensity (maximum expected modified Mercalli)	Ground motion (average peak horizontal acceleration g = gravity = 9.8 metres per second per second)
3.0–3.9	1950	25	II–III	Less than 0.15 g
4.0–4.9	7800	50	IV–V	0.15–0.04 g
5.0–5.9	39 000	110	VI–VII	0.06–0.15 g
6.0–6.9	130 000	200	VII–VIII	0.15–0.50 g
7.0–7.9	520 000	400	IX–X	0.50–0.60 g
8.0–8.9	2 080 000	720	XI–XII	Greater than 0.60 g

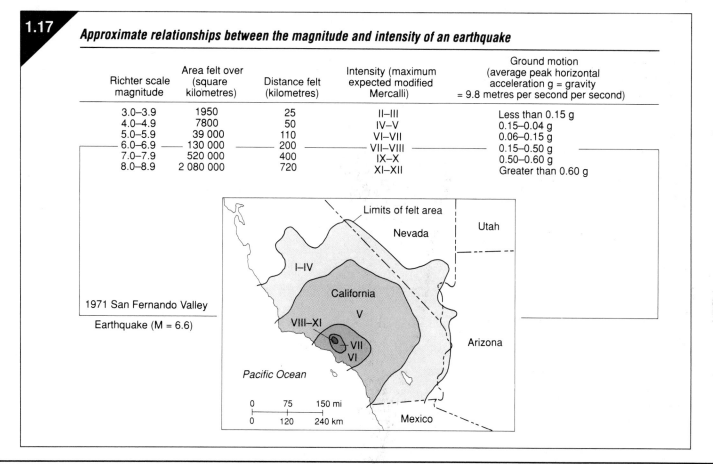

1971 San Fernando Valley Earthquake (M = 6.6)

Disastrous earthquakes will become more frequent and more devastating in future, seismologists meeting in the US warned last week. More than one-third of the world's largest and fastest-growing cities are located in regions of high seismic risk. Roger Bilham from the University of Colorado told a meeting of the American Geophysical Union in Denver, Colorado.

Bilham charted the regions of the world at high seismic risk and the siting of the 100 or so 'supercities' of the world — cities that will have more than 2 million inhabitants by the end of the century. Some 40 per cent of those cities, he told the meeting, are either within 200 kilometres of a tectonic plate boundary, or are close to where an earthquake has caused damage in the past. By the year 2035, 600 million people will be living in these cities. 'The stage is being set for an unprecedented disaster.' he said.

Poor countries are likely to bear the brunt of future earthquakes, but rich countries are far from immune. Even the best earthquake-resistant buildings may collapse. Tokyo, one of the most earth-quake-minded cities, would suffer 150 000 deaths and 200 000 injuries if struck by a large tremor, according to a new report.

The study, published at the beginning of this month, estimated the effect of a quake with a magnitude of 7.9 on the Richter scale, centred off the east coast of Japan and occurring on a weekday afternoon in winter. This is the type of quake that destroyed Tokyo in 1923, killing more than 100 000 people. Such a quake would destroy about 2.6 million buildings in and around Tokyo.

Japan already has strict regulations to reduce the vulnerability of buildings to earthquakes. All gas pipes have automatic shutoffs and tall buildings are mounted on shock-absorbent foundations. Engineers hope that modern technology will help reduce the risks. One construction company this year exhibited a concept study of a building mounted on hydraulic rams, controlled by computerised sensors to iron out the effects of tremors.

(Source: Ian Anderson and Michael Cross, *New Scientist* 17 December 1988)

Key understanding

◆ Scientists believe that many world population centres may be increasingly threatened by major earthquakes.

Activities

1 Using resource 1.18 mark and name on a world outline map, the 'supercities' which are at risk from earthquakes.

2 From resource 1.19, add these great earthquakes to your map of 'supercities.' Compare this map with your world maps showing world volcanicity (see page 3).

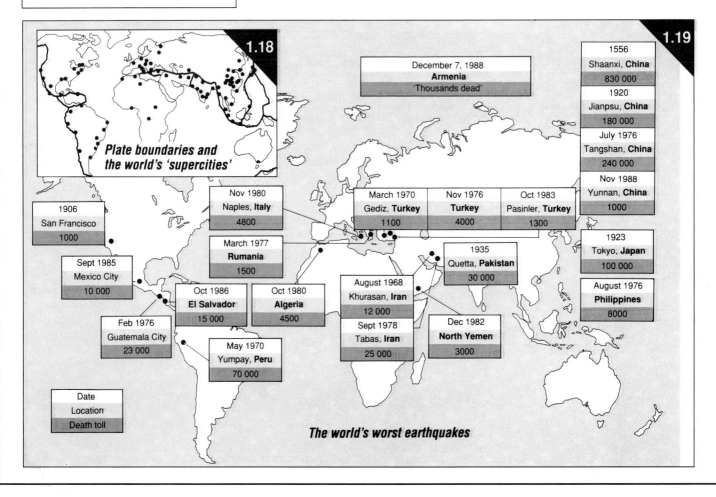

Plate boundaries and the world's 'supercities'

The world's worst earthquakes

CASE STUDY 1.8   *Oblique movements of plates, hot spots*

Scene: the Armenian city of Leninakan on 7th December 1988, following an earthquake of 6.9 on the Richter scale. The city, and the smaller town of Spitak were largely destroyed, and the death toll was at least 25 000 (resource 1.20). Tremors were felt across hundreds of kilometres in the whole region between the Black and Caspian Seas (resource 1.21).

1.20

The Armenian earthquake, 7 December 1988.

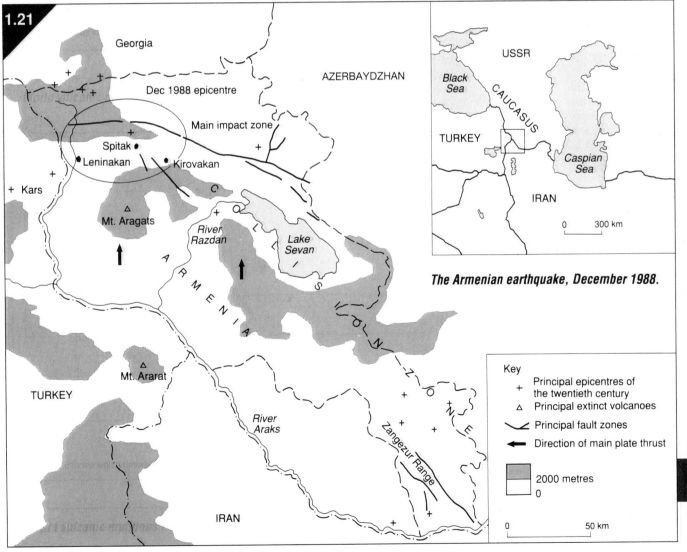

The Armenian earthquake, December 1988.

Key

+ Principal epicentres of the twentieth century
△ Principal extinct volcanoes
⨼ Principal fault zones
← Direction of main plate thrust
▨ 2000 metres
☐ 0

Why did it happen?

The Caucasus is a part of the huge belt of young fold mountains which runs from Gibraltar in the west through the Himalayas on the east. Plate tectonic theory tells us that this belt has evolved over some 150 million years, as crustal plates carrying Africa, Arabia and India northwards have collided with the Eurasian plate. At present, the African and Arabian components are rotating northwards, about a hinge near Gibraltar, at between 2 and 3 cm a year. Thus the collision with the Eurasian plate is still going on and there is a zone of tectonic activity and instability along much of the southern rim of the USSR.

The Caucasus region is a particularly active zone, e.g. there have been 1200 'significant' earthquakes in the 20th century, with Armenia suffering frequently. Leninakan itself was severely damaged by another earthquake in 1926. The most unstable zone runs across Armenia, north of Leninakan and Kirovakan, before curving round the north side of L.Sevan. This is a heavily faulted

zone, with a jerk along a major E – W fault providing the epicentre just north of Spitak for the December 1988 earthquake.

Beneath Armenia, a small plate is pushing northwards and upwards, causing shattering, faulting and frequent seismic activity. This rising and crumpling axis is the collision zone across the Caucasus Mountains and the southern part of the Caspian Sea. To the north the land is subsiding. On the west, Turkey sits upon a little plate of its own, and this is adding further compression to Armenia.

Despite the history of this region, the event appears to have been a surprise. Dr Clark, a geologist from Leeds University, is quoted as saying: 'This is a completely unexpected event. There has been nothing abnormal there in the way of seismic activity, and there has not been anything as big as this during this century. Sometimes earthquake prediction works. Sometimes it just sneaks up behind you and hits you.'

Why was it a disaster?

This earthquake became a disaster because it occurred in a densely populated area and because many of the buildings were not designed to withstand strong tremors. Many of the deaths occurred in concrete apartment blocks, commonly five to twelve storeys high. They were of the prefabricated-panel type of construction found in hundreds of thousands of blocks through the Soviet Union, including earthquake zones. Many lacked steel reinforcement and were rigid and brittle. They were unable to sway with the ground motion and therefore collapsed. Further, there is evidence that many were poorly built – low-quality concrete and badly designed joints.

'As 1989 began, the Soviet government announced that work would commence to rebuild the ruined cities, at a total cost of 9 million roubles. Spitak is to be rebuilt several kilometres away from its previous site. The new buildings will be low-rise, of no more than three or four storeys, and designed to be earthquake-proof. But no building is entirely earthquake-proof.'

Activities

1 Use your understanding of plate tectonics to explain why the December 1988 earthquake occurred. Try to put as much of your answer as possible in the form of labelled diagrams.

2 Why was the destruction so great and what can be done to prevent it happening again?

CHAPTER 2

Rocks, weathering and landforms

Introduction

Examples from all parts of the world tell us that one important factor influencing the landforms which make up the landscape is rock type. Granites, limestones, hard sandstones etc, all provide distinctive landforms in temperate and tropical environments (resource 2.1). Equally important are the ways wind, water, ice, temperature and plants work upon these rocks. The case studies in this chapter help you to understand the complex relationships between the various characteristics of rocks, weathering and erosion processes and the shapes we see in the landscape today. Such understanding is crucial in explaining human responses to different landscapes, e.g. settlements on 'spring lines', 'wet point' and 'dry point' sites.

Some landscapes are built upon a single rock type, e.g. the granite moors and tors of Dartmoor. Yet even within a so-called 'rock type', there are sufficient structural and lithological variations to cause different responses, e.g. not all limestones produce limestone pavements. (See box below.) More commonly, however, landscapes and even individual landforms are built of sets of quite different rock types (resource 2.2). The resulting complex and varied relationships are clearly illustrated in case studies 2.1 (North Pennines, Cumbria), 2.4 (Idanre Hills, Nigeria) and 2.7 (Bredon Hill, Worcester and Hereford).

2.1

Granite tor: Tanzania

Granite tor: Cairngorm Summit

Rock type and landform relationships are usually explained in terms of the properties of the rocks, which fall into two broad categories – **structural** and **lithological**. Structural properties include joints, bedding planes, faults, patterns of folding etc. Lithological properties can be subdivided into three aspects:

1 **Hardness**, i.e. resistance to abrasion, and **toughness**, i.e. resistance to crushing on impact.

2 Their **porosity, permeability, water absorption** and **specific gravity**, which determine the ease with which water is absorbed and moves through rocks. These properties influence a rock's resistance to processes such as frost action, swelling and softening, and to various forms of chemical weathering.

3 **Rock strength**, i.e. the ability to withstand compression, tension (stretching), and shearing (tearing) forces. This is affected by grain size,

cementing agents (cements which hold the grains together), minerals which make up the rock etc.

So the chemical properties and how they are affected by weathering are determined by the types of minerals which make up the rock. Physical properties, and the ways rocks can be modified, are controlled by the nature of the solid mineral grains, the type and extent of the spaces within the mineral aggregate, and how the mineral grains are bonded together.

Case studies 2.3, 2.4, and 2.5 from Sarawak, Nigeria and Guyana represent those hot environments which are moist enough to support complete and dense vegetation cover. In such environments, weathering in all its three forms is the dominant agent of landform and soil evolution (resource 2.3). The combination of consistently warm temperatures and abundant moisture supply energises: (i) High rates of mechanical and chemical activity, and (ii) Rapid cycling of mineral and organic materials through the regolith (weathered mantle). Note, however, that climate is only one of the influential inputs into the weathering system (resource 2.4).

Even in temperate environments, chemical weathering can be important where rock types are especially susceptible, e.g. the shakehole networks within the Pennine limestones in case study 2.2, which is presented as a fieldwork exercise.

Case studies 2.6, 2.7 and 2.8 focus on how slopes evolve, and the factors which influence them in warm, temperate and cool environments. The example from southern France (case study 2.6) illustrates conditions under which gulleying is the main process, while on Bredon Hill (case study 2.7), in central England, mass movement and geological structure have been dominant. Freeze-thaw activity and lithological character are shown to be the key influences in the harsh environment of eastern Canada (case study 2.8)

In order to use the case studies most effectively, you will find it helpful to check out the main chemical and physical characteristics of the rock types involved, from standard reference texts and dictionaries etc.

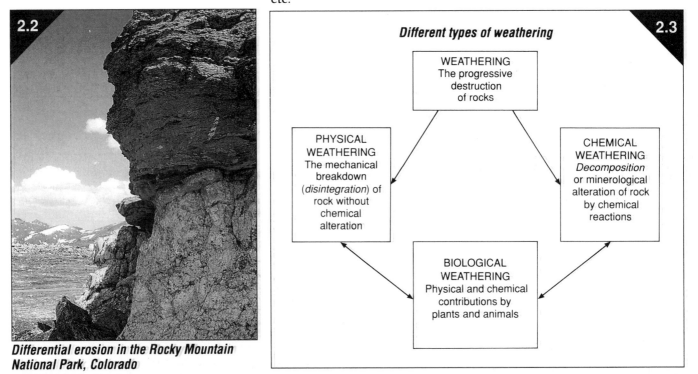

2.2

Differential erosion in the Rocky Mountain National Park, Colorado

2.3

Different types of weathering

WEATHERING
The progressive destruction of rocks

PHYSICAL WEATHERING
The mechanical breakdown (*disintegration*) of rock without chemical alteration

CHEMICAL WEATHERING
Decomposition or minerological alteration of rock by chemical reactions

BIOLOGICAL WEATHERING
Physical and chemical contributions by plants and animals

2.4	Factors affecting weathering depth in the humid tropics
Climatic	Consistently **high** temperatures accelerate rates of chemical reaction. **Rainfall** occurring in all seasons provides an ample supply of water, which is the main reagent in weathering processes.
Biotic	**Dense forest canopy** protects the surface from raindrop and rainwash impacts, yet provides litter from which organic acids are produced capable of chemical reaction with many mineral constituents of rocks.
Geomorphic	**Persistence of ancient landscapes** over extensive areas, often with **gentle slopes** and slow denudation rates, aids weathering penetration.
Site	Whenever topography etc. assists **free drainage**, chemical reactions and hence weathering are sustained over time.
Geologic	**Rock type and texture** vary in their mineral composition, and as minerals themselves vary in their susceptibility to decomposition, rocks are disintegrated by the alteration of the 'weaker' minerals by the active acids. Crystalline texture affects the ways in which the acids can penetrate the mineral structure.

CASE STUDY 2.1   *Relationships between rock type, structure and landforms*

Background

As we look at a landscape we are probably seeing the outcome of millions of years of hard work – by the tectonic forces illustrated in Chapter 1; by the natural agents and processes of erosion and weathering (water, ice etc); by humans over the last few thousand years. This landscape has been created by a long sequence of contrasting environmental conditions – from tropical oceans, to hot deserts, to ice sheets – all overlaid by increasing human endeavours. One way to study the landscape is to work out this sequence of events and to identify which elements belong to which phase in the succession and which processes were involved. Because of this multi-phase and multi-process history, most landscapes are said to be **polygenetic.**

For British landscapes, the simplest approach is to base a study on three broad phases: (i) pre-Pleistocene; (ii) Pleistocene glaciation; (iii) post-glacial. The first phase, covering in most landscapes many millions of years, is essentially concerned with the building of the geological framework and what the land looked like as the glaciers spread. The Pleistocene glaciation may be dated as approximately two million to 10 000 years BP (BP is geologists' notation for 'before the present'), when at maximum glaciation, ice sheets spread as far south as a line roughly from the Bristol Channel to the Thames estuary. The post-glacial period, referred to by geologists as the 'Holocene' or 'Recent' period, is the relatively brief time span during which the glacial landforms have been modified, stream systems established, soils evolved, vegetation successions developed and human imprints extended.

▶ *Before working through this case study, it will be useful for you to check your understanding of the following:*

**geological timescale;
sedimentary, igneous, metamorphic rocks and their modes of origin;
scarp and dip structures;
inlier, normal and thrust faulting;
contact metamorphism.**

Key understandings

◆ Geological framework has an important influence upon landscape evolution and character.

◆ Landforms can be explained in terms of rock characteristics and structural (tectonic) history, combined with the work of weathering processes over long periods of time.

◆ Rocks vary in their strength and resistance to erosion.

◆ Complex fault systems may provide the framework for distinctive sets of landforms.

Example from the North Pennines, Cumbria

The geological framework

For the 25 km between Penrith and the Lune Gorge, the M6 in Cumbria runs north-south near the boundary between two contrasting types of landscape, each built upon a quite different geological framework (resource 2.5). On the west rise the rugged, broken hill masses of the Lake District. To the east, the rolling agricultural landscape of the Vale of Eden extends to the foot of the well-defined profile of the Cross Fell Pennines. Both the Vale of Eden and the Cross Fell Pennines are built upon great thicknesses of sedimentary strata (layers), ranging

in geological age from Carboniferous (up to 350 million years BP) to Triassic (225 million years BP). The environments in which these sediments were laid down varied from tropical oceans (fossiliferous limestones) to harsh deserts (red sandstones and evaporite deposits — the large plasterboard factory at Kirkby Thore (647268) mines gypsum, an evaporite mineral from a desert playa). Since their deposition and consolidation to distinctive sedimentary rocks, these strata have been tilted and faulted by tectonic forces. Thus, the three major landscape units we see today (and identified on resource 2.5) — the Vale of Eden, the Cross Fell Inlier, and the Pennine escarpment — can be explained in terms of the geological framework established before the Pleistocene glaciation. Pleistocene and post-glacial processes have modified landforms and added detail (see case study 5.5) but this region offers an excellent example of the powerful influence that geologic and tectonic processes and forces can have upon landforms and hence upon human occupance. From west to east across the Vale, the scarp and dip succession becomes increasingly obscured by a veneer of glacial drift derived principally from the Lake District. In places the icesheets moulded this drift into one of the best drumlin fields in England. Furthermore, the great diversity of the drift, from heavy red boulder clay to lighter loams, has influenced the development of farming, e.g. the areas of poorly drained boulder clays can be recognised by reed patches in fields or land left under woodland.

The Cross Fell Scarp

The Cross Fell escarpment is a **fault scarp**, created by repeated uplift along the North Pennine Fault line. As we shall see later (page 27), this is not a single fault, but a complex network of faults with a very long history. Geologists base their reasoning upon the similarities and differences between the rock types of the Vale and the escarpment. The Carboniferous strata of both the Vale and the Pennine scarp are very similar in character and succession and are believed to have been deposited side-by-side. All the younger rock types, however, are found only within the Vale and there is no evidence that they were once more extensive. This suggests that the faults began to lift the scarp and lower the valley *before* the Permian and Triassic sediments were laid down. Indeed, the character of these younger rocks tells us that they were deposited in a basin surrounded by uplands in a semi-desert or desert environment. Furthermore, fragments of rock types found on the scarp are common in the Permian and Triassic rocks of the Vale of Eden.

Today, the scarp appears as a series of well-defined steps leading to the flat cap of Cross Fell itself at 893 m (resource 2.6). This stepped topography is typical of much of the Pennine range, for throughout their length the Pennines are built of thick piles of sedimentary strata, tilted, and broken into blocks by faulting. As the rock formations vary in their lithology and hence in their strength,

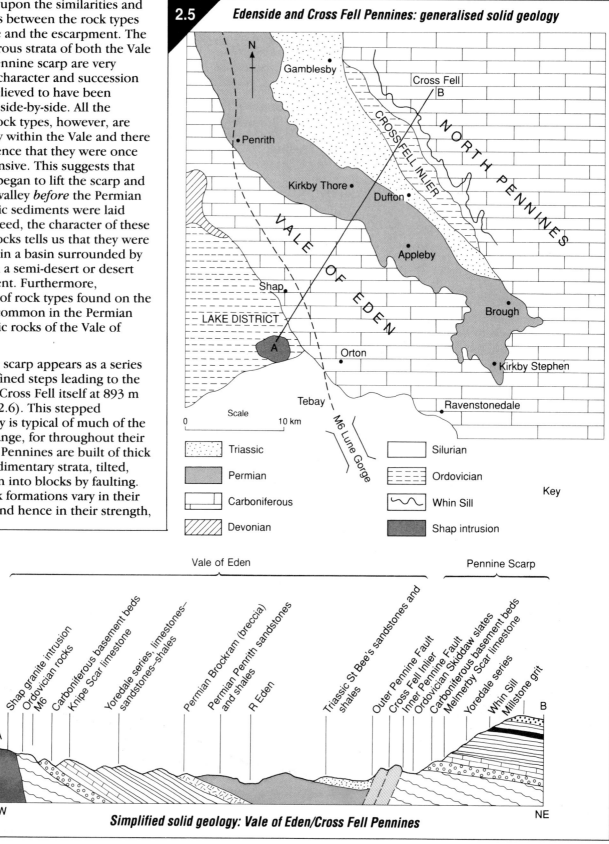

2.5 *Edenside and Cross Fell Pennines: generalised solid geology*

Key

- Triassic
- Permian
- Carboniferous
- Devonian
- Silurian
- Ordovician
- Whin Sill
- Shap intrusion

Scale
0 ___ 10 km

Simplified solid geology: Vale of Eden/Cross Fell Pennines

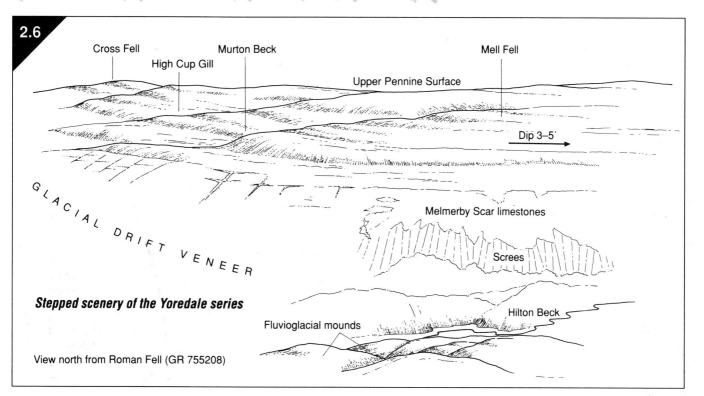

2.6

Cross Fell
High Cup Gill
Murton Beck
Mell Fell
Upper Pennine Surface

Dip 3–5˚

GLACIAL DRIFT VENEER

Melmerby Scar limestones

Screes

Stepped scenery of the Yoredale series

Fluvioglacial mounds

Hilton Beck

View north from Roman Fell (GR 755208)

differential erosion has created the steps, e.g. harder gritstones and limestones jut forth as steps and benches, with softer shales forming intervening slopes and hollows. In the Cross Fell Pennines, hard Millstone Grit forms the cap rock of Cross Fell, and the Melmerby Scar Limestone stands out as one of the most persistent steps along the full length of the scarp.

Resource 2.7 summarises the succession and illustrates the variation in rock type which is the basis for variety of landform.

There is a further significant question to be asked: is the Cross Fell scarp typical of escarpments and if so, representative of a type? Obviously in detail every scarp is different but geomorphologists have attempted to assemble scarps into a small number of categories. Resource 2.8 sets out one of the most straightforward descriptive classifications, suggesting that individual scarps may be either simple, compound or complex. In these terms, the Cross Fell escarpment becomes an excellent example of a complex scarp. Such a

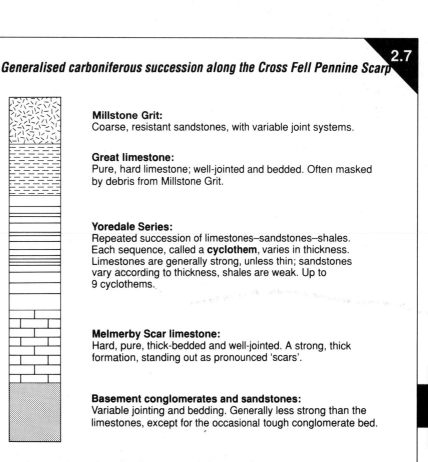

2.7

Generalised carboniferous succession along the Cross Fell Pennine Scarp

Millstone Grit:
Coarse, resistant sandstones, with variable joint systems.

Great limestone:
Pure, hard limestone; well-jointed and bedded. Often masked by debris from Millstone Grit.

Yoredale Series:
Repeated succession of limestones–sandstones–shales. Each sequence, called a **cyclothem**, varies in thickness. Limestones are generally strong, unless thin; sandstones vary according to thickness, shales are weak. Up to 9 cyclothems.

Melmerby Scar limestone:
Hard, pure, thick-bedded and well-jointed. A strong, thick formation, standing out as pronounced 'scars'.

Basement conglomerates and sandstones:
Variable jointing and bedding. Generally less strong than the limestones, except for the occasional tough conglomerate bed.

feature can be regarded as a multi-facetted slope and so we can explain its evolution and form in terms of slope processes. Resource 2.9 is a simple model of slope evolution which can be applied to the Cross Fell scarp and helps us understand and explain what we see in the landscape.

The Whin Sill intrusion

In some landscapes built upon a set of contrasting rock types, there may be one formation or set of beds which control much of the way the landscape has evolved. For example, across the Dark Peak of Derbyshire in the southern Pennines, very resistant Millstone Grit capping beds strongly influence the shape of the moorland landscape. Across the Cross Fell scarp, by far the strongest rock lithologically is the Whin Sill igneous intrusion (resource 2.10). This classic example of magma intruded along bedding planes of pre-existing rocks to solidify as dolerite, is Britain's largest intrusive sheet. It underlies much of the northern Pennines, outcropping on the Northeast coast at Bamburgh Castle and again intermittently along the Cross Fell scarp. Its most spectacular outcrop is at High Cup Nick where it forms a 20 m high cliff on the valley sides and controls the morphology of the upper section of the glacial trough. Today the exciting scenery created by the Whin Sill at High Cup is one of the highlights of the Pennine Way, as a section of this long distance footpath skirts the outcrop.

There are several pieces of evidence which tell geologists that this is not an extrusive lava flow which was spilled across the Carboniferous ocean bed. The most obvious evidence is that the Carboniferous beds both *above* and below the dolerite have been hardened by **contact metamorphism**. As this metamorphism was caused by heat, the overlying rocks must have been present when the hot liquid magma first appeared, i.e. that the magma was injected between pre-existing rocks.

Scarp development — a general statement

2.8

'A slope cut into nearly horizontal strata of unequal resistance is characterised by a step-like profile, where the exposed edge of the more resistant strata form the steep rises and some of the benches and the less resistant strata form the intervening slopes. The specific form of the landscape will be determined by the relative rates of weathering and removal of rock from the particular strata which, in turn, are influenced by the nature, thickness and sequence of those strata. Scarps may be classed as simple, compound and complex. **Simple scarps** are predominantly composed of one main rock type, and may be of two sub-types, one composed of relatively resistant rock and one composed of weak rock. **Compound scarps** are composed of two major rock types, a resistant cap rock and a weather underlying rock.... **Complex scarps** possess more than one sequence of resistant and less resistant rock.... On nearly horizontal strata, scarp form is independent on rock resistance as controlled by cementation and porosity, the orientation and spacing of joints and bedding planes, and the proportion of the scarp face composed of resistant rock.'

(Source: A J Gerrard, *Rocks and Landforms*, Unwin Hymans 1988,

---

2.9

A model and generalised statements for slopes, including escarpments, developed on sedimentary successions

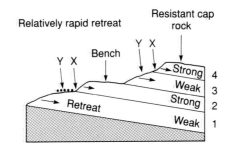

X Undercutting from erosion of weak formation causes collapse and retreat of strong formation

Y Boulder field and scree from collapsed rock face may slow down retreat of slope

Retreat rate may be controlled by balance between supply and removal of debris (Y), i.e. whether the slope is **weathering limited** or **transport limited**.

Definition
Weathering limited slope
Material is removed faster than it is being produced, therefore there is a thin regolith.
Transport limited slope
Weathering rate is greater than transport removal, therefore a thick regolith builds up.

1 How rapidly a rock formation recedes depends upon its position in the succession

2 The relative resistance of a formation is less important than this position

3 Weak formations capped by stronger formations become increasingly dominant by area as the landscape development progresses

4 Weak formations determine the rate of recession of higher, more resistant ones

5 Weak formations above strong formations are rapidly stripped away once the succession above is removed

2.10

The Whin Sill at High Cup Nick

Landforms of the Cross Fell Inlier

When faulting has occurred intermittently over millions of years, achieving vertical movements totalling thousands of metres, it is hardly surprising that the North Pennine Fault Line is not a single fault but a complex series of faults across a shattered fault zone (resource 2.11). The topography within this fault zone is quite different from that of the Vale of Eden to the west or the Pennine scarp to the east. The distinctiveness can be explained in terms of the geological framework, especially rock types and faulting history. In simple terms, the rocks within the fault zone are much older than the surrounding sedimentary strata, i.e. they represent an inlier.

Repeated tectonic activity along this fault zone has thrust blocks of rock upwards unevenly by as much as 2000 m until rock series millions of years apart in age now sit side by side. Each block is divided by the main outer and inner longitudinal faults and the internal network of shorter faults. This is the Cross Fell

inlier, one of the most famous geological locations in Britain. It is a complex assemblage of older rocks set within surrounding younger rocks by faulting. On a detailed geological map (see Geological Survey Special Sheet 1) this lens-shaped inlier, some 20 km long and up to 3 km wide, resembles a stained-glass window, each colour representing a different rock type. Resources 2.11 and 2.12 illustrate the complexity.

The Appleby Pyramids

The outstanding field evidence of the presence of the inlier is a series of conical hills, sometimes called the 'Appleby pyramids', after a nearby town. These hills, especially Knock Pike (686282), Dufton Pike (700266) and Murton Pike (735231), are built of Ordovician rocks up to 250 million years older than the Carboniferous and Triassic rocks which surround them. Their nearest 'relatives' are the Skiddaw Slates and ancient volcanic rocks which make up the Lake District hill masses away to the west.

These 'pyramids' owe their presence and their shape to (i) the complex faulting and (ii) prolonged erosion which has exposed them. Many of the faults provide lines of weakness along which the erosional agencies, principally ice and water, have been able to etch out these free-standing conical hills. Lithology too, has influenced their appearance. For example, Dufton Pike and Knock Pike, both fault-defined, are built of tough rhyolitic lavas, upthrust slivers of the Ordovician Borrowdale Volcanic Series which dominate the central Lake District. Murton Pike, on the other hand, owes its shape to a combination of lithological and structural factors: a low-angle thrust fault has placed the Ordovician Skiddaw Slates over the much younger Carboniferous limestones and created an asymmetrical shape (resource 2.12). The outcome is a set of landforms easily distinguishable from the stepped topography of the Pennine scarp, and from the drift-plastered scarp–and–dip scenery of the Vale of Eden.

CASE STUDY 2.1 *Relationships between rock type, structure and landforms*

Activities

1 Summarise the characteristics which support the claim that the Cross Fell scarp is a 'complex' escarpment.

2 What are the relationships between lithology, structure and erosion/weathering processes in creating the Cross Fell scarp?

3 Explain why the Cross Fell Inlier is such a complex geological and geomorphological feature.

4 What evidence is used to establish (a) the age of the North Pennine Fault line and (b) that the Whin Sill is intrusive not extrusive?

5 List examples identified in this case study which support the claim that rock character has a significant influence upon landforms.

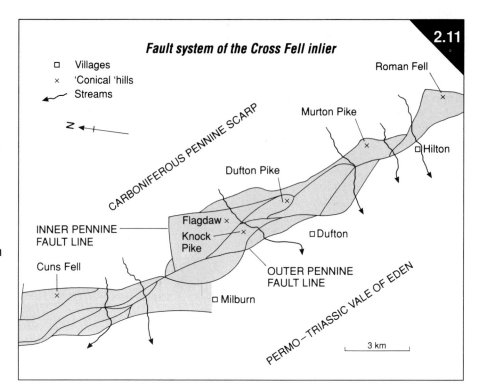

2.11

Fault system of the Cross Fell inlier

□ Villages
× 'Conical 'hills
↙ Streams

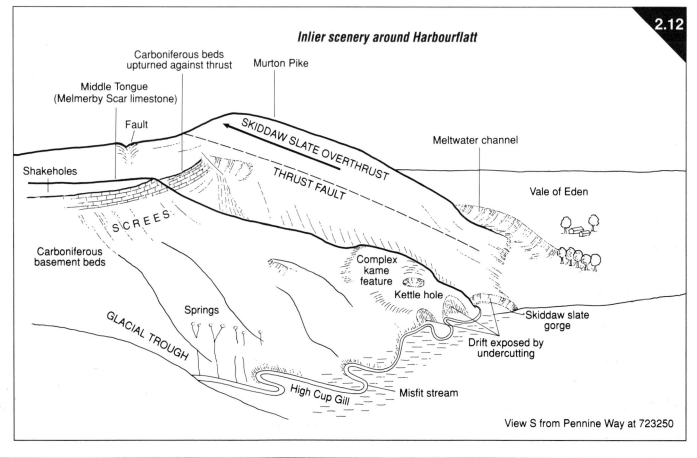

2.12

Inlier scenery around Harbourflatt

View S from Pennine Way at 723250

CASE STUDY 2.2 Localisation of weathering – the example of shakeholes

Background

An important feature of weathering is its localised impact. Many landforms show evidence of variations in the rate of weathering within the same rock formation, e.g. look at many older stone buildings in cities, where the blocks become ribbed or pitted. This differential weathering is related to the character of (i) the weathering process and (ii) the structure and lithology of the rocks. Nowhere is this more clearly illustrated than in the occurrence and development of shakeholes, a distinctive feature of a number of limestone districts (resource 2.13).

Shakeholes are cone-shaped depressions often about 3 m deep and 9 m across, and oval to round in shape. They occur frequently where gently dipping, well-jointed limestone is overlain by glacial drift. (Note the contrast with limestone pavements, which seem to require a stripped surface.

Solution beneath this superficial cover enlarges selected joints and cracks in the bedrock, causing the overlying drift to subside into the cavities (resource 2.14). Thus, shakeholes fall within the family of karstic enclosed depressions known generally as **dolines**.

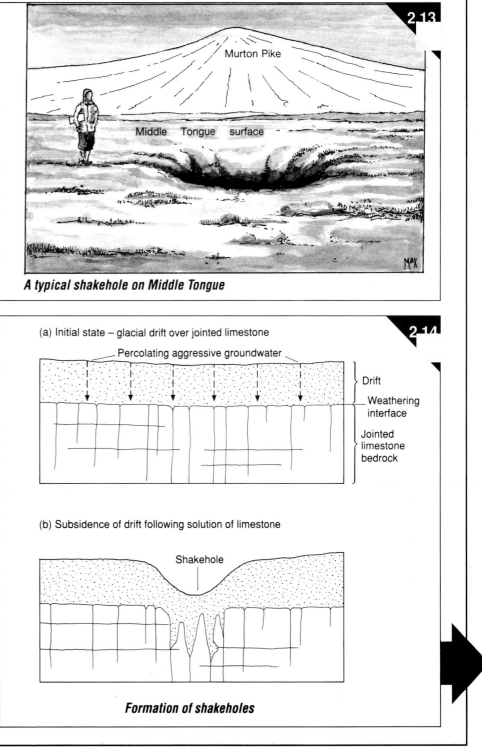

A typical shakehole on Middle Tongue

(a) Initial state – glacial drift over jointed limestone

Percolating aggressive groundwater

Drift

Weathering interface

Jointed limestone bedrock

(b) Subsidence of drift following solution of limestone

Shakehole

Formation of shakeholes

Key understandings

◆ A number of key variables influence the occurrence, size and shape of shakeholes:

(i) The amount and acidic status of the water reaching the sub-drift bedrock.

(ii) The thickness and character of the drift.

(iii) Local slope, e.g. gentle gradients mean less runoff and greater infiltration.

(iv) The catchment around each shakehole: wider catchments mean more water.

(v) Joint patterns of the limestone: shakeholes are most likely at intersections of major joints.

Middle Tongue, Cross Fell escarpment, Cumbria

In case study 2.1, it was shown that the Pennine scarp has developed as a series of well-marked steps and benches upon a thick pile of Carboniferous sedimentary formations. One of the strongest of these step-bench features marks the outcrop of the Melmerby Scar Limestone, a hard, thick-bedded, well-jointed formation. At several locations on these benches, sets of shakeholes have developed. One of the best is found on Middle Tongue, a scarp spur about 6 km North East of Appleby (resource 2.12).

A group of sixth form students measured a sample of 26 shakeholes on Middle Tongue (resource 2.15). Their results are tabulated on resource 2.16. They used the following equipment: data recording sheet for all items measured; a shakehole distribution map (as in resource 2.15); two metric tapes, or one tape and a piece of rope; a clinometer or abney level; a magnetic compass. (In a field exercise, each working group of three students would need this equipment.) The procedures are straightforward, but time-consuming, and are set out in resource 2.17.

(Adapted from: M Pemberton, 'Shakeholes: A morphometric field project for sixth-form geographers.' *Geography*, 65(3), 1980, pages 180 – 193)

Activities

1   Data analysis: The data of resource 2.16 may be analysed and interpreted around hypotheses to test relationships between variables. With a partner, set up a small number of hypotheses concerning characteristics of shakeholes and carry out graphical and statistical analyses to test them. If you have access to a micro-computer, then make a data-base to facilitate your analysis.

2   Note: Logic suggests that shakehole occurrence is related to jointing systems. The problem is that shakeholes tend to develop on drift-veneered surfaces, which makes joint measurement difficult. One possible solution is to locate an exposure of the same formation as near as possible to the shakeholes, measure the joint patterns, and use the results. What constraints on your shakehole analysis would you need to note?

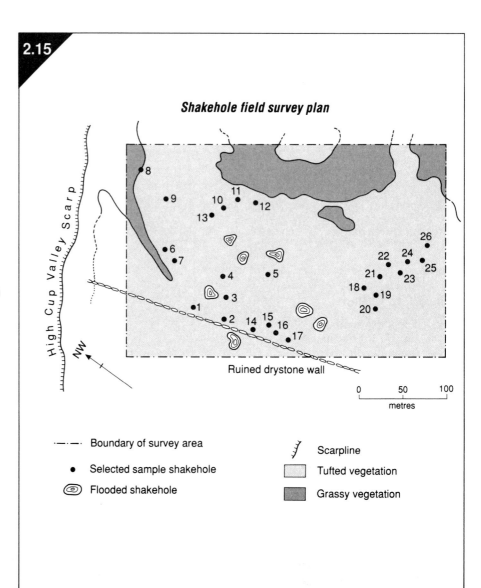

2.15

Shakehole field survey plan

--·-- Boundary of survey area

● Selected sample shakehole

◎ Flooded shakehole

Scarpline

Tufted vegetation

Grassy vegetation

Ruined drystone wall

0   50   100
metres

(1) Field reference number	(2) Long axis length (m)	(3) Long axis orn. (°)	(4) Depth (m)	(5) Short axis Length (m)	(6) Slope value (°)	(7) Slope orn. (m)	(8) Mean diameter (m)	(9) Elongation ratio	2.16
1	3.75	125	0.85	3.1	1.5	351	3.42	1.210	
2	2.30	268	0.75	2.2	1.0	14	2.25	1.040	
3	3.60	110	1.00	3.2	1.0	293	3.40	1.125	
4	6.4	8	1.80	6.3	0.5	310	6.35	1.010	
5	9.6	71	2.00	8.8	1.0	267	9.20	1.090	
6	3.9	310	0.50	3.65	5.0	351	3.77	1.070	
7	5.7	99	1.35	5.2	3.0	14	5.45	1.096	
8	2.5	328	0.40	2.3	7.0	340	2.40	1.086	
9	3.65	290	0.90	3.4	4.0	320	3.525	1.073	
10	5.1	350	0.65	2.9	2.0	2	4.00	1.760	
11	4.4	90	0.55	3.7	2.0	20	4.05	1.190	
12	5.85	75	0.80	4.2	2.0	288	5.025	1.392	
13	5.8	90	1.00	4.35	2.5	10	5.075	1.380	
14	3.12	190	0.90	3.1	2.0	90	3.11	1.006	
15	3.1	90	0.65	2.6	1.0	315	2.85	1.192	
16	3.2	230	0.80	2.7	1.0	71	2.95	1.185	
17	5.0	99	1.20	3.9	1.0	90	4.45	1.282	
18	5.3	288	1.10	3.6	4.0	180	4.65	1.472	
19	3.8	271	0.50	2.8	3.0	282	3.30	1.360	
20	3.7	266	0.60	2.2	3.0	177	2.95	1.680	
21	3.8	60	0.70	3.2	3.0	178	3.50	1.190	
22	4.1	69	0.90	2.8	2.0	144	3.45	1.460	
23	3.8	230	0.70	2.2	2.0	200	3.00	1.720	
24	3.7	254	0.40	2.9	4.0	197	3.30	1.275	
25	4.5	102	0.37	2.4	5.0	206	3.45	1.875	
26	4.8	340	0.60	3.0	5.0	200	3.90	1.600	

Field procedures 2.17

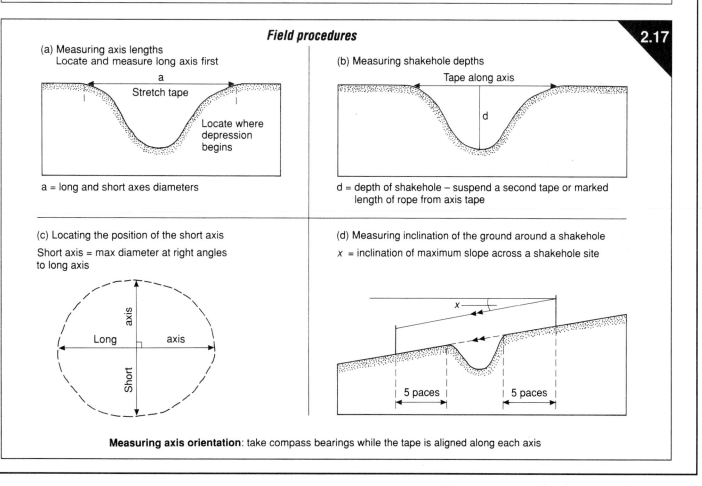

(a) Measuring axis lengths
Locate and measure long axis first

Stretch tape

Locate where depression begins

a = long and short axes diameters

(b) Measuring shakehole depths

Tape along axis

d

d = depth of shakehole – suspend a second tape or marked length of rope from axis tape

(c) Locating the position of the short axis

Short axis = max diameter at right angles to long axis

Long axis
Short axis

(d) Measuring inclination of the ground around a shakehole

x = inclination of maximum slope across a shakehole site

x

5 paces | 5 paces

Measuring axis orientation: take compass bearings while the tape is aligned along each axis

CASE STUDY 2.3 *Karst landscapes of the Mulu*

Background

One of the key questions in examining the relationships between rocks and landforms is: If we have a similar rock type, but change the environmental conditions, e.g. the conditions for weathering processes, what effect will this have upon the resulting landforms? This case study is an aid to answering this question. The Mulu Mountains of Sarawak are built of limestones. They are not dissimilar in structural and lithological properties to those of the Pennines which are examined in case study 2.2, but they exist in an equatorial environment.

The Mulu National Park landscape

Much of the Mulu National Park provides the optimum environmental conditions for intense chemical weathering: thick, pure limestones (97 per cent Ca CO_3); an equatorial climatic regime where every month has mean temperatures of more than 22°C and rainfall of more than 100 mm (pH 5.5); a climax vegetation of rainforest. The result is a classic tropical **karst** landscape, and although the main aim of the National Park is to conserve specialised and luxuriant

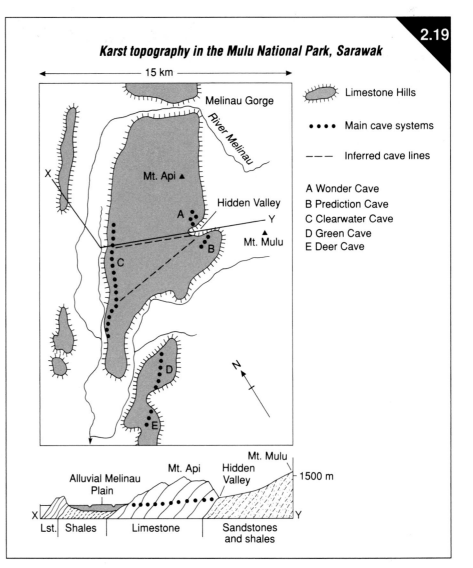

2.19

Karst topography in the Mulu National Park, Sarawak

← 15 km →

Limestone Hills

•••• Main cave systems

— — — Inferred cave lines

A Wonder Cave
B Prediction Cave
C Clearwater Cave
D Green Cave
E Deer Cave

Melinau Gorge

River Melinau

Mt. Api ▲

Hidden Valley

▲ Mt. Mulu

N

Mt. Mulu
Hidden Valley
Mt. Api
Alluvial Melinau Plain
1500 m
Lst. | Shales | Limestone | Sandstones and shales

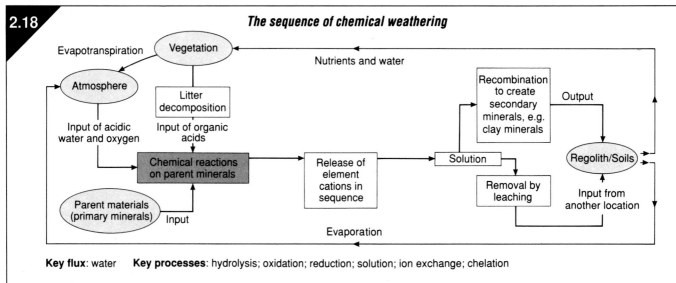

2.18

The sequence of chemical weathering

Evapotranspiration

Vegetation

Nutrients and water

Atmosphere

Litter decomposition

Input of acidic water and oxygen

Input of organic acids

Chemical reactions on parent minerals

Parent materials (primary minerals)

Input

Release of element cations in sequence

Solution

Recombination to create secondary minerals, e.g. clay minerals

Output

Removal by leaching

Regolith/Soils

Input from another location

Evaporation

Key flux: water   **Key processes:** hydrolysis; oxidation; reduction; solution; ion exchange; chelation

Key understandings

Resource 2.18 summarises the chemical weather process. Before using the case studies, work carefully through the diagram, checking that you understand what it shows. Refer to standard reference texts as necessary, for this is a complex topic, as the range of key processes indicates. The following are some important points to help you:

◆ The essential **flux** for chemical weathering is water (H_2O). Decomposition of a rock involves the breaking down of the internal structure of the primary minerals. This is achieved by the water surrounding a mineral or penetrating its structure through microopenings and the atomic structure, thereby setting off a set of chemical reactions.

◆ Chemical reactions are accentuated by the fact that percolating water is not 'pure' H_2O, but is mildly acidic. For example, CO_2 may be added to create weak carbonic acid. Organic acids from vegetation decay also assist.

◆ Each mineral has a unique composition and internal structure, and resists or responds to the weathering processes in a special way.

◆ Each rock type is composed of a distinct assemblage of minerals and will thus vary in its response to the weathering processes.

◆ Some elements are readily attacked and removed from mineral structures, i.e. they have **high mobility**, while others are resistant, i.e. they have **high immobility**.

$(Ca, Mg, Na) \rightarrow K \rightarrow Fe2 \rightarrow Si \rightarrow Ti \rightarrow Fe3 \rightarrow Al$

Mobile ⟶ Immobile

Calcium(Ca)
Magnesium(Mg)
Sodium Na
Potassium(K)
Iron (II) (Fe2)
Silicon(Si)
Titanium(Ti)
Iron (III) (Fe3)
Aluminium(Al)

If we know the mineral composition of a rock, then we can predict its response to chemical attack — rocks rich in calcium or potassium should weather more readily than rocks rich in aluminium.

◆ In any given rock type there will be a sequence of decomposition, with the more mobile elements being removed first.

◆ The end-product is a weathering profile is the weathered layer between surface and bedrock whose characteristics depend upon (i) the parent materials, (ii) the predominant processes, (iii) the timespan involved.

---

rainforest, the designated area does contain some of the finest examples of landform features developed on limestone in the world.

The central landform system is a line of precipitous limestone hills rising abruptly more than 1000 m from the surrounding plains (resource 2.19). They are fringed by spectacular white cliffs up to 500 m high and cut by deep gorges such as that of the River Melinau (see case study 4.1 for details of this river). The steeply dipping strata, with the tallest cliffs along the east-facing scarp, possess the features of mechanical strength and structural control necessary for limestone cliff formation: very high proportion of $Ca\ CO_3$; low primary porosity; poorly defined bedding; well-defined, widely spaced joint system; some variations in lithology, leading to differential erosion.

The processes

The chemical activity of acid-bearing rain and soil waters is concentrated on exposed surfaces, and along joints, bedding planes, and root channels. The essential process is that of solution ($Ca\ CO_3 + H_2O + CO_2\ Ca\ (HCO_3)_2$. This is especially aggressive near the margins where arriving waters tend to be fairly acid and low in calcium bicarbonate. As they penetrate the limestones the waters rapidly become saturated, the rate of solution decreases and is sustained only by the addition of further CO_2, e.g. from organic materials. The effect can be seen in the criss-cross network of linear depressions, up to 50 m deep, scoring the hill surfaces, related directly to the joint systems. Where joint sets cross, extensive depressions are formed. Sub-parallel groups of close-set joints may be separated by lines of fretted and fluted white pinnacles up to 30 m tall, emerging through the forest like rows of giant teeth. The intricate patterning of the pinnacles is the result of differential solution rates during the passage of water over the surfaces, whereby an initial irregularity is accentuated over time.

The cave system

As in so many limestone landscapes, the concentration of the solution activity leads to cave formation and subterranean drainage systems. Recent exploration has shown that 'the Mulu Park now ranks as one of the world's great cave regions'. Resource 2.19 shows that waters flowing west across the sandstones and shales of Mount Mulu reach the limestone at Hidden Valley and disappear to emerge in the Clearwater Cave system (C on resource 2.19). Hidden Valley is a blind cliff-sided gorge some 500 m deep, probably formed by the roof collapse of an earlier cave. The main stream flow in Clearwater Cave is 3 m per second, through a chamber 20 m wide and 30 m high. This East-West system may be an intermediate stage in the creation of a gorge cutting through the hill mass (compare the huge Melinau Gorge).

These currently active cave systems, totalling hundreds of kilometres, lie in the **vadose** zone, i.e. above permanent ground water level, the **water table** being determined by the relatively low altitude of the Melinau Plain. In the past, however, this alluvial plain, underlain by limestones and shales, lay much higher, thereby sustaining a higher water-table through the limestone hills. Under these conditions, an even more spectacular cave system evolved in the **phreatic** (permanently flooded) zone. Running North to South the remnants are shown as A, B, D, E on resource 2.19. Prediction Cave, now filled with sediment, is 100 m wide, while the 1 km main tunnel of Deer Cave which is 'probably the largest cave passage in the world' is up to 170 m wide and 120 m high and is the home for one million bats!

Activities

1 Across the limestone hills the soils are generally thin and need rapid organic cycling to support specialised types of rainforest (resource 2.20). Suggest what is happening on this surface and how it will evolve.

2 The second type of landform system developed on the local Melinau limestones is that of the **limestone flats**: undulating and hummocky plains veneered with alluvial clays and peats, acid in reaction except when in direct contact with the limestones. The hummocky terrain is the result of settling and collapse from solution, while differential weathering produces irregular lines and patches of bare pinnacles. Suggest why this regolith and soil should be thin on pure limestones in hot, moist conditions. (Remember this contrasts with the thick weathered mantle common in many humid tropical environments.)

3 Describe and account for the limestone flats topography shown on resource 2.20.

4 On resource 2.20 what is the relationship between the cliff notch and the water table?

5 Describe the processes and sequence operating at the hill/flat junction and how they help to explain the lowering and extension of the limestone flats surface.

6 **Group research and discussion:** Compare the Karst landscape of the Mulu Hills with that developed on limestones in mid-latitudes, e.g. the Pennines in Britain (see case study 2.1). Suggest reasons for similarities and differences. (Note: focus on processes.)

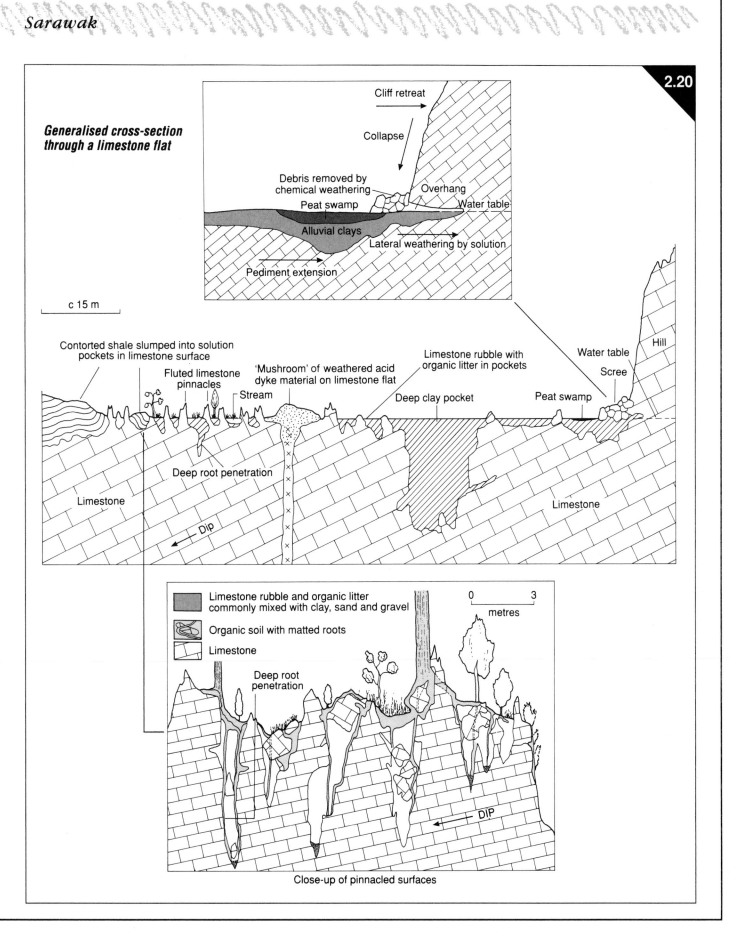

2.20

Generalised cross-section through a limestone flat

Cliff retreat

Collapse

Debris removed by chemical weathering

Overhang

Peat swamp

Water table

Alluvial clays

Lateral weathering by solution

Pediment extension

c 15 m

Contorted shale slumped into solution pockets in limestone surface

Fluted limestone pinnacles

Stream

'Mushroom' of weathered acid dyke material on limestone flat

Limestone rubble with organic litter in pockets

Deep clay pocket

Peat swamp

Water table

Hill

Scree

Deep root penetration

Limestone

Limestone

Dip

Limestone rubble and organic litter commonly mixed with clay, sand and gravel

Organic soil with matted roots

Limestone

0   3
metres

Deep root penetration

DIP

Close-up of pinnacled surfaces

Background

From preceding case studies in this chapter, we know that in temperate environments, the composition and structural characteristics of rocks play an important part in landscape evolution. But are there similar relationships in humid, tropical environments? As weathering is influenced by temperature and rainfall, we might expect that where conditions are warm and moist through much of the year, weathering will be vigorous. Such activity is likely to produce distinctive landforms. Yet lithology and structure may well be vital ingredients. This case study of the Idanre Hills of Western Nigeria illustrates the interactions between climate, geology and topography in the humid tropics.

Key understandings

◆ The mineral composition of rocks is especially significant in environments where chemical weathering is predominant, e.g. in warm, moist conditions.

◆ Jointing patterns exert a strong control upon landscape character.

The Idanre environment

The Idanre Hills (7°N 5°E) occupy some 320 km between the Owena and Ofosu rivers, in the Western Plains and Ranges physical province of Nigeria. Annual rainfall averages 1600 mm with a double maxima and a four month dry season (November to February) although relative humidities remain high (more than 70 %) and water balance deficits occur in only two months. Vegetation was rainforest, but this is a well-populated district and much has been cleared, to give extensive savannas and bare rock surfaces, environments liable to accelerated rates of weathering and erosion.

In this area the hill mass rises abruptly from the surrounding plains, a characteristic which is very common in the tropics, and one for which there seems to be no single explanation. In this instance the answer lies in the contrasting weathering and erosion responses of different rock types: the hill mass is

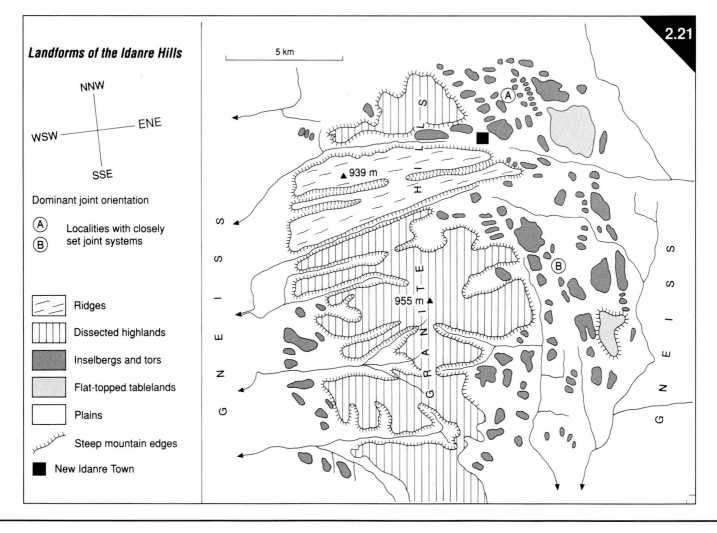

Landforms of the Idanre Hills

2.21

Dominant joint orientation

Ⓐ
Ⓑ Localities with closely set joint systems

Ridges

Dissected highlands

Inselbergs and tors

Flat-topped tablelands

Plains

Steep mountain edges

■ New Idanre Town

built of ancient granites, while the plain is underlain by less resistant metamorphic gneisses. Thus, the bounding escarpments seem to be primarily the outcome of surface lowering of the gneisses rather than scarp retreat across the gneisses and then the granites.

Rock type, structure and landform

The Idanre Hills are a landform system within which two major units may be identified (resource 2.21):

(a) an inner zone of prominent sub-parallel ridges and dissected highlands

(b) a fringe of flat-topped tablelands and **inselbergs/tors.**

Variation in composition of the granites influences the ruggedness of the terrain, with especially coarse granites yielding the highest, strongest relief. However, the most important control upon the landform evolution appears to be the well-developed joint system. If resource 2.21 is examined with the pre-dominant joint orientations in mind, then it can be seen that the landform boundaries are aligned WSW–ENE and NNW–SSE.

Joint spacing further differentiates the landscape: areas with high joint densities tend to develop as ridges and inselbergs. However, the relationship is not entirely consistent, as resource 2.22 suggests, i.e. the weathering and erosion processes operating on expanses of close-set joints tend to produce relatively fragmented terrain. Stream patterns too, are closely related to joint systems (resource 2.22). Downcutting which is still active in most streams, is achieved by pot-holing, with debris provided from valley widening processes, especially exfoliation along valley sides.

(Source: adapted from: L K Jeje, Effects of rock composition and structure on landform development: The example of Idanre Hills of Western Nigeria (*Journal of Tropical Geography*, 39, 1974, pages 43–53))

2.22

Joint density/drainage density relationships, Idanre Hills, Nigeria

Terrain type		Joint density	Drainage density
Dissected highlands		1.4	2.8
Inselbergs	(a)	3.7	3.5
Inselbergs	(b)	1.9	3.2
Ridges		2.6	2.8

(density units = length in kms/sq.km.)

Activities

1 Place tracing paper over resource 2.21. From the features shown on the map, mark on, as carefully as you can, lines indicating joint systems.

2 Using resource 2.21 and the patterns revealed by your trace overlay suggest what relations there may be between joint systems and landscape components.

3 Suggest reasons why joint systems should be especially influential in landform evolution in the humid tropics.

Background

Even in the aggressive weathering environment of the humid tropics, weathering processes are only one dimension of slope evolution, that is, a control on the location, character and amount of debris supply which makes up the regolith or weathered mantle. This case study introduces other influential variables, including vegetation, and illustrates the complexity of slope development.

The Rupununi-Kanuku landscape

The Rupununi savanna (3°N 60°W) is some 13 000 sq km of gently undulating lowland (100–140 m above sea level), which is moderately dissected by streams flowing north from the Kanuku Mountains (1000 m). These mountain ridges are outcrops of an ancient **pre-Cambrian** crystalline shield (consisting of granites, gneisses, schists) and have supplied the materials for the younger sedimentary strata (shales and alluvium) which underlie the savanna. The thin soils of the mountain slopes are clad in rainforest, grading downward to deciduous forest, supported by rainfall of more than 2000 mm distributed through much of the year. The semi-continuous forest canopy at 8–15 m permits the development of a shrub layer of 2–4 m height.

The extensive and thick **laterites** (see case study 10.4 for laterite development) of the savanna support grassland and variable tree cover, with 75 per cent of the mean annual total of 1500 mm arriving in the May–August wet season. The forest and shrub vegetation, with a surface litter mat, provides almost total ground cover, but the savanna bunch grasses leave approximately 50 per cent of the surface bare.

The slopes

Resource 2.23 summarises the findings of a study of three slopes, two on the savanna and one on the forested hillside, and shows clearly how the inputs, processes and outputs of slope evolution may vary over space. For instance, Slopes 1 and 2, both on the savanna, lie only a few kilometres apart, yet for the study year 1965–66, their rainfall totals illustrate the highly localised nature of tropical storms (table 2) (See Chapter 8, pages 165 – 176). When slope angles are compared (table 1) and combined with the rainfall totals, the contrasts in runoff, sediment yield and denudation rate become partially explicable (table 3). If similar comparisons are made between the savanna slopes and the forested slope, relationships become complex, and other variables such as characteristics of vegetation cover and soil surface materials, must clearly be taken into account.

The processes

Of the main erosional processes – raindrop impact, **rilling** and overland flow – only the last is significant locally. Interception by vegetation and the protection by the surface litter, minimise raindrop impact on the forest slope, while rilling is reduced by the litter acting like roof shingles, encouraging sheetwash. On the savanna, raindrop impact would be expected to be more important because of the partially bare surface. However, its role on the slope components A and C (resource 2.23) is primarily that of particle dislodgement rather than significant transport, while rilling is discouraged by the compact nature of the surface.

(Source: adapted from: R H Kesel, 'Slope runoff and denudation in the Rupununi savanna', *Journal of Tropical Geography*, 44, June 1977, pages 33–42.)

Activities

1 Overland flow, sediment yield and denudation are greatest at the lower end of slope component A and the middle section of component C (resource 2.23). How would you account for this?

2 Slope component B is dominated by a layer of coarse gravel (up to 50 mm grain size). How does this help to account for the finding that raindrop impact, rilling and overland flow are all reduced across this component of the slope?

The data can be used for the testing of hypotheses and correlation analysis. With a partner propose two hypotheses, and use correlation techniques to test them. What additional information might you require to improve the quality of your analysis?

2.23

Table 1: Run off/sediment yield relationships, Rupununi, Guyana

Rainfall episode	Slope 1 (Savanna)		Slope 2 (Savanna)		Slope 3 (Forest)	
	Runoff[a]	Sediment[b]	Runoff[a]	Sediment[b]	Runoff[a]	Sediment[b]
1	1.0	2.0	7.0	4.0	2.0	7.5
2	3.0	1.0	8.0	5.0	2.5	5.0
3	4.0	8.5	10.0	12.5	3.0	5.5
4	4.0	3.0	11.5	5.0	3.0	17.5
5	6.0	6.0	27.0	11.0	4.5	10.5
6	6.5	14.0	41.0	17.0	5.0	11.0
7	7.0	8.0	59.0	21.0	5.5	6.0
8	7.0	11.5	79.0	24.0	7.5	16.0
9	8.5	10.5	112.0	32.0	8.0	11.5
10	10.5	14.0	132.0	45.0	18.0	30.0
11	14.0	18.0	151.0	46.0	26.0	29.0
Mean Gradient	6°		15°		16°	
Maximum Gradient	11°		28°		23°	

(a) cm³ × 1000;

(b) grammes

Table 2: Slope characteristics, Rupununi, Guyana

Slope	Altitude(m)	Vegetation	Rainfall (1965–66) (mm)			
			Surface[a] under canopy	Total[b]	Max rain intensity (mm/hour)	
1	110	Savanna	–	1288	70	
2	140	Savanna	–	3281	170	
3	500	Forest (canopyheight 8–15m), with shrub layer, (2–4m)	1591	3612	220	

(a) Raindrops dripping on to surface from leaves, branches etc. Another c. 40% reaches surface via stemflow.

(b) Total rainfall recorded on neighbouring open plot.

Table 3: Relationship between Runoff and Denudation, Rupununi, Guyana

Slope	Av. runoff (% of total ppt)	Max. runoff (% of total ppt)	Total sediment yield (gms)	Denudation rate (mm/1000 years)
1	7.7	12.3	706.8	125
2	14.0	21.5	1662.8	291
3	14.9	33.0	1845.1	323

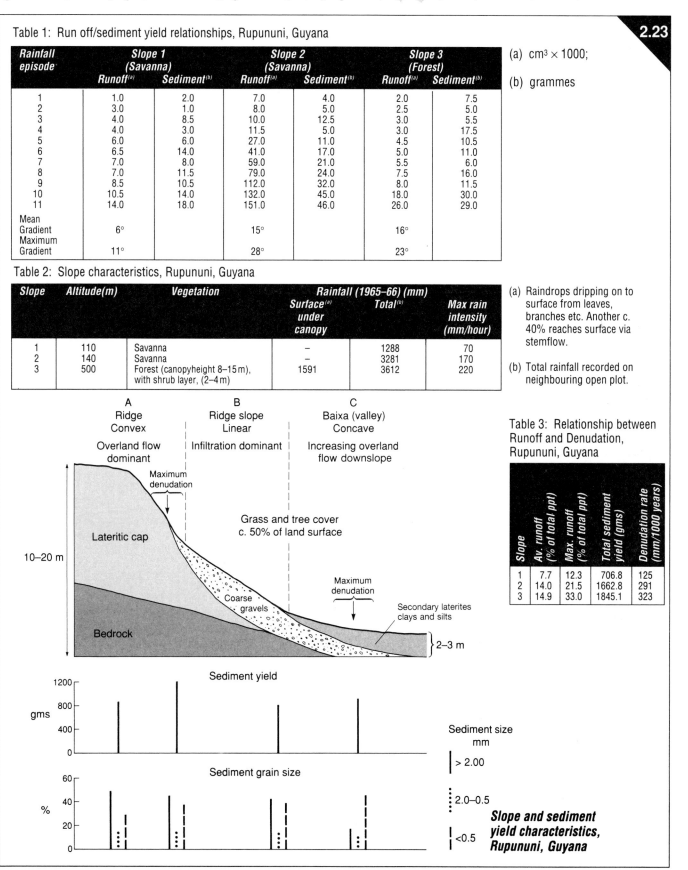

Slope and sediment yield characteristics, Rupununi, Guyana

CASE STUDY 2.6 Gully networks and slope

Background

It is now generally accepted that landscapes evolve not by steady progression, but through surges of change separated by periods of relative quietude or equilibrium. The evolution of most slopes fits this general statement or model: episodes of instability interrupting periods of stability. Slopes across much of southern Europe seem to be undergoing such a dynamic episode at the present time, with repeated evidence of accelerated erosion. This varies in intensity from gradual downslope movement of individual soil particles by rainsplash, to shallow rill systems and eventually to deeply gullied sites exhibiting intense erosion. Clearly, this change is being triggered by some critical shift in the way these slope systems work, e.g. changed environmental conditions, human interference.

'In theory, accelerated erosion of the exposed regolith on a steep slope, cut in rocks of low resistance, proceeds as follows. In any heavy rainstorm which produces significant overland flow, slight hollows on the steep slope focus the surface water. The downslope increase in the capacity to transport will then begin to exceed the downslope rate of increase in the amount of sediment available for transport. Rills then develop downhill from these locations. This has a self-enhancing or positive-feedback effect, so that when rocks of low resistance underlie the regolith, the rills develop into gullies. Thereafter the network expands with any new storm, and should develop in time to reach some sort of equilibrium.'

As an equilibrium or state of balance is achieved, the surge of change, i.e. the instability episode, should come to an end.

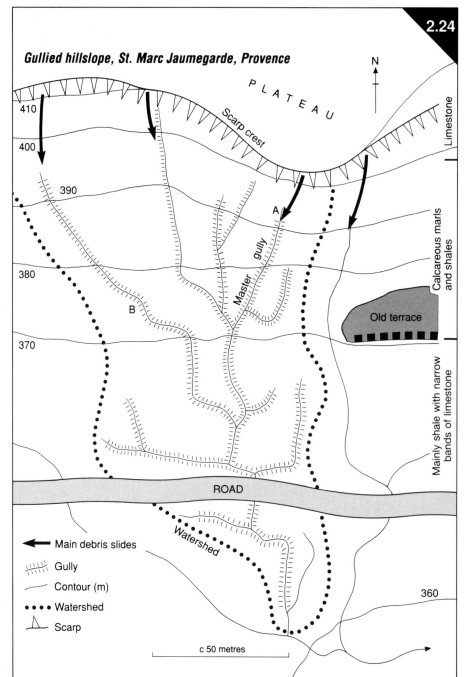

Gullied hillslope, St. Marc Jaumegarde, Provence

Main debris slides
Gully
Contour (m)
Watershed
Scarp

c 50 metres

Key understandings

◆ Landscapes undergo surges of change interspersed with longer periods of relative stability.

◆ Episodes of accelerated change may be triggered by changes to inputs, stores and outputs of an environmental system.

◆ Accelerated change may be caused by the interaction of several factors.

Gullies at St. Marc Jaumegarde, near Aix-en-Provence

The slope was once cultivated and partially terraced, but has been abandoned and scrub woodland is taking over. The last active gullying episode seems to have begun during the 1960s (resource 2.25).

The rim of the valley is formed by a pervious, well-structured formation of sandy limestone. This juts forth as a tabular cliff of cap-rock, lying **unconformably** upon steeply dipping sedimentary strata, a sequence of calcareous marls and shales beneath which limestones lie. The marls and shales are relatively soft and form the mid-slope, while the footslope is built upon the somewhat harder limestone beds (resource 2.24).

The cap-rock acts as a water store, with water emerging at the base and via the main vertical joint system. The water disintegrates the basal layers of the cap-rock and erodes the softer underlying stratum, thus causing undercutting. These processes cause repeated rock falls, thereby providing a ready debris supply for rock slides in tracks across the mid-slope. These tracks deepen into gullies and continue across the footslope. The gullying is particularly well-developed where vegetation is sparse. The thin, stony regolith has been stripped, and the gullies are cut deeply into the solid rock below.

The search for causes

Vegetation cover

There is a partial canopy of Aleppo pine with a dense shrub layer up to 2 m in height. Debris-slide tracks have cut swathes through this woodland, and gullying has been more extensive on sparsely vegetated areas. The absence of a grass mat is particularly important, as once there

Severe active gullying scars a small, steep-sided valley

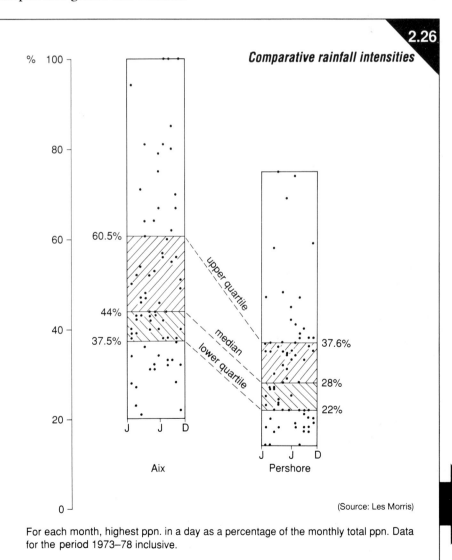

Comparative rainfall intensities

(Source: Les Morris)

For each month, highest ppn. in a day as a percentage of the monthly total ppn. Data for the period 1973–78 inclusive.

is a gap in the tree and shrub canopy, bare ground is exposed.

Climate characteristics

Climatic controls are known to influence the widespread gullying of this part of France. At Aix-en-Provence, the mean annual rainfall is similar to that of Pershore, a town in the county of Worcester and Hereford, but the variability and above all the intensity are much greater (resource 2.26). Thus, the rainfall at the study site seems to be erratic and strongly episodic. These characteristics encourage gullying. Studies from other local sites suggest that winter cold spells followed by snow and rain cause accelerated erosion: the surface is first broken up by ice needle expansion. The subsequent snow melt and rain quickly saturate the loosened material, which then moves downslope as a series of localised mudflows. In summer, desiccation during dry spells can cause deep cracks, plus a surface crust. The occasional heavy rainstorms give rapid runoff across this crust, with funnelling into the desiccation cracks, causing gullying. The ample debris supply for entrainment as abrasive bed load, facilitates this process. Finally, soil moisture status can be critical: a spell of steady rain followed by a heavier burst, first saturates the regolith, causing rapid runoff as the heavier fall arrives. This may trigger sheetwash, leading to rilling and gullying.

Geology

The three components shown on resource 2.24 clearly have influential roles. Firstly, the cap-rock controls the form of the upper slope and supplies the debris store used for gouging the gullies below. Some sections of the cap-rock are receding more rapidly than others and give more ample supply, which, in turn, helps to determine the main debris-slide tracks. Secondly, the marls and shales of the mid-slope are susceptible to erosion, especially when bare or sparsely vegetated. Thus, the gully density is greatest across these beds. For the first 40 m or so below the cap-rock scar, the slopes are steep (30 – 32°) and this zone may be an equilibrium slope of parallel retreat, i.e. gullies and interfluves are both retreating at about the same rate. Thirdly, the limestone of the lower mid-slope and the footslope is somewhat more resistant, giving a gentler gradient, and controlling gully alignment through joint systems, e.g. the angular path of Gully B on resource 2.24

(Source: adapted from: B H Adlam, A J Gerrard and L Morris, 'Accelerated erosion near Aix-en-Provence, Southern France.' *Department of Geography, University of Birmingham*, WP.25,1983.)

Activities

1 The research on which these findings are based is ongoing, but using the results so far, suggest what factors appear to be influencing the accelerated rate of gullying and hence slope development at this site

2 Does the gully development at this site seem to be following the theoretical process set out on page 41?

3 A slope is often quoted as an example of a system, e.g. a cascading system; a process-response system, etc. Construct a system diagram which represents the dynamics of the master gully at the study site.

CASE STUDY 2.7 *Mass movement and slope forms – Bredon Hill*

Background

As is seen in the case study on the Cross Fell Pennines escarpment (pages 23 – 28), topography which is developed on rock formations of varying strength, structure and lithology, is likely to display a series of steps, e.g. Gerrard's 'complex' scarps (page 26). Mass movement in its several forms usually plays a significant role in the evolution of these composite slopes. These slopes are excellent examples of the geomorphic principle that most landforms develop via intermittent surges of change, separated by periods of relative stability. These episodes of accelerated change may occur at different timescales, e.g. slumping, mudflows and solifluction at times of spring snowmelt, or following heavy rain-storms. Massive slope failures over several decades may be associated with medium term climate fluctuations or vegetational changes. As we study landscape today, the evidence of mass movement may be 'fossil', i.e. no longer active, or may be ongoing. An example which illustrates all these characteristics is the northern flank of Bredon Hill in Hereford and Worcester.

Key understandings

◆ Variables such as geology, climate, vegetation and human activities are important in slope development.

◆ Processes which help to form slopes operate over different timescales and may change over time as the slope evolves.

◆ A complex slope is usually the result of a variety of processes at work over a long period of time.

Note: *This case study includes detailed fieldwork results. Therefore, before studying it, you should be familiar with slope processes, such as rotational slip, and saturated slumping*

Bredon Hill

Bredon Hill is an **outlier** of the Cotswold escarpment and is built of a succession of **Jurassic** sedimentary strata varying from strong limestones to easily erodible silts and mudstones (resource 2.27). Its northern flank is a complex mixture of scarps, spurs, landslides, rotational slumps and debris-choked valleys. Resource 2.28 shows that the result of detailed morphological field mapping is not perhaps at first easy to 'read', but on careful scrutiny the elements become clear:

(i) two main scarps are formed by the Oolite cap-rock and the Middle Lias Marlstone Rock;

(ii) the weaker formations between the key scarp formations have suffered repeated slope failures, the resulting slides, slumps and flows partially masking the scarps and clogging the valleys;

(iii) valleys have serrated the slope into an alternating series of spurs and embayments.

Resource 2.27 gives a simplified summary of these elements, indicating the four zones into which the slope may be divided. Each zone exhibits distinctive process-form relationships.

Mass movement forms and processes

Bredon Hill presents a landscape which can only be understood in terms of the various processes of mass movement and the forms they create. Varied evidence suggests that the slope failure forms range in age from Late Devensian to the present day. (The Devensian is a late stage in the Pleistocene glaciation which ended around 10 000 years ago.) This continuum of mass movement must have diminished gradually in scale and vigour as the climatic and biotic factors changed, as the slopes were deeply modified and as the

retreat of the Inferior Oolite cap rock reduced the catchment supplying water to the fundamentally important ground water reservoir.

Today, the slopes possess varying degrees of stability. On the upper parts of the hill, highly localised conditions are critical in explaining why one slope may be undergoing active slump while another which is close by and of greater overall angle remains stable. The important factors are geology and structure relative to ground water springs, and site location relative to Middle Lias spurs and benches. On the lower hillslopes, the potential for mass movement is more restricted. Debris slides can occur on the Middle Lias scarp slope. The old flow lobes, on the other hand, are generally stable unless their upper ends become loaded by the addition of water and debris from above. Given enough loading, slopes which seem to be well below the threshold angle become critical and move in an effort to achieve a new equilibrium.

Woollashill mudslide

At a site near Woollashill (GR.944403), mass movement is active today from the Oolite scarp right down to the footslope (resource 2.28). On the Upper Lias slopes, rotational slips have fresh scarps and well developed slip depressions, usually water filled. The average slope here is 9°. Pressure ridges and counter scarps are present, indicating a complex slip sole. Well defined shears mark this panel of movement from the crest down to 180 m OD and can be traced down almost the whole slope to a position well below the Middle Lias scarp. The upper area is fed by a cluster of springs where ground water emerges from beneath the regolith at a level which is somewhat below the foot of the Oolite scarp. Downhill the landslips feed into a bowl-shaped depression where the

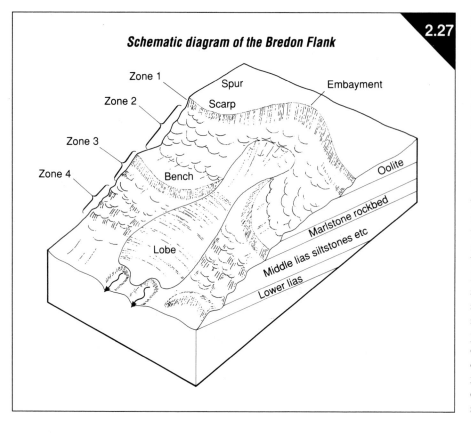

Schematic diagram of the Bredon Flank

2.27

Labels: Zone 1, Zone 2, Zone 3, Zone 4, Spur, Scarp, Embayment, Bench, Oolite, Lobe, Marlstone rockbed, Middle lias siltstones etc, Lower lias

slip sole is shallower and also steeper. Movement becomes increasingly translational and complicated, and includes debris fall and debris or slab slide. Even minor mudflow can occur. From the bowl the debris is channelled over the Marlstone Rockbed into two feeder runs or chutes. Through these, debris and water is supplied, usually in a piecemeal manner, to the head of the flow lobe choking the valley.

The mechanism generating movement seems to be that of undrained loading in which debris and water from above is augmented by spring water from the Middle Lias. The impact of a quantity of saturated mud and debris from above may produce critical loading and consequently extremely high pore water pressures which triggers off a mudslide. Lower down, the debris rides up onto the mud in front. At times the mechanism is effective enough to cause low angle and apparently stable slopes well

Zone 1 Scarp slope of the Oolite cap rock

The scarp is made up of a set of alternating embayments and spurs, the result of unequal scarp retreat. The scarp is strongest where the removal of the debris and slumped material is most efficient, e.g. where valleys have broken through the Middle Lias formations below. Above the remaining Middle Lias benches, the debris from the repeated landslips is removed slowly, and so has built up to obscure the scarp face.

Zone 2 Landslipped Upper Lias mudstones and shales

Mass movement is recurrent on these weaker formations, especially at times of heavy water content following winter-freezing. The upper component of this zone is a confusion of rotational slips and landslides. The lower component consists of toe holes where the debris spills out on to the Middle Lias benches or depressions which are debris feeder stores for the valley heads notched into the Middle Lias bench.

Zone 3 Middle Lias escarpment

The scarp is broken into a series of marked spurs, most of which are capped by the strong Marlstone Rockbed. The benches on top of this formation vary in size, dependent on how much debris has slumped and then slid from the overlying formations. The scarp face below the cap rock is made up of a succession of fine siltstones, clays, mudstones and the limestone beds. Slope failure is common and there are large slips. Between the scarp spurs the valleys are partially choked by the lobes of past mudflows and slides, supplied by the copious debris supply from the Oolite and Upper Lias formations.

Zone 4 The footslope

The valleys which spill out between the Middle Lias spurs are so choked with material deposited as the underlying gradient decreased, that the present surface is convex. Below this series of lobes, present-day streams are cutting their heads into the toes of these lobes producing a series of seepage depressions or spring heads. The lobes of debris are a set of fragmenting spurs which are irregular small scarp and bench features, the slip blocks from multiple slope failure of the Middle Lias scarp. Occasional hills of the Lower Lias mark the edge of this footslope zone.

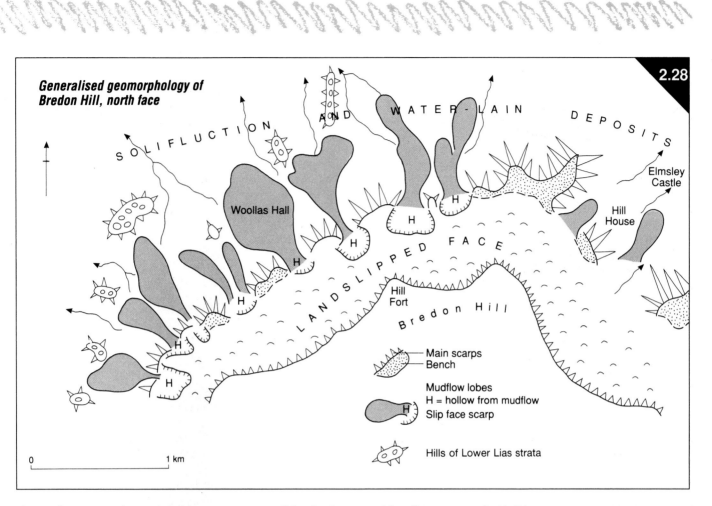

Generalised geomorphology of Bredon Hill, north face

2.28

SOLIFLUCTION AND WATER-LAIN DEPOSITS

Woollas Hall

Elmsley Castle

Hill House

LANDSLIPPED FACE

Hill Fort

Bredon Hill

Main scarps
— Bench

Mudflow lobes
H = hollow from mudflow
Slip face scarp

Hills of Lower Lias strata

0   1 km

---

down the accumulation lobe to move. But given the right combination of weather events, antecedent ground water and certain conditions in the temporary debris store provided by the runs, exceptional mass movement can occur. This is a mixture of mudflow and mudslide. In the wake of such movements, striated switchback tracks and mudflow levees are left. Lower down, however, on the accumulation lobe, where the movement runs out, convex toe lobes are created. The accumulation lobe filling the valley on the footslope is an amalgam of flows of wide age range. The disruptive effect of contemporary movements on this mass of flows is reflected in marginal and other shears, in slip scarps and in pressure ridges.

Exceptional mass movements at this site have been reported on various occasions. Grove (1953) recorded a movement of 15 m in 30 minutes in one of the feeder runs. This flow travelled 180 m downslope, but Grove refers to an earlier movement of 300 m at the same site. On another occasion in 1960, the lobe extended 215 m downhill from the runs. Because of this activity, the site has been monitored since 1968, at first for exceptional movement, but now to include the slow, longer term shift of debris. Since 1969, there have been only two exceptional flow slides, neither of a magnitude as great as the movements listed so far. In May 1972, the lobe ran 95 m and in June 1973 60 m downhill from feeder runs.

(Source: adapted from: L Morris, and A J Gerrard, 'Mass Movement Forms and Processes on Bredon Hill', *University of Birmingham, Department of Geography*, 1974.)

Activities

1 Use tracing paper to draw the outline of resource 2.27. From the morphological map (resource 2.28) and the summary text of the four zones, label the diagram as fully as you can, i.e. features, processes and geology.

2 Use the Woollashill site to illustrate how a slope may be thought of as a cascading system e.g. inputs → throughputs (process and material) → stores → outputs.

3 Using a trace overlay on a 1:25 000 map of this area (OS Sheet no: SO 93/94), mark on the geological and morphological zones.

Background

It is generally accepted that frost action is one significant factor in the mechanical disintegration of rocks in seasonally cold and periglacial environments. The most commonly quoted mechanism is **frost wedging**: as water lying in cracks and joints within rock outcrops freezes, it expands, thereby increasing the tension in the surrounding rocks. After thawing, the ice cracks and joints remain partially open and so are capable of holding more water, which on re-freezing, stresses the surface rocks still further. It is the continuous repetition of this freeze-thaw cycle which causes progressive weakening of the rocks and eventual disintegration, resulting in rock slope retreat and landforms such as talus slopes and blockfields.

Clearly rock type is an important variable. Truly 'solid' rocks, i.e. those with poorly developed networks of minor joints and cracks are not easily susceptible to frost wedging. In contrast, rocks which have such networks are more easily penetrated by water, and so more likely to suffer from freeze-thaw activity. (Remember, the water we are considering here is not the water held within the pore-structure of rocks but water moving and lying along joints and cracks. The freeze-thaw cycle of such pore water also affects rock strength.) Yet as we study the effect of freeze-thaw activity, it becomes clear that the amount of rock disintegration varies considerably, even within similar rock types. In other words, rock character alone cannot account for the variations in mechanical disintegration of rocks in cold environments.

Recent studies have focused particularly on the characteristics of the **freeze-thaw cycle**: how often it occurs; how intense it is; how rapidly it evolves and how long it lasts. A freeze-thaw cycle is usually defined as that period of time beginning with the fall of temperature to below freezing point and ending when temperature rises above freezing point once more. Perhaps the most obvious hypothesis for us to propose is that the more frequent the freeze-thaw cycle at a location the more severe will be the rock disintegration. The results of the research study used below, from the Great Kabes region in Canada, shows that the relationship is not quite so straightforward. Notice that the research illustrates the modern trends towards in-depth studies of overall sites, yielding detailed results. This detail is valuable, but of course, may be applicable only to the study site. Therefore, comparisons between studies are important.

Key understandings

◆ Freeze-thaw mechanisms are particularly effective when surface and near-surface rocks contain small-scale joint and crack networks.

◆ Intensity and length of the freeze-thaw cycle may be as important as frequency in achieving rock disintegration.

◆ Factors such as altitude, aspect and now cover may have a significant influence on the character and effectiveness of the freeze-thaw mechanism.

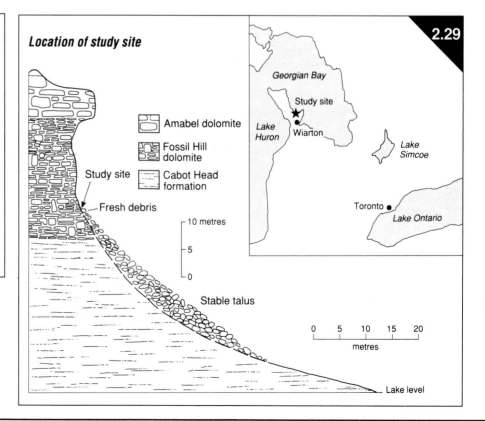

Location of study site

2.29

Amabel dolomite

Fossil Hill dolomite

Cabot Head formation

Study site

Fresh debris

10 metres

5

0

Stable talus

Georgian Bay

Study site

Lake Huron

Wiarton

Lake Simcoe

Toronto

Lake Ontario

0 5 10 15 20
metres

Lake level

Characteristics of the study site, Bruce Peninsula, Canada

The escarpment, overlooking Georgian Bay, consists of two main elements: (a) a 15 m vertical rock face capped by a strong overhang; (b) a talus (debris) slope with an angle of rest of 37° (resource 2.29). The strong dolomite beds (hard limestones) which make up the cliff face, overlie the much weaker shales of the Cabot Head Formation. The cap-rock of Amabel Dolomite has provided most of the block debris for the talus slope which is now partially vegetated with pine and birch trees, indicating that it is no longer being actively fed from the cap-rock. It is a 'fossil' feature formed in the colder conditions after the ending of glaciation about 12 000 years ago. In contrast, the upper part of the talus slope is active, with a fresh veneer of smaller debris derived from the Fossil Hill Dolomite.

The study area used in this case study (study site on resource 2.29) is a small section of the Fossil Hill Dolomite, near the base of the free face. The selected rock patch is well jointed, with spacing of between 25 cm and 16 cm, with numerous minor fractures (less than 60 mm wide and less than 10 cm deep) criss-crossing the surface. The fragments falling on to the upper talus slope average 12 cm long, 7 cm wide and 2.5 cm thick. The site faces south east and is rarely snow-covered, although the winters are severe (January mean temperature –7.5°C), yielding around 350 mm of snow. The data was collected over 115 days from December 1983 to April 1984, during a winter which showed typical variations around the longer term mean figures (resource 2.30).

The results of the study

The graphs in resource 2.31 summarise the results for the main types of information gathered during the 1983–84 winter:

(a) the amount and timing of debris falling from the rock face;

(b) the air temperature at the rock face;

(c) the bedrock temperature from the surface;

(d) the amount and timing of ground water seepage emerging at the rock face.

Most of the debris fell in two episodes, in February and March, with various releases in December and January (resource 2.31(a)). It was estimated that if the rate of debris fall from this 15 m² area was typical of the whole free face at the site then the cliff face would have retreated by 0.1 mm during that winter. This suggests an average retreat rate of 10 mm/century. Having measured the debris fall, we now need to explain it by examination of the other data.

The air temperature graphs (resource 2.31(b)) tells us that there were 27 freeze-thaw cycles in the 115 days of measurement. Notice that from mid December to late January the temperatures remained permanently below 0°C and so there were no freeze-thaw cycles. February shows a pattern of freeze-thaw cycles of varying length, from diurnal (the daily rhythm) to 9 days. Much of March was dominated by long freezing spells, before the freeze-thaw cycle was established late in the month and continued into early April. Follow the pattern of temperatures at 1 cm depth in the bedrock (resource 2.31(c)) and you will see that while the overall rhythm is similar to the air temperature, there are some detailed differences. Resource 2.31(d) shows that groundwater seepage on to the rock face was episodic, with two main episodes in February and March. These, and an early episode in December, coincided with debris falls.

The researchers found that temperature range and hence the freezing-cycle potential decline rapidly beyond 1 cm into the bedrock.

	1951–1980			1983–1984		
	Mean monthly temperature (°C)	Precipitation (mm)	Snowfall (mm)	Monthly temperature (°C)	Precipitation (mm)	Snowfall (mm)
Nov	2.9	94.7	39.4	5.7	127.6	53.7
Dec	–3.7	107.4	92.5	–6.3	170.4	197.0
Jan	–7.1	97.0	102.0	–9.8	77.0	124.0
Feb	–7.5	64.1	60.5	–2.2	60.6	42.3
Mar	–2.8	65.0	42.9	–5.9	65.6	35.9

2.30 Mean monthly temperature and precipitation 1951–1980 and the monthly averages for the 1983–84 field season at Wiarton

Thus frost action occurred within the upper fewer centimetres, rarely occurring beyond 5 cms. This accounts for the relative thinness of the debris blocks found on the upper talus slope.

(Source: adapted from: B D Fahey, and T H Lefebure, 'The freeze- thaw weathering regime at a section of the Niagara escarpment on the Bruce Peninsula, Canada', *Earth Surface Processes and Landforms*, 13(4), June 1988, pp. 293–304.)

Activity

Use the information and data presented to support the following conclusions reached by the researchers concerning the relative importance of cycle frequency, duration, and intensity of rock weathering:

1   'The results suggest that long periods of comparatively intense freezing followed by temperatures well above 0˚C represent the most favourable conditions for debris production. Shorter, more frequent events, even when accompanied by quite severe freezing intensities are much less productive, suggesting that the duration of freezing is more important than intensity'.

2   'Frost wedging in pre-existing fractures is the primary mechanism responsible for the release of material from the free face. The timing of maximum release closely corresponds with maximum groundwater seepage, and with high intensity, long duration cycles, i.e. those in which the freezing phase lasts three to five days reaching −14˚C in the air and −8˚C to −10˚C at 1 cm bedrock depth'.

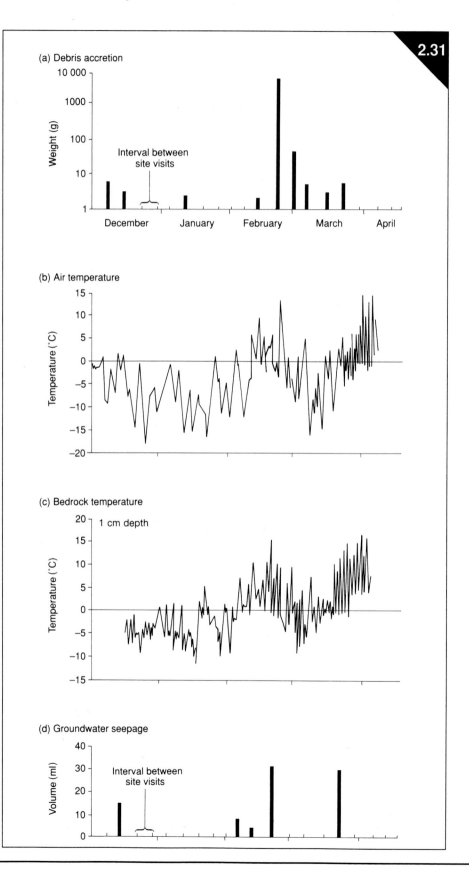

CHAPTER 3

Coastal processes and management

Introduction

Nowhere do the energies of natural processes and the power of human technology come into more direct and unrelenting conflict than along coastlines. The coastline is the interface between the oceanic and terrestial realms. If you look at a world population map, you will see immediately how attractive coastal locations seem to be. This narrow zone can be studied as an open system, and is known as the **littoral zone,** constructed of a set of components or subsystems as summarised below. You should check your understanding of the terminology and characteristics before using the case studies.

Definition of the littoral zone

The environment that exists between the outer (seaward) limit of wave action upon the underlying surface and the inner (landward) limit to which significant quantities of materials are transported and deposited.

The first two case studies are taken from California, whose popular name 'The Golden State' is partly due to its famous beaches and Pacific sunsets. Competition for space along the 1800 km of Californian shoreline is intense, and often in the scramble, little thought has been given to coastal processes. With increasing frequency, the ocean is making us pay for our thoughtlessness. These themes of pressures and impacts are central to the rest of the case studies, taken from different regions, for example, Africa, the eastern USA, Britain and the USSR, and from different coastlines, for example, offshore bars and estuaries.

The clastic material composing marine beaches presents a wide range of compositions and sizes. Although most commonly quartzose, some tropical coasts have coral sand and other volcanic coasts with rapid erosion may have beach material predominantly of ferromagnesian minerals. The coarsest sand material appears in the two zones of maximum turbulence or high energy where larger and smaller waves break (i.e. the breaker and transition zones: resource 3.1), and it is here that sorting is poorest. The coarsest material of all (i.e. gravel, cobbles and boulders) is commonly found in the backshore zone where it has been thrown by storm waves. This coarser material is subjected to considerable abrasion by high-energy wave action and, for example, it has been estimated that a 10 cm cube of limestone would become well rounded after only about one week under the action of 0.5 m high waves. Beach cobbles are well rounded but are commonly of low sphericity due to wave sliding action, compared with the low roundness and high sphericity characteristic of many stream cobbles. Each littoral zone possesses its own distinctive sedimentary structures but the most important of these are the cross-laminated sands dipping seawards at low angles characteristic of both the foreshore and the longshore bar.

Key understandings

◆ Two influential variables in coastal morphology and dynamics are wave energy and shoreline geology.

◆ Human activities have significant effects upon the storage and movement of energy and materials through the coastal system.

◆ Human response to hazard may have both positive and negative environmental impacts.

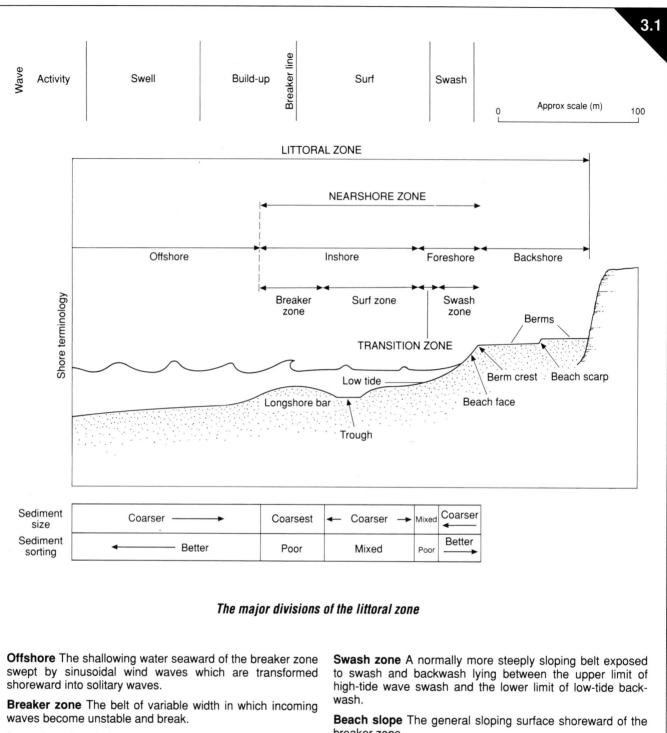

The major divisions of the littoral zone

Offshore The shallowing water seaward of the breaker zone swept by sinusoidal wind waves which are transformed shoreward into solitary waves.

Breaker zone The belt of variable width in which incoming waves become unstable and break.

Longshore bar A low ridge, or series of ridges, aligned parallel to the shore, usually composed of sand, which are formed within the high-water breaker zone and may be exposed at low tide.

Surf zone The zone between the breaker and swash zones swept by turbulent borelike translation waves following the initial wave breaking. Together with the breaker zone, this forms the location of longshore currents.

Longshore trough An elongated depression on the shoreward side of the longshore bar.

Swash zone A normally more steeply sloping belt exposed to swash and backwash lying between the upper limit of high-tide wave swash and the lower limit of low-tide backwash.

Beach slope The general sloping surface shoreward of the breaker zone.

Beach face The part of the beach profile usually exposed to wave swash.

Backshore The part of the beach above the level of normal high-tide wave swash.

Berm A low-gradient surface built by sediment deposited by receding waves. The berm crest is its outer edge and multiple berms may be separated by beach scarps which are normally less than 1 m high.

CASE STUDY 3.1 *Rocks, rollers and real estate in Santa Cruz county, California, USA*

Background

The sedimentary rocks exposed along the Santa Cruz coastline vary considerably in their resistance to erosion. This is due to differences in exposure, degree of cementation, structure, and stratigraphy. The presence of joints, faults, and erodible beds have led to average long-term erosion rates of about 30 cm per year, or greater in some areas. Much of the erosion, however, is episodic, and occurs during major storms.

Considerable damage has occurred along the coast during past winter storms. Valuable beach-front property has disappeared, roads have been destroyed, homes have been undercut, damaged, or ruined. The 1977–78 winter storms caused damage, even though extensive shore protection devices had been installed.

The city of Santa Cruz lies on the northern edge of Monterey Bay along the central California coast (resource 3.2). It is a cliff coastline, with cliff height varying from 6 m to 27 m, built of sedimentary formations and capped by uplifted marine terraces. The geological character has a significant control on the weathering and erosion processes. (This is summarised in resource 3.5.) Lithological variations within the main formations affect the cliff form and erosion rates as shown in resources 3.3 and 3.4.

Coastal erosion or seacliff retreat is caused by both marine and terrestrial processes. Surf action is usually the dominant agent, producing both hydraulic (wave) impact and abrasion. The rate of seacliff retreat is dependent upon the following natural factors:

1 available wave energy and exposure (including the presence or absence of a protective beach at the base of the cliff),

2 lithology of seacliffs and their resistance to erosion,

3 geologic structure including joints, faults, and folding,

4 height of the seacliff.

Runoff and human activities are factors that can add significantly to the rate of cliff retreat.

Erosion and protection of the Santa Cruz coastline

Wave energy

Waves (both sea and swell) reaching this coastline come from all sectors of the northwest and west-southwest. The largest waves are caused by winter storms, and a significant number of these arrive in the arc between northwest and southwest. Deep water waves with heights of 3.5 m can be expected five times a year, and those with heights of 6 m occur every eight to ten years. The open coast north of Santa Cruz is directly exposed to these waves. Protective beaches are almost totally lacking except at the mouths of the small coastal streams.

Lithology: the rocks of the seacliffs

Seacliffs bear the brunt of the wave attack, although they are protected in some areas by shore platforms (resources 3.3 and 3.4). *Use these diagrams carefully as you follow the text below.* Shore platforms develop best where bedding planes in the Santa Cruz mudstone dip gently seaward, but are also found where dips are landward.

Despite the direct exposure to strong wave attack, the resistance of the Santa Cruz mudstone to the hydraulic impact of the waves and abrasion generally has produced only moderate rates of coastal retreat. Between the city of Santa Cruz and the town of Davenport, 16 km to the north, aerial photo measurements indicate average values of 0 to 21.5 cm/year of cliff retreat over a twenty year period. Periodically an arch or sea cave in the seacliffs will collapse, which locally produces rapid retreat of up to 24 m in some instances.

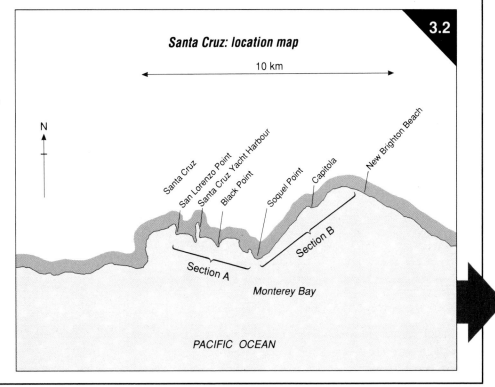

3.2

Santa Cruz: location map

10 km

N

Santa Cruz
San Lorenzo Point
Santa Cruz Yacht Harbour
Black Point
Soquel Point
Capitola
New Brighton Beach

Section A

Section B

Monterey Bay

PACIFIC OCEAN

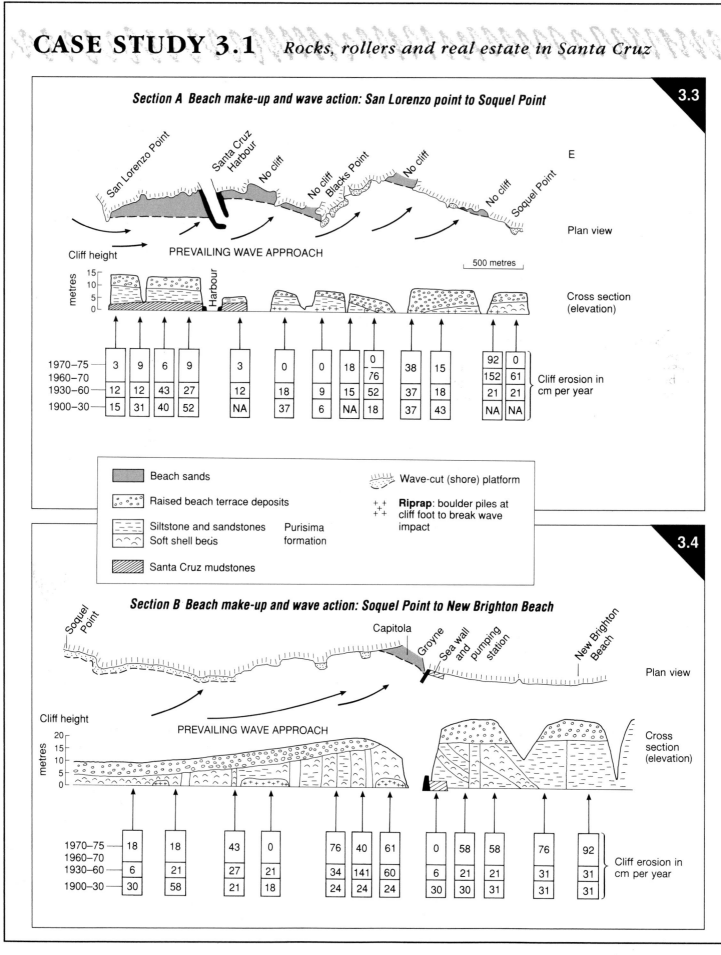

3.3

Section A Beach make-up and wave action: San Lorenzo point to Soquel Point

San Lorenzo Point • Santa Cruz Harbour • No cliff • No cliff • Blacks Point • No cliff • No cliff • Soquel Point • E

Plan view

Cliff height PREVAILING WAVE APPROACH

500 metres

Harbour

Cross section (elevation)

1970–75	3	9	6	9	3	0	0	18	0 / 76	38	15	92	0
1960–70												152	61
1930–60	12	12	43	27	12	18	9	15	52	37	18	21	21
1900–30	15	31	40	52	NA	37	6	NA	18	37	43	NA	NA

Cliff erosion in cm per year

Legend:
- Beach sands
- Raised beach terrace deposits
- Siltstone and sandstones — Purisima formation
- Soft shell beds
- Santa Cruz mudstones
- Wave-cut (shore) platform
- **Riprap**: boulder piles at cliff foot to break wave impact

3.4

Section B Beach make-up and wave action: Soquel Point to New Brighton Beach

Soquel Point • Capitola • Groyne • Sea wall and pumping station • New Brighton Beach

Plan view

Cliff height PREVAILING WAVE APPROACH

Cross section (elevation)

1970–75	18	18	43	0	76	40	61	0	58	58	76	92
1960–70												
1930–60	6	21	27	21	34	141	60	6	21	21	31	31
1900–30	30	58	21	18	24	24	24	30	30	31	31	31

Cliff erosion in cm per year

Erosional resistance due to stratigraphic variation is very noticeable in the seacliffs, both within the Purisima formation and along its contact with the overlying terrace deposits. Where unconsolidated or poorly compacted beds are exposed to surf action at the base of the seacliff, undercutting usually occurs in the form of notches, seacaves or arches, followed by collapse of the overlying material.

Within Monterey Bay, the seacliffs are protected from direct wave attack. The predominant waves from the west-north-west are refracted almost 90° before striking the coast, and wide sandy protective beaches begin to appear. The coastal cliffs throughout most of the city of Santa Cruz are composed of erodible sediments of the Purisima formation. Rapid erosion has cut back the cliffs, changing the trend of the coastline and creating the embayment known as northern Monterey Bay. Although the bay configuration protects this area from direct wave attack, erosion rates in these sandstone and siltstone beds (Purisima formation) are still greater than the rates in the Santa Cruz mudstone along the open coast to the north. The erosion rate of the Purisima formation is influenced by the varying hardness of different lithologic units (sets of beds) within the formation, the orientation of well developed joint sets, and the presence of faults.

The unconsolidated deposits which lie unconformably on the marine terrace that forms the top of the present day seacliff are exposed to surf action where the terrace has been extensively downwarped and so lowered to near sea level. In these locations, the bedrock portion of the cliff may be 1.5 to 3 m high, or less, leaving little resistance to wave action. In these cases, the terrace deposits are usually stripped off the platform, and cliff retreat is rapid, up to 50 cm/year.

Structural influences

Faults affect erosion rates in two ways. First, they act as zones of weakness along which erosion is accelerated. Second, inside the bay, numerous faults have set beds side-by-side within the Purisima Formation which have varying resistance to erosion. Much of the local coastal geomorphology can be ascribed to this process. Directly up and downcoast from Capitola average erosion rates in weak units in the surf zone were as high as 1.5 m/year. The headlands which form natural longshore drift barriers are a result of a resistant bed being present in the surf zone along sub-parallel faults between less resistant material. Measured erosion rates at these points are low relative to adjacent areas.

Seacliff height

Cliff height sometimes exerts an indirect control on erosion rates. The quantity of material produced by a given amount of coastal retreat is directly related to cliff height. For example, cliffs have been undercut and have subsequently failed, and large blocks have broken out along joint sets and fallen to the beach below. To the extent that this material remains in place at the foot of the cliff, it serves as temporary 'riprap' to buffer the cliffs from direct wave attack. However, the large sandstone and siltstone blocks produced by breakdown of the Purisima Formation last only a few years in the surf zone.

Impact of coastal erosion

Human activities

Human activities can affect natural rates of coastal retreat. Those actions which have been the most widely observed and documented are those which lead to the formation of a beach or loss of protective beaches. The construction of groynes, jetties, and breakwaters are good examples of synthetic structures that alter

beach-shore conditions. In addition, structures at the top of the seacliff can produce direct increases in cliff failure (resource 3.5).

Two jetties constructed as part of the Santa Cruz small craft harbour have had an effect on coastal processes in northern Monterey Bay. A broad protective upcoast beach formed where severe erosion (up to 90 cm per year) had been occurring. The interruption of longshore drift and loss of sand downcoast led to increased erosion, and private property owners had a buffer or riprap placed to prevent erosion along the ocean front. At Capitola, several kilometres downcoast, a groyne was constructed to trap sand moving downcoast in order to form a protective beach. The existing beach disappeared following the upcoast construction of the harbour at Santa Cruz. The downcoast side of the groyne is devoid of a beach and is adjacent to a vertical concrete wall which encloses a sewer pumping station. The lack of sand, combined with the concentration of wave energy immediately downcoast from the retaining wall, produces above average erosion rates.

The stretch of coast from Capitola Beach southwestward to New Brighton Beach is composed of well-jointed erodible beds within the Purisima Formation. The combination of erodible material and lack of a significant protective beach has led to severe cliff retreat along 1.5 km of ocean front. The lack of a protective beach is due to the fact that the cliff line is oriented in a direction conducive to high rates of longshore drift, and also because there is no structure downcoast to trap littoral materials. The average erosion rate in this area over the past 100 years has been about 30 cm/year. Since 1970, rates of 45 to 90 cm/year have been occurring. As a result, the foundations of apartment buildings on the seacliff have been gradually undercut, leaving portions of the concrete foundations unsupported. A similar failure continues to occur in the

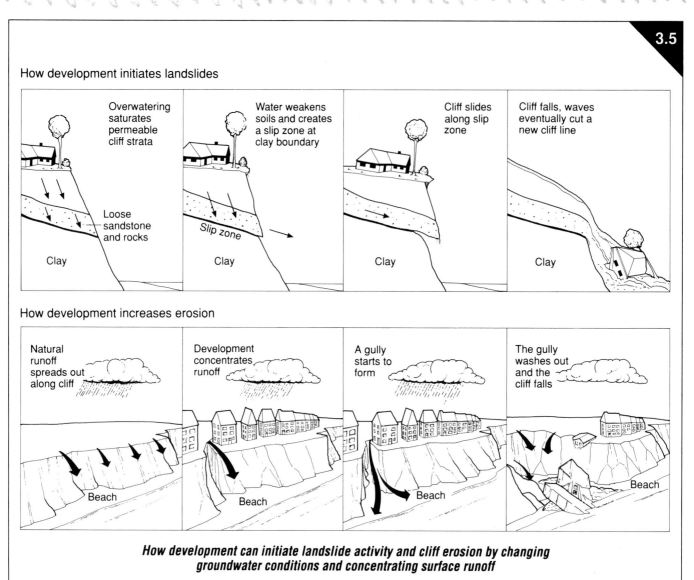

How development initiates landslides

Overwatering saturates permeable cliff strata

Loose sandstone and rocks

Clay

Water weakens soils and creates a slip zone at clay boundary

Slip zone

Clay

Cliff slides along slip zone

Clay

Cliff falls, waves eventually cut a new cliff line

Clay

How development increases erosion

Natural runoff spreads out along cliff

Beach

Development concentrates runoff

Beach

A gully starts to form

Beach

The gully washes out and the cliff falls

Beach

How development can initiate landslide activity and cliff erosion by changing groundwater conditions and concentrating surface runoff

area; the exceptionally severe storms of the 1977–78 winter caused numerous failures along this stretch of coast. No structures were immediately endangered during the 1977–78 winter but some may be endangered within five to ten years.

Vehicle traffic along a road located at the top edge of the seacliff, the saturation of the cliffs by storm drain discharge, and the wedging action of tree roots along joint sets have all contributed to rapid cliff retreat in this area. Although vegetation may serve to stabilise steep slopes in some locations, deep rooted plants may actually increase erosion along near-vertical seacliffs.

In an area of naturally high erosion rates, the effects of human activity have accelerated cliff retreat even more. Human habitation of the bluff top and along the back beach itself is nearly continuous along much of northern Monterey Bay. Although many of the cliff-top residences may have been initially built with some setback from the cliff edge, continued erosion has threatened many of the homes and led to the expenditure of hundreds of thousands of dollars to place protective riprap. However, even this precaution does not ensure permanent protection from surf action. Undercutting and settling

necessitate periodic replenishment of riprap at additional cost. Effects of reflected or altered wave action in transferring damaging erosion to adjacent unprotected properties can also be a serious problem.

1978 Storm damage

Continued heavy wave action, combined with high tides, during January of 1978 caused severe damage to a number of beach-front residences along northern Monterey Bay south of New Brighton Beach. Most of these houses had been recently built at the base of a seacliff on a back beach area. Although a 30 to 60 m wide beach normally protected the homes, the severe wave action of the storm and high tides removed the entire beach, undermined foundations, broke glass windows, and led to the loss of decks, patios, stairways, and landscaped front yards. One residence with a shallow concrete wall foundation partially collapsed as the foundation was undercut. Although this beach is normally in equilibrium, it is only a matter of time before the 50 or 100 year storm will totally remove the beach and destroy these homes.

Episodic seacliff retreat

Numerous observations indicate that major cliff retreat occurs episodically when large blocks fail or collapse due to undercutting or weakening. Much of this activity occurs during severe storms when wave action is intense and the cliffs are weakened by saturation from rainfall and runoff.

Summary

In the aftermath of the 1977–78 winter storms, individuals and groups of homeowners are applying to local government for permission to install riprap, bulkheads, and seawalls in a variety of sizes and shapes. The expenses are considerable and the secondary effects of such protective structures are not always known or understood. Local planning agencies are working to develop a uniform plan of coastal protection. The California Coastal Commission (CCC) has the authority to make decisions on such proposals in addition to planning ahead for future land usage.

(Source: G B Griggs, and R E Johnson, U C California at Santa Cruz, 'Coastline Erosion, Santa Cruz County' *California Geology*, April 1979, pp. 67 – 76.)

Activities

1 a What is the prevailing direction of wave approach along the Santa Cruz coast?

b Describe the characteristics of waves arriving along the Santa Cruz coast, and suggest why they should be high energy waves.

c Explain the development of Monterey Bay.

2 a Draw a diagram to show the effect of the shape of the coastline in resource 3.2 on the direction of wave approach in Monterey Bay.

b Your diagram should show that waves are refracted by up to 90° as they roll ashore along northern Monterey Bay. This should reduce their energy but this part of the bay is still suffering from erosion. Why?

3 Using resources 3.3 and 3.4 and the text,

a describe the coastline of the Santa Cruz area;

b evaluate the statement that erosion along this stretch of coast can be explained in terms of the geology.

4 Does the data of resources 3.3 and 3.4 tell us whether rates of coastal erosion are increasing or decreasing?

5 a What effects has the building of Santa Cruz harbour had upon the evolution of this coastline?

b Why has the town of Capitola had to build a groyne?

6 By the use of a labelled diagram of the northern part of Monterey Bay, set out evidence to support the assertion that human interference with natural processes at one location, has impacts upon other locations i.e. it has a knock-on effect.

7 What effects has continued erosion had upon cliff-top properties, and to what extent is this due to thoughtless or poorly planned development? What responses have local property owners and planners made?

8 How does this case study illustrate the idea that most environmental systems exist for much of the time in a state of balance, or dynamic equilibrium, interrupted by brief surges of change?

9 In 1981, the California State government decided that an overall plan for the 1800 km of California's coast is needed. Why should such a comprehensive plan be more effective than leaving the planning to each local authority along the coastline?

Background

As development along the Californian coastline intensifies and the impacts and hazards it creates become more obvious (see case study 3.1, and resource 3.5) the need for comprehensive management becomes more urgent. A crucial element for effective management is a full and reliable data-base, i.e. information on which decisions can be made. One result was the setting up, in 1981, of the Coast of California Storm and Tidal Waves Study (CCSTWS). This twenty year programme is being carried out by the US Corps of Engineers, and administered by the California Coastal Commission. The 1800 km of coastline has been divided into six regions. The San Diego region in the south is to be studied first. This has been given priority because of the intensity of human activity and because it has 'a long history of shoreline erosion, and suffered $116 million in damages during the severe winter storms of 1982–83'.

This case study reports on the Oceanside cell, which is a complex unit with cliffs, lagoons and variable drift directions, which have been critically influenced by human activities (resource 3.6 and photo below).

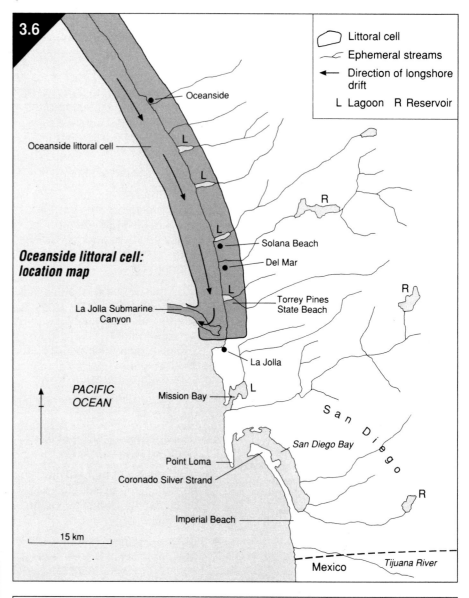

3.6

Key:
- Littoral cell
- Ephemeral streams
- Direction of longshore drift
- L Lagoon   R Reservoir

Oceanside

Oceanside littoral cell

Oceanside littoral cell: location map

La Jolla Submarine Canyon

Solana Beach

Del Mar

Torrey Pines State Beach

La Jolla

PACIFIC OCEAN

Mission Bay

San Diego

San Diego Bay

Point Loma

Coronado Silver Strand

Imperial Beach

15 km

Mexico   Tijuana River

Plastic covering to prevent further collapse at Del Mar

Key understandings

◆ The most important unit of study being used to build the data-base is the **littoral cell**: *a segment of coastline that is involved in a complete cycle of littoral transportation and sedimentation.*[2]

◆ It works as an open system (resource 3.7): energy and materials e.g. water and sediments, enter the cell (*inputs*), move through (*throughputs*) and are stored in the cell (*stores*), and finally leave the cell (*outputs*).

◆ The workings of this littoral cell system are measured by its **sediment budget**: the balance between inputs, stores and outputs. Using this framework and measurements, forecasts can be made about the future of a particular stretch of coastline. For instance, if sand inputs to a beach store exceed outputs of sand from that beach, (i.e. more sand arrives than is removed), then the beach will grow (aggrade). If removal exceeds arrival, then the beach will shrink (degrade).

3.7

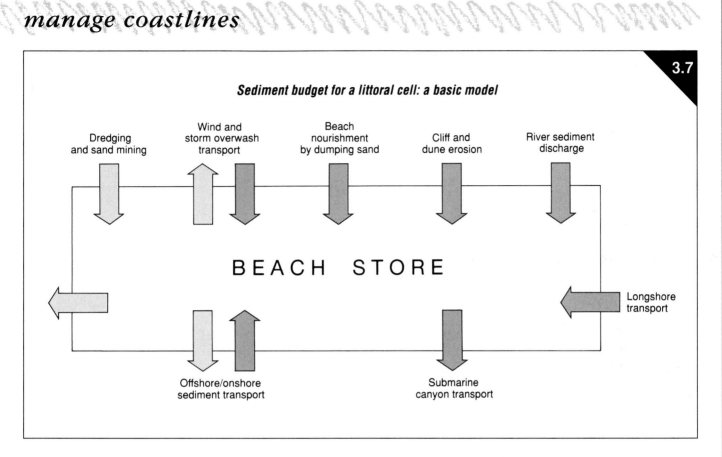

Sediment budget for a littoral cell: a basic model

Sediment budgets for the Oceanside littoral cell

A sediment budget describes the movement of sand-sized and larger sediments into, out of, and within a defined coastal segment, the littoral cell. The objective of the sediment budget is to permit assessment of shoreline change given changes in the factors affecting the quantity and movement of sediment. The sediment budget predicts net change in the amount of sediment along a defined reach. Since it is a reflection of the net effect of natural forces over the long-term, it can be used to assess general trends and to identify the impacts of proposed structures. It generally assesses the average annual change in sediment resource along a segment of shoreline based on a review of historical and current conditions.

The factors which are included in a sediment budget analysis are:

1 Sediment sources (rivers, cliffs, near-shore deposits of sediment, artificial beach nourishment).

2 Factors which affect the movement of sediment within the littoral cell (near-shore wave conditions, nearshore currents, tides, sediment characteristics, changes in sea level, sea bed character, structures altering sediment transport, wind and wave overwash).

3 Sediment sinks (stores of sediment) e.g. submarine canyons, shoals, sediment mining, offshore sediment loss.

The result of a sediment budget analysis is a long-term understanding of how these factors combine to alter the amount and distribution of sediments along the shoreline. Using a sediment budget, it is possible to assess the potential impacts of major storms, of floods, of dam construction, of harbour construction, and of other human activity along the shoreline. It is also possible to assess long-term shoreline stability under a variety of conditions.

The 53.5-mile (84 km) long Oceanside littoral cell (resource 3.6)

is a complex system with beaches backed by cliffs, several major rivers and numerous coastal streams, major lagoons, and a major small craft harbour. The cell has a long history of coastal erosion problems, particularly those associated with the harbour at Oceanside.

Most recent studies of longshore sediment transport have estimated net southerly transport at Oceanside at from 102 000 to 254 000 yds³/year. All agree that net transport is to the south.

In addition, the movement of sediments into and out of the cell is highly episodic. Most river sediment discharge in the region is the result of infrequent major storms; the floods caused by these storms both bring large amounts of sediment to the shoreline and flush out accumulated sediments from the lagoons along the coast. (Southern California has a 'Mediterranean' climate, with rain mostly occurring in a few winter storms.)

3.8

Oceanside Harbour breakwater and dredger

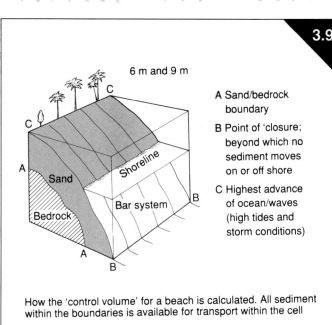

3.9

6 m and 9 m

C

C

A

Sand

Shoreline

Bedrock

Bar system

B

A

B

A Sand/bedrock boundary

B Point of 'closure; beyond which no sediment moves on or off shore

C Highest advance of ocean/waves (high tides and storm conditions)

How the 'control volume' for a beach is calculated. All sediment within the boundaries is available for transport within the cell

Complicating this picture is the presence of Oceanside Harbor, which has changed natural longshore transport significantly since initial construction in the 1940s. The harbour interrupts sediment transport in both a northerly direction (which tends to move into the harbour entrance and form bars) and in a southerly direction (which builds up sand on the north side of the harbour breakwater and is diverted offshore) (resource 3.8).

Variables in the sediment budget

There are a number of key variables in construction of a sediment budget (resource 3.7). The main ones used in the Oceanside cell study are:

The control volume

At a certain depth offshore, sediments on the bottom cease to be affected by waves and nearshore currents. (resource 3.9).

The volume of sediment in the littoral zone is determined by the depth at which sediment movement due to wave and current effects is negligible. This depth is called the 'depth of closure', and the volume of sediment shoreward of this depth is called the 'control volume', this depth is between (6 m) and (9 m) for the Oceanside Cell.

Longshore transport

Annual transport to the south has been estimated at from 643 000 yds³/year to 807 000 yds³/ year. With annual transport to the north estimated at from 540 000 yds³/year to 553 000 yds³/year.

For purposes of this sediment budget, a net southerly transport of 194 000 yds³/year is used.

Gross transport in both directions along the coast is important in this cell because the harbour at Oceanside blocks transport in both directions.

Onshore and offshore transport

Sediments move onshore and offshore in both seasonal cycles (driven by wave action) and permanently (driven by rip currents). Based on numerous studies, an offshore loss of sediments due to rip currents of 100 000 yds³/year was used as the basis for this sediment budget.

Riverine sediment sources

There are numerous river sediment sources in the Oceanside littoral cell. In a given year, their contribution to the littoral sediment resource may be negligible or significant, depending on the extent of rainfall in the inland watershed. Rivers in the region tend to produce most of their sediment contribution during infrequent winter flooding.

Cliff-derived sediments

The cliffs contribute little sediment to the littoral cell on a regular basis, but may contribute significant amounts during infrequent periods of heavy runoff and or following landslides.

Beach nourishment

From 1954 to 1979, an average of 270 000 yds³/year were added to the beaches, most in the vicinity of Oceanside Harbour as a result of dredging operations. Since 1979, an additional 2 000 000 yds³ has been placed on the beach, most at Oceanside. Much of the sediment placed on Oceanside Beach to the south of the harbour has been eroded within a short time period after nourishment, indicating that the southern beach is out of equilibrium.

A substantial portion of sediments placed on the beach by nourishment programs are fine sands and silts from harbor dredging. Most will be carried quickly offshore as they are sorted on the beach by wave action.

Sediment sinks

The primary sediment sink in the cell is the Scripps-La Jolla Submarine Canyon, which extends to the nearshore zone (resource 3.6). Virtually all sediment moving downcoast is lost to the submarine canyons.

Harbour shoaling

Shoaling in the harbour and at the entrance to major lagoons usually involves finer grained sediments than exist on the beaches. Oceanside Harbour traps several hundred thousand cubic yards of sediment each year. Sediment accumulation in the harbour has declined from 450 000 yds^3/year from 1950–1971 to 293 000 yds^3/year from 1971 to 1981. This suggests that there is a declining supply of finer sediments in the nearshore zone.

Sea level rise

As sea level rises relative to the shoreline, there is an apparent shoreline regression. Sea level rise in the Oceanside Cell is estimated at .02–.05 feet per year. The impact of this rise is negligible in the short term.

Preliminary conclusions of the sediment budget analysis

The most accurate and precise sediment budget data are for the immediate vicinity of Oceanside Harbour. These data suggest that for the period following contruction of the harbour (1962 to 1972) there was a net annual accretion north of the harbour, a net offshore loss of sediments moving around the harbor breakwater, and a net accretion south of the harbour. This accretion was almost entirely the result of beach nourishment.

Since 1972, conditions along the coast have changed. A period of mild weather has been replaced by a period of relatively intense winter storms, with major events occurring in 1978, 1980, 1982–83 and 1987–88. These storm periods, the third of which coincided with a major El Niño event (see case study 7.1), caused major coastal erosion along the entire cell. For example, approximately 900 000 yds^3 of beachfill placed on Oceanside Beach in 1981 was washed away during the 1982–83 winter storms. There was significant cliff erosion as well.

Among the more significant findings of this analysis is the discovery of an offshore bar, beyond the 9 m depth line, beginning immediately offshore of the harbour and extending downcoast (resource 3.13). This bar probably represents sediment deflected offshore by the harbour and subsequently moved downcoast by bottom currents. This deflection is estimated at 240 000 yds^3/year for the period 1962–1972.

The analysis also suggests that the harbour has altered the natural longshore sediment transport for the harbour area significantly. Sediments moving south are either trapped by

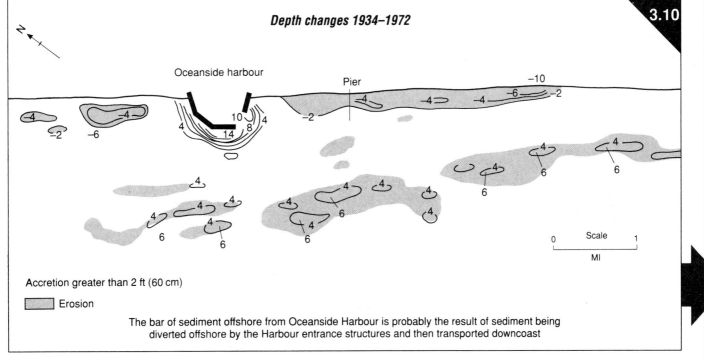

Depth changes 1934–1972 | 3.10

Accretion greater than 2 ft (60 cm)

Erosion

The bar of sediment offshore from Oceanside Harbour is probably the result of sediment being diverted offshore by the Harbour entrance structures and then transported downcoast

the breakwater, forming a bank of sand, or are diverted offshore. There is thus a net loss in longshore sediment transport to Oceanside Beach. This is certainly consistent with the history of erosion along this stretch of beach. When sediment transport shifts to a northward direction, the sediment in the fillet of sand at the breakwater spreads out along upcoast beaches, accounting for the slight accretion noted in this region. Sediments from below the harbour area are trapped by the harbour, particularly finer sediments.

A conceptual sediment budget for the Oceanside littoral cell

The harbour at Oceanside is the key factor in the sediment budget for the entire cell. It has altered upcoast (north) and downcoast (south) transport of sediments with the general effect that upcoast beaches have retained sediments which would have moved downcoast under natural conditions. Likewise, downcoast beaches have not received sediments which they would have under natural conditions. River sediment contributions have probably decreased somewhat, although the sediment resource within the river beds in the lower reaches is still significant. The long-term impact of dams in the upper watersheds may not yet have been felt.

From Dana Point to Oceanside there appears to be a net downcoast transport, with offshore transport due to rip currents. At Oceanside Harbour, sediments may be deflected offshore to a deposition zone which may extend to the submarine canyons at Scripps-La Jolla. Sediments in this offshore zone are not moved onshore, but instead are moved downcoast by a coastal current generated by the predominantly northwesterly winds. Theoretically, this current could move sand-sized sediment downcoast whenever wind velocities exceed 15 knots (about 6% of the time). The beaches shoreward of this deposition zone are cobble or cobble with a thin layer of sand-sized sediments. They are eroding slowly.

(Case study adapted from: *CCSTWS Annual Report*, 1987, L A 1988 and *CCSTWS Quarterly Bulletin*, April 1988)

Activities

The California Coastal Commission report on the Oceanside littoral cell, draws these key conclusions:

- **The harbour blocks downcoast transport.** There is a build up of sediment north of the harbour and erosion to the south.

- **Sediment moving downcoast may be deflected offshore.** There is evidence that sediment moving downcoast is deflected offshore and carried downcoast parallel to the shoreline, rather than moving landward to the beach.

- **Impact of dams has not been felt yet.** Dams have trapped sediment, but the residual sediment in river beds has continued to provide sand to beaches.

- **Spoil from harbour dredging does not stay on the beaches.** The harbour traps fine sediments, which easily wash off the beach under wave attack. Sediment from the harbour itself has limited long-term value for beach restoration.

1 Use labelled maps, diagrams and sketches to illustrate what each conclusion means and to explain what is happening.

2 State briefly how the sediment budget for this cell has been altered.

3 List the 'gains' and the 'losses' resulting from the construction of Oceanside harbour, and assess the likely long-term environmental impact of this development.

4 **Review exercise**: Is the sediment budget of Californian beaches changing?

Many Southern Californians are convinced that their glorious beaches are disappearing. But are their fears justified? The two extracts below suggest somewhat different scenarios: (A) is from a research paper, published in 1978; (B) is from a 1988 report.

a Summarise the position taken by each report and identify the differences.

b Use the materials on the Oceanside littoral cell to explain:

(i) why Californians might be so worried, and

(ii) which of the two scenarios seems to be supported by the CCSTWS data.

(A) Modification of the natural system

Perhaps the most serious and least obvious modification to the natural system is the termination of the natural sand supply to both the Silver Strand and Oceanside littoral cells by the damming of coastal streams for water reclamation and flood control. A dam placed on a stream course is an effective barrier to water flow, but it is also a total barrier to sediment transport. Thus, a dam severs the sediment producing drainage basin from the coastline.

Data indicates that about 33% of the sand supply to the Oceanside littoral cell is severed from the coast by dams, so that of the 350 000 yds /yr potentially available in the natural system only 230 000 yds /yr can still reach the coastline. Thus, the apparent surplus in sand supply to the Oceanside cell does not exist, and with the limited precipitation in the area in recent years the littoral cell is deficient in sand.

In the Silver Strand littoral cell to the south, damming has severed 72% of the sand supply from the coastline. In this case, the 660 000 yds /yr natural sand supply is reduced to 180 000 yds /yr, which is insufficient to maintain Silver Strand Beach. The problem of insufficient sand supply is already apparent at the south end of the cell where the community of Imperial Beach is undergoing beach erosion.

Since the available data indicate that the littoral cells in San Diego County are now experiencing a shortage of sand, it is apparent that beach erosion is going to become an increasingly prevalent problem. As the sand presently moving through the cell is ultimately lost, the wave energy will be used in active erosion of the sea cliffs.

Planning will necessarily involve: 1) proper location and set-back of sea front structures from the shoreline; 2) proper design and construction of protective measures necessary for existing structures; 3) consideration of proposed dams and flood control channels that involve coastal drainage basins in terms of sediment supply to the coastline; 4) consideration of artificial replenishment of beach sand by nearshore disposal of sand dredge spoil and sand construction spoil; and, 5) research and development into procedures for recycling beach sand through the littoral cell rather than continue to allow its loss from the nearshore environment.

(B) Are the beaches really disappearing

Recently, articles in *Time* and in *Oceans* have suggested that beach erosion has reached crisis stage in many areas. According to Time, 82% of California's beaches are eroding at a rate of 6 inches to two feet per year.

This gloomy picture is not supported by CCSTWS study, at leady in the San Diego Region. CCSTWS Project Manager Tom Dolan: 'In Southern California, the beach width has not changed significantly over the last century, except for beaches directly affected by human activity, for example, Oceanside and Silver Strand.'

CCSTWS review of historic shoreline change showed that about 80% of the beaches in LA, Orange, and San Diego counties have experienced accretion rather than erosion since 1875. This generally positive picture is partly the result of sound coastal engineering and beach nourishment projects. The beaches at Newport and Coronado are good examples of stable, well-engineered beach projects.

What about the eroding beaches, such as Oceanside, Sunset Cliffs, Imperial Beach? What about cliff erosion and failure at San Clemente and Del Mar? Here, the problem has often been development without careful consideration of coastal impacts. Overwatering of lawns on cliff tops is causing much of the cliff failure in southern California. At Oceanside, the wartime harbor construction was completed without time to thoroughly consider coastal impacts.

What does the future hold? Generally slow erosion is likely, as development inland chokes off sediment flow to the coast. But, according to Tom Dolan, 'we can probably solve this problem using CCSTWS data to develop sound coastal engineerii.; programs.'

CASE STUDY 3.3 *Coastal management – or mismanagement? Abidjan, West Africa*

Background

The Californian case studies (pages 51 – 61) highlight two important understandings: firstly, how easily the sediment budget balance along a coastline is disturbed by human activities. These activities may be along the coast itself, or far inland. Secondly, the need for co-ordinated planning and management along the whole coastline. Such co-ordination is difficult, even within one State, but when different countries are involved, decision-making is far more complex, as this case study from West Africa illustrates.

Activities

1 The stretch of West African coastline discussed in resource 3.11 is a large-scale littoral cell (compare with resource 3.7).

   a Summarise how this cell worked in its natural state, i.e. before any construction projects.

   b Use a labelled map or diagram to show how construction projects have altered the working of the cell.

2 List the projects mentioned, their purpose, and the principal environmental impacts of each.

3 a Identify who has 'gained' and who has 'lost' from each project.

   b What can and should be done to solve this problem? (Think in terms of the littoral cell and its sediment budget.)

4 Group discussion: In what ways are the West African and Californian examples comparable and distinctive, in terms of (i) physical processes, and (ii) decision-making processes?

3.11

Dam blamed as West Africa's coastline disappears

Ocean currents sweeping along the coast of West Africa are washing huge chunks of coastland into the sea, threatening villages, tourism and industry in the region. A new dam is being blamed.

The Guinea current, one of the strongest in the world, is nibbling away at 2000 kilometres of coastline between the Ivory Coast and Nigeria. It carries off some 1.5 million cubic metres of sand each year. The consequences for Ghana, Togo and Benin are potentially catastrophic.

Experts trace the origin of the problem to the construction in 1961 of the Akosombo hydroelectric dam in Ghana. They say it obstructs the flow of sediment along the River Volta to the coast, 110 kilometres away. This means there is less sand to replace what has already been washed out to sea and the land retreats before the ravages of the current.

Little remains of the Ghanaian town of Keta, 30 kilometres east of the Volta estuary. Most of it has tumbled into the sea. Other coastal towns are threatened.

In neighbouring Togo, other artificial structures contribute to the erosion. In the mid-1960s, the country's capital, Lomé, opened a new deepwater port to improve trade with landlocked neighbours — Mali, Niger and Burkina-Faso.

The port is shielded by a 1300-metre breakwater. It obstructs the Guinea current which flows from west to east. Sand carried by the current collects on the westward side of the breakwater only, leaving the other side open to erosion.

Already, the current has washed away coastal roads in Togo. In 1984, it took just 24 hours to swallow up 100 metres of what used to be the main road between Ghana and Benin. Fortunately, engineers had built a new stretch of road further inland.

Residents of the holiday village of Tropicana, 9 kilometres east of Lomé, watched the sea advance 100 metres inland between 1978 and 1983. Government and aid officials fear that the town, a key source of tourist revenue for Togo, could disappear altogether unless the erosion is checked.

Erosion there has eased since the sea met a bank of sandstone uncovered by the erosion, but this natural barrier also disrupts the course of sand deposition.

The erosion also threatens commercial enterprises further to the east. At Kpeme, 18 kilometres from Tropicana, Togo exports some 2.5 million tonnes of processed phosphate from a jetty. These exports account for more than half the country's foreign exchange.

The jetty may collapse if the erosion of its base continues. Engineers have shored-up its foundations with boulders, but this is a short-term solution.

A recent study funded by the EC recommended that stone breakers perpendicular to the coast be erected at regular intervals. They would gather pockets of sand between them, guarding against further erosion.

Local engineers are sceptical, however. They believe that sand will only collect on the westward side, where the breakers meet the Guinea current. And if the breakers only protect Kpeme, then the town of Aneho, to the east, will be exposed, they say. For this reason, both stretches of coast should be protected. But the cost is huge. It costs £1-2 million to protect just one kilometre of coastline.

Donors, including the EC have pledged £25 million to save the coastline.

But if Togo saves its coastline, the erosion could accelerate in neighbouring Benin, where the foundations of coastal oil wells may be threatened.

(Source: Michael Bourke, Abidjan, *New Scientist,* 15 January 1987)

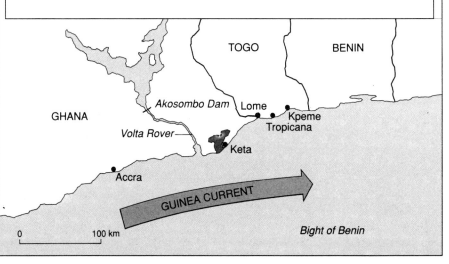

CASE STUDY 3.4 *Coastal barriers of the USA*

Background

Coastal barrier is a general term which includes a group of littoral features built of sand: offshore islands, bars, spits and tombolos, and their associated wetlands, lagoons and inlets (resources 3.12 and 3.13). Such barriers fringe low-lying coastal plains along many of the world's shorelines. One of the longest and most continuous series borders the Atlantic and Gulf coasts of the United States, for about 4000 km from Maine to Texas (resource 3.14).

Key understandings

This case study focuses upon the tensions and conflicts between these three statements:

◆ Coastal barriers are highly changeable and dynamic environments

◆ Humans tend to create non-changing, stable environments in order to reduce hazards

◆ Coastal barriers are attractive environments for human activities.

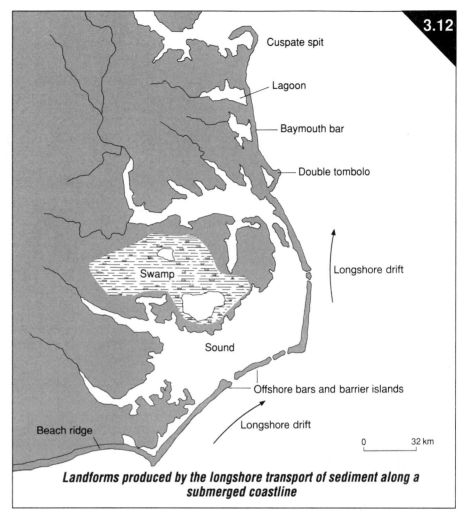

3.12

Cuspate spit

Lagoon

Baymouth bar

Double tombolo

Longshore drift

Swamp

Sound

Offshore bars and barrier islands

Longshore drift

Beach ridge

0   32 km

Landforms produced by the longshore transport of sediment along a submerged coastline

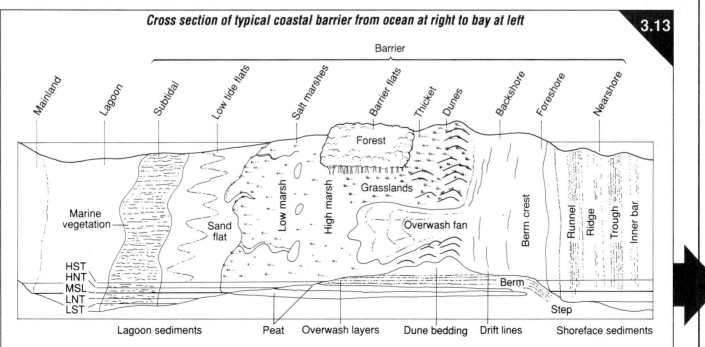

Cross section of typical coastal barrier from ocean at right to bay at left

3.13

Barrier

Mainland | Lagoon | Subtidal | Low tide flats | Salt marshes | Barrier flats | Thicket | Dunes | Backshore | Foreshore | Nearshore

Forest

Marine vegetation

Low marsh

High marsh

Grasslands

Overwash fan

Sand flat

Berm crest

Runnel | Ridge | Trough | Inner bar

HST
HNT
MSL
LNT
LST

Berm

Step

Lagoon sediments | Peat | Overwash layers | Dune bedding | Drift lines | Shoreface sediments

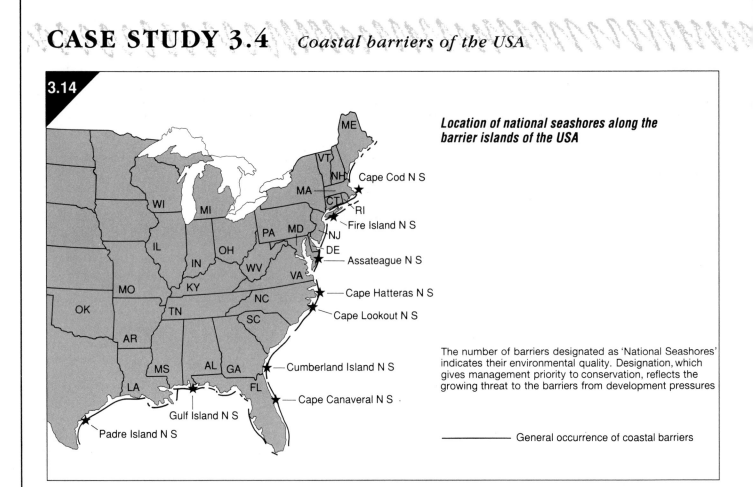

3.14

Location of national seashores along the barrier islands of the USA

Cape Cod N S

Fire Island N S

Assateague N S

Cape Hatteras N S

Cape Lookout N S

The number of barriers designated as 'National Seashores' indicates their environmental quality. Designation, which gives management priority to conservation, reflects the growing threat to the barriers from development pressures

Cumberland Island N S

Cape Canaveral N S

Gulf Island N S

Padre Island N S

———— General occurrence of coastal barriers

3.15

Miami Beach – a fully developed coastal barrier with lagoon infilling

The struggle for the barrier

The early inhabitants recognised that the coast has always been a hazardous place, settled on the bay side of the barrier islands, as far inland from the beach as possible. Over the past several decades that pattern has been reversed. Construction now takes place as close as possible to the shoreline. Today, such resorts as Atlantic City, Miami Beach (resource 3.15) and Galveston Island occupy barrier islands, and summer homes crowd many of the beaches. Naturally, pressure for public works to protect the islands and beaches is strong.

It is impossible for a northeaster or a hurricane to move onshore without affecting the coastal barrier. Hurricanes are more powerful but less frequent than the winter northeasters, particularly along the Atlantic coast. For example in September 1989, Hurricane Hugo moved onshore around Charleston, South Carolina causing extensive damage to the littoral zone and to property. The impact was most severe and evacuation of people most urgent along the coastal barriers. About 30 times a year, storms from the northeast generate waves with sufficient force to erode the beaches and front dunes. Every 100 years or so one of these winter storms has a devastating impact. Along the Gulf Coast, on the other hand, hurricanes cause most of the damage.

Formative processes

When the last period of glaciation ended between 12 000 and 14 000 years ago, sea level was some 100 m lower than it is today, and the shorelines of the Atlantic and Gulf coasts were from 35 to 110 km seaward of their positions now. As the icesheets melted, sea-level rose, reaching within a few metres of the present level 6000 years ago. Most of the barrier islands formed 4000 to 6000 years ago as the sea-level stabilised. Since then they have continued to change. Peat and tree stumps – remnants of forests that once stood on the bay side of the islands – are now being found on ocean beaches. In other words, the islands have been moving towards the mainland, the recession varying over several thousand years as sea level rose, sediment availability and wave energies have changed.

Migrating islands

The two most important factors in the landward movement of the island barriers are the overwash of water and sediment and the formation of inlets. During severe storms the beach zone and the dunes are overtopped by high water and waves. As the sediment-charged mass of water spills across the beach and flows toward the bays and lagoons on the landward margins of the barrier islands, sediment is removed from the beach and added to the island's interior. This process transforms the shapes and positions of the islands but conserves their total sediment mass (resource 3.16).

Temporary inlets are formed during storms when the narrower parts of islands are overwashed and breached, creating openings to the lagoons and bays behind the beaches. Sand moves through the open inlets and is deposited on the inside of the island as a large fan-shaped shoal (overwash fans on resource 3.13). These shoals may be

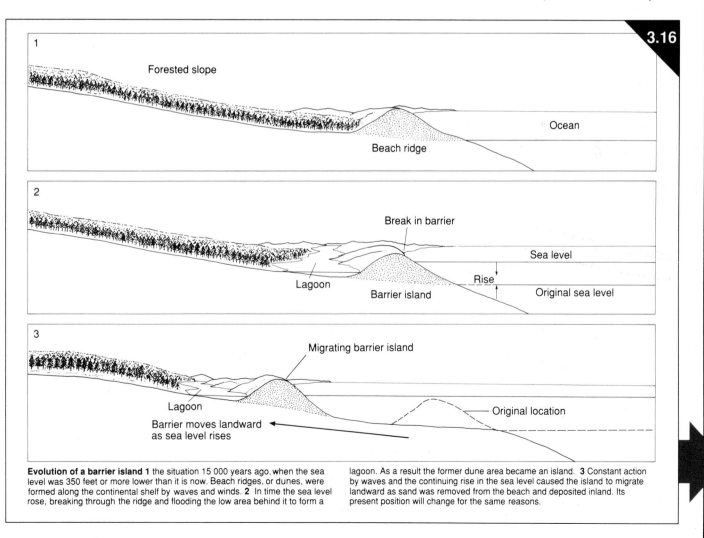

3.16

Evolution of a barrier island 1 the situation 15 000 years ago, when the sea level was 350 feet or more lower than it is now. Beach ridges, or dunes, were formed along the continental shelf by waves and winds. **2** In time the sea level rose, breaking through the ridge and flooding the low area behind it to form a lagoon. As a result the former dune area became an island. **3** Constant action by waves and the continuing rise in the sea level caused the island to migrate landward as sand was removed from the beach and deposited inland. Its present position will change for the same reasons.

exposed at low tides and eventually become salt marshes. Along the Atlantic coast, sea level is rising at about 15 cm a century, and coastal recession rates vary from 0.5 to 1.5 m a year. However, rates vary according to the direction of storm tracks, direction of wave approach and orientation of the shoreline, e.g. along the Gulf coast annual erosion rates of 7 m are being recorded in Louisiana.

Human occupance of coastal barriers

Left to the play of natural forces, barriers are little affected by gradual migration. Beaches restore themselves from sand supply from offshore bars, dune systems and erodible uplands. Vegetation recolonises overwash areas and wetland habitats flourish. But the process of migration wreaks havoc with human attempts to occupy coastal barriers. Buildings and lives are endangered by exposure to wave action, storm surges, high winds and shore erosion. Resource 3.17 shows the growing human pressures on the coastal barriers, despite the hazards.

Forms of response

1 Shore protection and beach restoration

As population and investment at risk on coastal barriers have increased, so have demands for public action to stabilise oceanfront shorelines. Between 1936 and 1978, the US Army Corps of Engineers assisted coastal communities in the construction of 75 projects costing $109 million. Until recently, the 'hard' engineering approach of shore protection has been the most common, e.g. structures such as jetties or groyne fields extending perpendicular to the shore to trap drifting sand, or sea walls in place of the vanishing beaches in front of properties (resource 3.18). These measures, particularly seawalls, have

3.17

Land use change on Atlantic and Gulf coastal barriers					
	1955		1975		% Change
	Acres	%	Acres	%	1955 – 75
Built up	90400	5.5	228700	13.6	+153.0
Agricultural	14700	0.9	10200	0.6	−31.0
Rangeland	101000	6.1	98800	5.9	−2.0
Forest	161200	10.2	152200	9.1	−10.0
Water bodies	102000	6.2	101200	6.0	−0.7
Wetlands	918000	55.6	838900	50.0	−9.0
Barrier dunes	256400	15.5	249200	14.8	−8.0

3.18

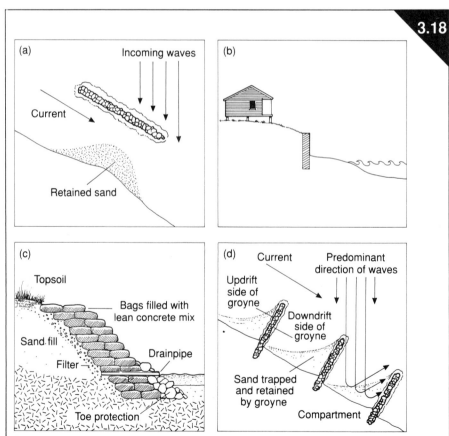

Protective structures represent the 'hard' approach to preventing or reducing erosion of a beach. A breakwater (a) intercepts waves before they reach the beach. A seawall (b) separates the sea from the beach. A revetment (c) is built on the beach to prevent waves from removing sand. A groyne (d) juts out from the beach and retains sand on the side facing the current. An alternative to hard structures is the 'soft' engineering technique of replenishing the sand on a beach periodically. The sand comes from offshore.

often hastened the loss of beach due to increased scour and interference with access to replenishment sand (see case studies 3.1 and 3.2,). Even the common practice of erecting fences to collect sand and enhance the dune barrier can be dangerous as it tends to lead to a narrower beach and steeper dune face, allowing wave action directly against the dune face (resource 3.19).

The failures of such structural approaches and the continued loss of beaches in front of major resort communities has led to a shift towards expensive beach restoration projects, i.e. the 'soft' engineering approach. Between 1980 and 1982, the Corps of Engineers restored a 17 km, 100 m-wide section at Miami Beach, Florida at a cost of $80 million. Another scheme, proposed for Sea Bright, New Jersey, would cost $100 million.

2 Public preservation

A different form of response has been to preserve certain barrier beaches and associated ecosystems through public acquisition and management. The most extensive of these efforts has been the establishment of nine national seashores (resource 3.14). These include 180 000 ha., of which 60 per cent is on coastal barriers. The US Fish and Wildlife Service has 38 national wildlife refuges covering 80 000 ha. Complementing these federal programs are a number of state and local government schemes, so that at least 50 per cent of all coastal barrier area is under some form of protection and management.

3 Flood insurance

The National Flood Insurance Program, set up by government in 1968, offers flood insurance cover to owners of flood-prone land, providing the communities in which they stand are operating acceptable flood management policies. This has accelerated pressures for development of the barriers, as it provides improved hazard cover.

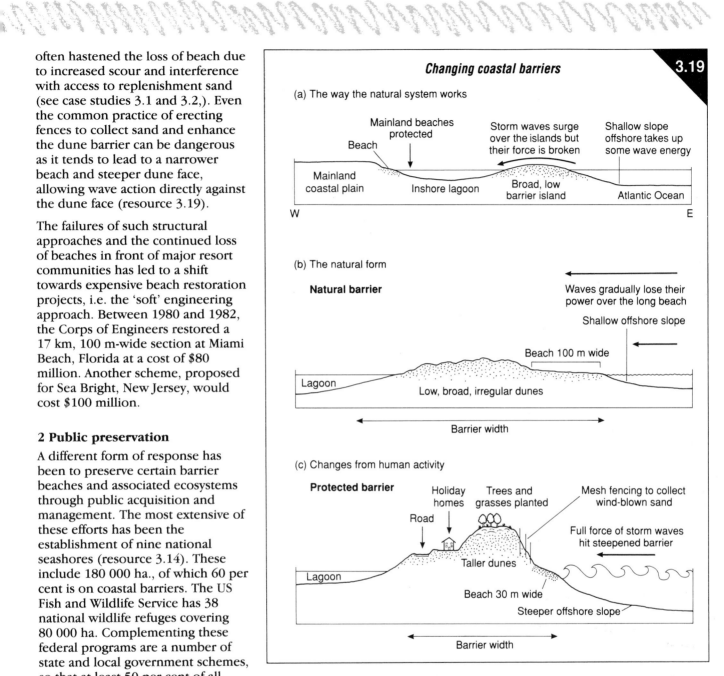

Changing coastal barriers 3.19

(a) The way the natural system works

Mainland beaches protected
Beach
Storm waves surge over the islands but their force is broken
Shallow slope offshore takes up some wave energy
Mainland coastal plain
Inshore lagoon
Broad, low barrier island
Atlantic Ocean
W · E

(b) The natural form

Natural barrier
Waves gradually lose their power over the long beach
Shallow offshore slope
Beach 100 m wide
Lagoon
Low, broad, irregular dunes
Barrier width

(c) Changes from human activity

Protected barrier
Holiday homes
Trees and grasses planted
Mesh fencing to collect wind-blown sand
Road
Full force of storm waves hit steepened barrier
Taller dunes
Lagoon
Beach 30 m wide
Steeper offshore slope
Barrier width

4 Coastal Barrier Resources Act

It has been realised that the flood insurance scheme and other federal support programs have been encouraging development. Thus in 1982, the government passed the Coastal Barrier Resources Act, whose key purposes are to identify 'undeveloped coastal barriers' and deny federal subsidies for developments on them, and to control more closely 'developed' barrier areas. About 29 per cent of the coastal barrier area has 'undeveloped' status. But remember that 40 per cent of the shoreline is 'developed', and is still in a hazard zone.

(Source: R H Platt, 'Overview of Developed Coastal Barriers', in 'Cities on the Beach', *Univ. of Chicago, Dept. of Geography, Research Paper No. 224,* 1987, pp. 1–16.)

Conclusion

The beaches and barrier islands are migrating out from under coastal development, making each building in turn a beachfront property. Many communities that reduced the risks by building dunes, groynes, seawalls etc. during the 1940s and 1950s now face rapidly increasing maintenance costs, no matter what protective efforts are mounted.

If the predicted 'greenhouse effect' brings about global warming, then sea level will rise more quickly and shoreline recession will accelerate. The alternatives are limited: to build hard structures and add sand as the sea encroaches or to retreat landward as the sea engulfs the developed beaches and barrier islands.

Power to the people: a local scheme

Massive projects like that at Miami Beach may get all the publicity, but increasingly local communities are introducing and controlling their own schemes. This is one example.

Mantoloking is a heavily developed coastal barrier between Bay Head and Normandy Beach, north of Island Beach State Park, New Jersey. Development began in the late 1800s and was particularly rapid between 1960 and 1980. The barrier is developed from the bay side to the beach, with two roads running the length of the town (which is about 2 km long) and almost every beachfront lot contains a house. In 1985 there were 117 owners of beachfront property.

Nearly all the buildings in town still have a dune between them and the sea. Much of this dune was destroyed during the 1962 Ash Wednesday storm, but it has been rebuilt by natural processes and human efforts. However, during the 1970s it was evident that human-caused dune deterioration was accelerating. This alarmed the residents who recognise the value of the dunes as a barrier against storm damage.

So in 1980 the Borough Council passed 'An Ordinance (local law) to Regulate, Preserve, and Protect the

Beaches and Dunes within the Borough of Mantoloking'. The law prevents any construction beyond a defined setback line (a line at a certain distance back from the dune front) and below a certain height above sea level. It prohibits people from walking on the dunes and requires landowners to maintain only one pathway across their dune. It prohibits disturbing natural vegetation or removing sand from the beach or dunes and motor vehicles may not be used on any dune.

Landowners may not lower the dune and must build up their dune if it is less than a recommended height. They are required to plant dune vegetation, erect fences and to restore and build up the dune system on the advice of the town 'dune consultant'. There is also a Dune Inspector who has the power to prosecute. The Borough has built a set of public dune and beach access paths. These boardwalks are raised and have gaps so that the sand can move freely and vegetation can grow, i.e. the natural processes are minimally impeded.

At least twice a year the dunes and beaches are measured and inspected. The officials and any interested townspeople walk the entire shoreline and inspect each landowner's dunes. A report is then made, recommendations are given out and landowners are expected to act on them. So far, the scheme seems to be working: there were severe storms in the winter of 1984, and although the beach was cut back, the dune crest was not breached. Soon after, the beach began to aggrade and some landowners speeded the process by bulldozing sand on to the dune face. Fences and grass plantings were placed on the new dune face and the pre-storm profile was established. By late 1985, there were few traces and the natural equilibrium had been restored.

Conclusion: Residents of Mantoloking know that the only thing standing between them and

the ocean is that narrow strip of sand held together by beach grass. What will happen however, in the long term, with the rising sea level and regional shoreline retreat, remains to be seen.

(Source: P J Godfrey, 'A successful local program for preserving and maintaining dunes on a developed barrier island: Mantoloking, New Jersey,' in *Cities on the Beach*, 1987)

Activities

1 Make a list of the main components of a coastal barrier system.

2 Summarise how a natural coastal barrier works, in terms of energy, material, process, form and time.

3 Compare the merits and weaknesses of 'hard' and 'soft' approaches to barrier beach management.

4 To what extent is it true to say that the Mantoloking community are attempting to sustain their Barrier Beach by inputs which support rather than change natural processes?

5 With a partner discuss this assertion: There is a fundamental conflict between the forces constructing and sustaining coastal barriers, and the way humans are using these barriers. This is a conflict humans are certain to lose.

CASE STUDY 3.5 *Environmental impacts of using tidal power – the Severn Estuary*

Background

An estuary is 'a semi-enclosed body of coastal water within which seawater is diluted with fresh water.' A map shows that for its size, Britain is well endowed with estuaries. It is hardly surprising that for many years there has been much interest in using these extensive inlets. Yet unlike the Dutch with their massive Yssel Meer and Delta Plan projects, Britain has only the recently completed Thames Barrage, the purpose of which is flood control. The line of gates are closed when necessary to prevent a combination of high tides and North Sea storm surges passing upstream through London. Nevertheless, over the past 30 years there have been a number of feasibility studies, such as The Wash, for increased farmland and improved drainage; Morecambe Bay, to create a fresh water reservoir; the Severn Estuary, to generate

electricity. All have so far failed to overcome the twin hurdles of cost and environmental impact.

However, uncertainties over coal, oil and natural supplies in the long

term, the controversial nature of nuclear power generation, the spatial logistics of harnessing solar and wind energy, the opposition to further inland HEP schemes all

---

Key understandings

◆ Generating electricity from tidal energy is a simple concept. Since many estuaries are funnel-shaped, they tend to have high tidal ranges, e.g. 7 m in the Severn Estuary. So if a barrage is built across an estuary and the incoming and ebbing tidal water flows are concentrated through turbines, the result is 'free' energy!

◆ The reality is not so simple. The proposed project outlined below makes it clear that a barrage

across the broad Severn Estuary would be very costly and have considerable environmental impact. This impact would not only be visual, but would involve severe changes to water movement and hence to sediment transport and deposition. This in turn, would affect beaches, mud-flats, harbours, coastal erosion and wildlife habitats. The study highlights too, how uncertain scientists still are about many of the potential impacts.

3.20

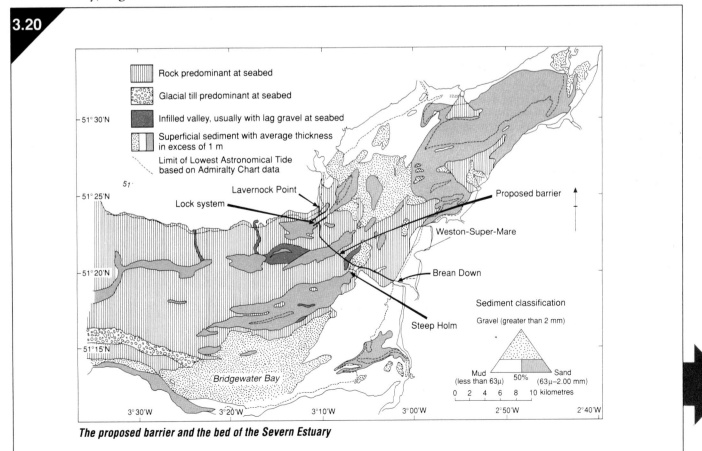

Key:
- Rock predominant at seabed
- Glacial till predominant at seabed
- Infilled valley, usually with lag gravel at seabed
- Superficial sediment with average thickness in excess of 1 m
- Limit of Lowest Astronomical Tide based on Admiralty Chart data

Labels: Lavernock Point, Lock system, Proposed barrier, Weston-Super-Mare, Brean Down, Steep Holm, Bridgewater Bay

Sediment classification: Gravel (greater than 2 mm), Mud (less than 63μ), Sand (63μ–2.00 mm), 50%

0 2 4 6 8 10 kilometres

The proposed barrier and the bed of the Severn Estuary

Impacts of barrage construction

The impact prediction covers three phases.

Phase I: Construction period

1 A key problem is the highly mobile and easily erodible sediment regime. The main concern, therefore, will be to minimise fine sediment erosion and redeposition.

2 Construction techniques, sequence and barrage orientation must take this problem into consideration. The proposed method uses a series of sluice gates to allow a complete crossing while retaining the freedom of the water and its sediment load to move in and out.

3 The construction would extend from the English side as quickly as possible to provide shelter for the fine sediments in Bridgewater Bay, because as construction proceeds there may be acceleration of current velocities in some areas.

4 Sea locks would be built at an early stage to allow navigation to continue.

5 It is intended that the sediment regime, water quality, dredging and spoil disposal practices would be able to continue with minimum disruption throughout the nine year construction period.

Phase II: Closure of the barrage

1 At closure, the tidal range and current velocities will change. These changes will be accompanied by a rise in mean water level within the basin. The main sediment regime change will be large scale and extensive deposition. Up to 30 mt will be deposited within the first year.

2 One of the crucial management tasks will be to close the sluice gates in a sequence which will control and direct the sedimentation to where it will have least impact or even most benefit, either above or below the barrage. This is particularly important for shipping lanes and harbour entrances.

Phase III: After the construction

Predictions become most uncertain in this phase.

1 We do know that more than 60 per cent of the intertidal area will be lost, and what we need to know is whether improvements in quality of the sediment regime will compensate for the loss in area.

2 The intertidal zone is particularly important in view of its internationally recognised status as an over-wintering area for wading birds and ducks.

3 The predictions need to consider the alterations in sediment regime, e.g. change in tidal mudflat profiles, materials, strength, time needed to become established etc. Long term impacts are uncertain.

4 Coastlines may become erosional or depositional, which would, in turn, affect holiday beaches, saltmarsh generation, land drainage, industrial cooling water intakes and effluent outfalls. There could then be further knock-on effects through the ecosystem foodchains.

5 The likelihood of less sediment in suspension and more deposited as stable bed layers should bring ecological benefits. However, possible disadvantages include the retention of pollutants and the risk of eutrophication if river nutrient and sewage inputs continue at the present rate.

6 After closure of the barrage, sediment inputs from rivers to the estuary basin behind the barrage will remain roughly the same, at 0.75 mt per year. This should cause few problems unless deposition is concentrated in a few areas. Incoming tidal currents will remain strong but the ebb flow will be much weaker. This may cause increased silting of river mouths in the upper estuary, because of greater net up-estuary movement of sediment.

7 Outside the barrage, the tidal range will only change a little but current velocities will be greatly reduced. As less sediment will pass through the barrage, the floor of the western estuary has little erodible sediment (and the sediment input from seaward is unknown), there is, therefore, a danger that the Bridgewater Bay muds may suffer severe erosion from storm waves.

combine to make energy policy a complex and urgent problem. Thus, interest has been revived in harnessing the enormous energy of the oceans, especially since the success of the French Rance Estuary scheme.

Environmental impacts of a Severn barrage

Tidal power goes part way to the dream of an inexhaustible, free, and non-polluting energy source with negligible impact upon the surrounding environment. It may be inexhaustible and non-polluting, but barrage costs are so high that it can hardly be regarded as free. Similarly, the impact upon the natural environment is greater than that of many other energy sources.

The scheme receiving the largest attention is the government funded investigation of a 16 km barrage across the Severn Estuary roughly from Cardiff to Weston-super-Mare.

This site has the greatest potential in Europe, but also some very difficult waters (resource 3.20). It would cost £5.5 billion (at 1984 prices), generate up to 9 per cent of UK electricity needs and be the equivalent of two major nuclear power stations. Unit costs would be comparable with those from coal or nuclear sources. To complete the research and the 9 year construction programme, it would not be operational much before 2005.

Two major problem areas being investigated are geological foundation conditions and environmental impacts (resource 3.21). The greatest uncertainties of prediction lie in the latter. A barrage will alter the water movement (hydrodynamic) regime over a large area, both above and below the barrage. For example, inside the barrage the tidal range will be halved, tidal current velocities will be halved and the rise in mean water level will cause more than 50 per cent of the existing tidal mudflats to be permanently covered. However, due to the relationship between current velocities and sediment carrying capacities, by far the greatest impacts will be upon the sediment regime. In the area above the barrage, the quantity of fine sediment carried by spring tides will fall from 30 mt to 2 mt. The sediment regime is crucial – it influences the design of the barrage, land drainage, coastal stability, holiday beaches, navigation, dredging, water quality and wildlife.

Present sediment regime

The Severn Estuary is well known for the large amounts of fine sediments constantly being moved around, most of which are in suspension. Indeed, the present ecosystem, unlike any other estuary in Europe, is suppressed by the high suspension load and the instability of the bed materials. The high current velocities mean that much of the bed itself is sediment-free or has only a thin veneer, as resource 3.21 shows. The coarser materials seem to operate in two cells. To the west of a line from Minehead to Abertaw, the net movement is offshore, towards the edge of the continental shelf. To the east, the net drift is upstream into the estuary. In contrast, much of the finer sediments circulate within Bridgewater Bay.

Conclusion

Unlike the foundation geology, where the technology for prediction and construction are well established, there is much less certainty about prediction of environmental change. The problems are regional in scale, involve complex interactions of physical, biological and chemical processes which are in many cases poorly understood. Further, the technology for investigating change, e.g. computer models, is still primitive and unreliable.

(Source: adapted from: R Kirby, 'Sedimentological implications of building the Cardiff-Weston barrage in the Severn Estuary,' *Proceedings of the Ussher Society*, 7(1), 1988, pp. 13-17.)

Activities

1 From resource 3.20 summarise the bed characteristics of the estuary

a inside, and

b outside the proposed barrage.

2 Suggest reasons for the location of the barrage.

3 a The present-day ecosystem of the estuary is referred to as 'suppressed'. What does this mean and what is the cause?

b Why might the estuary ecosystem benefit from the completion of the barrage?

4 Outline the hydrodynamics and sediment regime of the estuary:

a today, and

b after the building of the barrage.

5 Summarise the likely environmental impacts of the barrage and list the main areas of uncertainty.

6 From a small group discussion, construct two lists:

(i) giving three main points in support of the project

(ii) giving three main points in opposition to the project.

7 Compare and contrast the Leningrad (St. Petersburg) Dam (resource 3.22) and the Severn Barrage proposal, in terms of:

a the problem and the processes involved,

b the engineering solution,

c the purposes and uses of the solution,

d the environmental impacts of the schemes.

Leningrad (St. Petersburg) keeps out the floods — and motorists will benefit

London is by no means the only city to be threatened by floods. The problems of Leningrad, sited at the point where the River Neva flows into the Gulf of Finland, are even greater. That is why the Soviets have embarked upon a huge project to build a 25 km dam, 4.5 m above sea level, right across the estuary. The structure will contain two gates to let shipping through; at times of high tides the gates will slide shut to seal off the city from the sea.

Since Peter the Great founded the city in 1703, no less than 245 floods have been reported.

The two worst floods to hit Leningrad occurred within exactly 100 years of each other. In November 1824 the water rose 4.2 m and 569 people were killed. A century later, nearly half of the city was flooded and many industries were badly damaged.

Why is Leningrad continuously hit by floods while other cities in the Baltic, Stockholm for instance, are reasonably dry? The city's location provides a clue: it is in the most narrow and shallow part of the Gulf of Finland. Soviet scientists believe that the origins of the floods are deep depressions, which are generated near Iceland. In a depression, the water level rises. Danger occurs when a depression moves eastward towards the Baltic and the Gulf of Finland. It brings with it a powerful wave, which grows when it is forced into the narrow and shallow gulf. Strong winds reinforce this effect.

When the dam is finished in 1990, the gates will close within half an hour of a flood warning.

The barrier will run from near Gorskaja at the northern shore of the gulf, over an island called Kotlin (which houses the Kronstadt naval base) to Lomonosov in the south.

Not everyone agreed that a dam was the best way of stopping the floods. One possibility was to build banks of earth along the shores — but that would have made

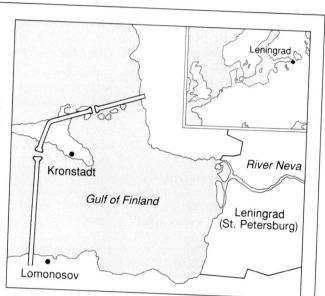

the city ugly beyond recognition. Another idea, to build a canal to drain the city centre, proved impracticable.

The most serious objections to the dam came from environmentalists. They pointed out that the structure would block off 400 sq km of the Gulf of Finland and could have serious implications. The water inside the barrier would get less salty and plant life and organisms would be disturbed.

Two passages, 200 m and 110 m wide, will let ships through.

The barrier will also have 64 smaller openings, each 24 m wide. They are designed to be closed in five minutes with gates that fall from above like a portcullis. Car drivers will benefit from the dam: it will act as the base for a motorway which will form part of Leningrad's ring road. The structure could even turn into a major tourist attraction: restaurants, harbours for small boats and bathing places should make the dam a popular place for a day out. To make the construction attractive, the two wider openings will be framed by pairs of huge wings, while the narrower openings will be decorated with spires.

(Source: *New Scientist*, 5 November, 1981)

CHAPTER 4

Water on the land – rivers at work

Introduction

The case studies in this chapter illustrate how surface water behaves in humid and sub-humid environments, and the implications for human activities (Arid environments are the theme of Chapter 6). The standard unit of study is the drainage system, i.e. focusing upon the input, throughput, storage and output of water (resource 4.1). An alternative and more comprehensive approach is to add the sediment and landform dimensions to create a fluvial system (resource 4.2). You should note that this latter approach does allow for the sediment component to be included in drainage basin analysis, i.e. that the processes of all three 'zones' occur within the drainage basin. This is important to bear in mind in studying the case studies which follow. How this fluvial system works and the landscapes it creates, depend upon a set of interacting variables (resource 4.3).

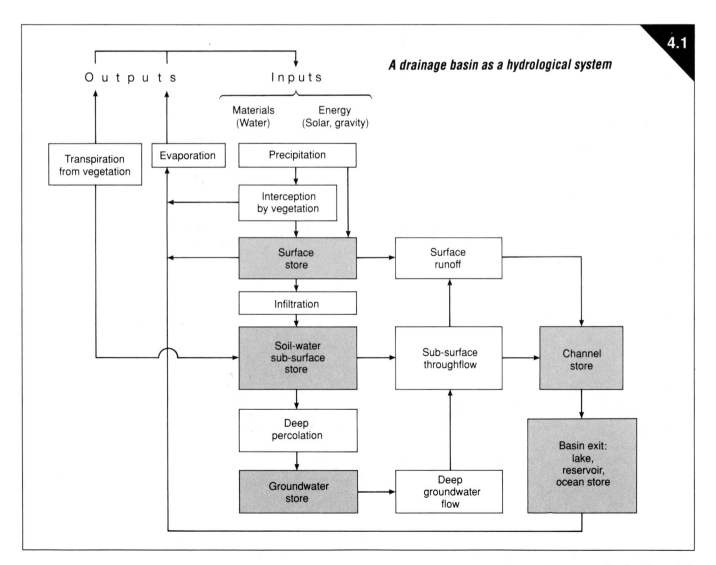

4.1

A drainage basin as a hydrological system

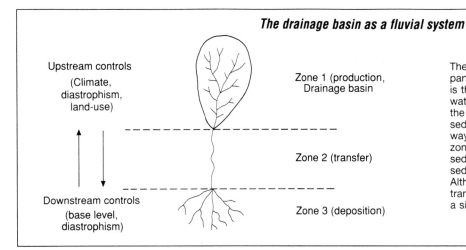

Upstream controls
(Climate,
diastrophism,
land-use)

Downstream controls
(base level,
diastrophism)

Zone 1 (production,
Drainage basin

Zone 2 (transfer)

Zone 3 (deposition)

The fluvial system may be divided into three parts: referred to as zones 1, 2, and 3. Zone 1 is the drainage basin or water shed from which water and sediment are derived. It is primarily the zone of sediment production although sediment storage occurs there in important ways. Zone 2 is the transfer or transportation zone, where major streams move water and sediment from zone 1 to zone 3, which is the sediment 'sink' or zone of deposition. Although sediments are stored, eroded and transported in all of these zones, within each a single process is usually dominant.

The second fundamental component in the study of rivers is the channel itself, i.e. the main pathway for the movement of energy, water and material through the system. The characteristics of river channels are determined by the interactions between water discharge, the quantity and character of the sediment discharge, and the nature of the bed and bank material (resource 4.4).

Water discharge and sediment availability vary continuously, creating detailed channel modifications, but over time, the stream works to achieve a condition of dynamic equilibrium. Negative feedback mechanisms adjust the stream system to variations in inputs and outputs.

Case study 4.1 on the River Melinau, Sarawak, illustrates a well developed natural river system at work, and asks us to question some common understandings about rivers in the humid tropics. The second, too, raises questions, but in this instance, about how people manage and use great river basins such as the Colorado River, USA. In contrast, the third case study takes the River Coln, a small tributary of the River Thames, to explore some basic principles of hydrology. Using examples from the USA, New Zealand, Australia and Japan the final set of three case studies (4.4, 4.5) focuses attention on the dynamics of rivers, especially their channels, and the ways they adjust to changed conditions, both natural and human-induced.

Drainage system variables 4.3

1 Time

2 Initial relief

3 Underlying geology— structures and rock types

4 Climate and weather characteristics

5 Vegetation

6 Relief in relation to base level

7 Hydrology — runoff, sediment yield, transport and deposition

8 Drainage network

9 Hillslope form

10 Channel and valley form

11 Sediment characteristics

12 Human activity and management

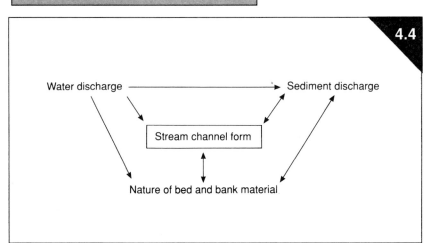

4.4

Water discharge

Sediment discharge

Stream channel form

Nature of bed and bank material

CASE STUDY 4.1 *Rivers at work – the River Melinau, Sarawak*

Background

The paper upon which this case study is based sets out to question several popular generalisations about rivers in humid tropical environments, draining catchments whose natural vegetation is rainforest:

1 That bedload (i.e. coarse debris of gravel size and larger) is less important than in mid-latitude rivers, with the suspended and solute components making up unusually high proportions. For example, one study of Amazon basin rivers found that bedload was only 5 per cent of the total. A well-known textbook, published in 1972, states: 'the transportation of coarse debris ... is exceptional'.

2 That the long profiles are irregular, with rapids and falls alternating with gentler stretches. This has been explained by the relative scarcity of coarse material able to carry out aggressive abrasion and hence 'smooth' the profile.

3 That braided channels and strongly developed meander belts are less common and channel forms more stable and shallower than in mid-latitude rivers.

Again, all these features are 'explained' by the predominance of fine grained material in the load of humid tropical rivers.

These characteristics are attributed to the relatively constant flow regimes and to the blanket of rainforest which protects the surface from rapid erosion. Rivers transporting coarse gravels and pebbles are exceptions and are accounted for by catchments with steep slopes or without rainforest cover, or the erosion of coarse alluvial terraces. The aggressive rate of chemical weathering leads to rapid comminution (reduction to

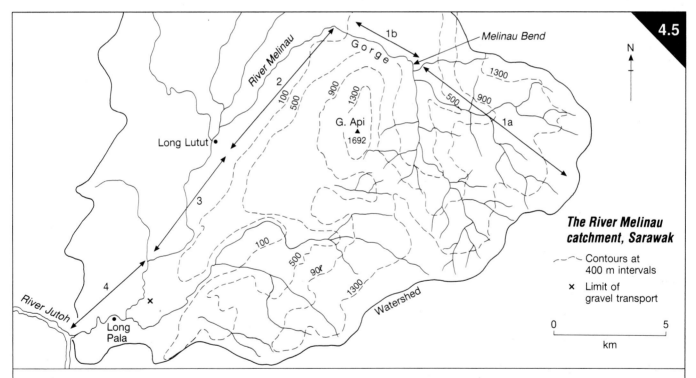

The River Melinau catchment, Sarawak

- - - - Contours at 400 m intervals
× Limit of gravel transport

0 _____ 5
km

4.5

Basin data

Catchment: 260 sq.km; channel length: 38 km; local base level at the confluence with River Tutoh; altitude fall: 2357 m; mean annual rainfall: >5000 mm; natural vegetation: unbroken rainforest.

Discharge: 28.3 cumecs mean annual; 175.6 cumecs maximum; 127 cumecs bankfull at Long Pala. The wide discharge fluctuations are caused by the intense storms and steep, impermeable slopes in the headwater catchment. Bankfull capacities are exceeded several times a year.

Load and erosion: Solute load of 47800 tonnes a year, giving a chemical denudation rate of 76 mm/1000 years, averaged over the catchment – basin rates on limestone areas are higher. Mechanical denudation in the headwater catchment is estimated at 3000 mm/1000 years.

smaller fragments) of the debris. However, as more studies of humid tropical rivers are made, these generalisations are increasingly being questioned.

Key understandings

◆ Rivers, their channels and valleys in the humid tropics are varied and complex.

◆ River valleys can be divided into distinct sections according to the inter-relationships between processes and landforms.

◆ A river basin may be conceived of as an open system operating in a condition of dynamic equilibrium.

The river at work

Resource 4.5 (on page 75) shows that once the tributaries have come together above Melinau Bend, the main River Melinau may be divided into four distinct sections. In the upper three sections it has the competence to transport debris of gravel size and larger. The consistent decline in competence to transport debris, i.e. size limit of the load, suggests that material is being actively transported

along the bed and that the Melinau long profile is adjusted to the sediment transported. As the cross-sections of resource 4.7 show, there are gravel terrace deposits along the valley, but these are used very little. The study concludes that 'the deposits currently being transported by the Melinau are ... derived almost entirely from the headwater regions, with only minute components of sediment derived from locally eroded limestones or gravel deposits'.

Channel and floodplain morphology

1 (a) **Headwater section:** High density stream network draining steeply sloping, rugged terrain. No floodplain, and channels are rock controlled.

(b) **Gorge section** (cross-section A): A floodplain is generally absent, with occasional boulder bars flanking the channel. The rock controlled channel may be cut 20 m deep and active incision is continuing.

2 **Braided channel with a braided floodplain** (cross-section B): The main channel is braided, with boulder and gravel bars in mid-

channel and along the sides. The floodplain is built of similar coarse materials and is itself criss-crossed by braided channels. Many are anastomosing (dispersing) from the main channel and some are occupied only at extreme flood events. Notice that the floodplain is slightly domed from the aggradation along the main channel. This accounts for the braided side channels which can only re-enter the main channel at infrequent deep pools. The braided form includes signs that the main channel shifts, and shows clearly that the river is aggrading its bed, using the abundant load carried through the gorge section. This has the effect of steepening the long profile from this point downstream.

3 **Braided channel with overbank floodplain** (cross-section C): The main channel becomes increasingly sinuous, with many gravel bars along its sides and some mid-channel bars. The floodplain which is raised above the channel bars, is smooth, and has no anastomosing channels. This tells us that the channel and the floodplain are being formed by different processes: the

---

4.6

Properties of the River Melinau

River Section	Altitude Range (m)	River Length (km)	River Gradient (m/km)	Valley Length (km)	Valley Gradient (m/km)	Sinuosity
Gunong Mulu–Melinau Bend	2357–183	11.4	191.6	11.4	191.6	1.0
Melinau Bend–Head of Alluvium	183–123	2.2	27.6	2.1	28.0	1.01
Head of Alluvium–Long Lutut	123–32	9.8	9.4	8.8	10.4	1.11
Long Lutut–Malinau Paku	32–20	11.1	1.1	8.2	1.4	1.35
Melinau Paku–Long Melinau	20–19	3.8	0.2	2.6	0.4	1.49

DOWNSTREAM

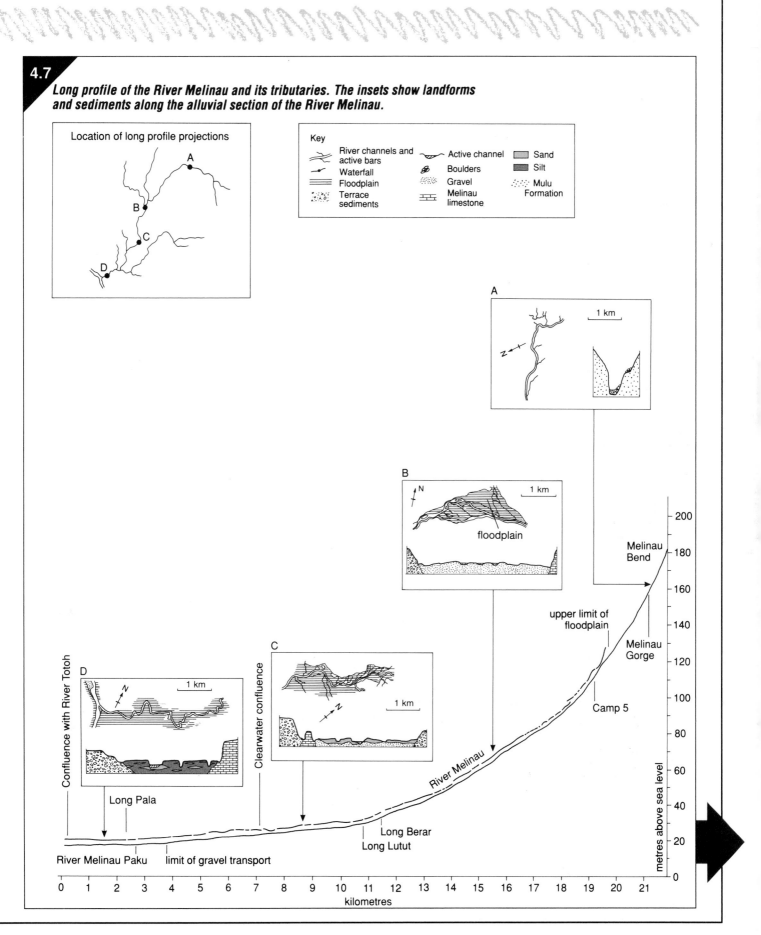

4.7

Long profile of the River Melinau and its tributaries. The insets show landforms and sediments along the alluvial section of the River Melinau.

Location of long profile projections

Key

River channels and active bars

Active channel

Sand

Waterfall

Boulders

Silt

Floodplain

Gravel

Mulu Formation

Terrace sediments

Melinau limestone

A

1 km

B

1 km

floodplain

C

1 km

D

1 km

Confluence with River Totoh

Clearwater confluence

Long Pala

Long Berar
Long Lutut

River Melinau Paku   limit of gravel transport

River Melinau

Camp 5

Melinau Gorge

upper limit of floodplain

Melinau Bend

metres above sea level

200
180
160
140
120
100
80
60
40
20
0

0 1 2 3 4 5 6 7 8 9 10 11 12 13 14 15 16 17 18 19 20 21

kilometres

bedload is being moved along the braided channel, while the floodplain is built partly from these gravels when the river shifts its course, and by silt and sand layers left by overbank flooding.

4 **Meandering channel with overbank floodplain** (cross-section D): Typical meander patterns, with sand point bars etc, and a silt and sand load, i.e. no gravel. The floodplain is up to 4 m above the main channel and is separated from it by a low sand level. The floodplain is crossed by narrow channels, scoured out during rising and falling stages of flood events.

Factors influencing the river and valley form

Once the River Melinau leaves its gorge section it is **aggrading** its valley floor. More load is being transported than can be carried through the middle and lower valley. The load is, therefore, deposited sequentially, the coarsest material first and the finest last. In the process of transport the debris is abraded and comminuted, with soft and soluble rocks being reduced first. The study proposes four possible factors:

1 **Tectonic control** There is evidence of ongoing uplift in the headwater catchment. This rejuvenation encourages incision and erosion by streams and so increases the available load.

2 **Climatic control** Rainfall records are inadequate, but there is some evidence of increased precipitation, or perhaps of storm intensity. This could lead to increased slope failure in the headwater catchment and hence to the increased availability of load.

3 **Vegetation cover** This influences sediment yield to the river through its control of rainfall interception, infiltration and soil strength. There is no sign, however, in the Melinau catchment of deforestation, yet in resent years landslips have become increasingly common and extensive. It seems likely that this mass movement is being triggered by increased inputs of rainfall which take the steep slopes beyond their stability thresholds, even though the rainforest cover is still intact.

4 **Factors within the river system** As available energy and materials vary, so patterns of erosion and deposition change constantly in rivers, causing shifts in channel shape and location. However, these dynamics tend to be highly localised, and seem unlikely to be a significant cause of the overall pattern of net aggradation along the Melinau.

Conclusions

- The steadily curved long-profile is in adjustment with its load

- This profile is slowly steepening, and with it the competence of the river to transport material

- Increased slope failure in the headwater catchment is increasing sediment availability

- Gravel deposits will spread progressively downstream

- The river course will become increasingly braided.

Activities

1 Explain:

   a why valley aggradation is at its maximum along section 2 of the Melinau course,

   b how this steepens the channel long profile, and

   c what effects this may have on the downstream valley.

2 Use the Melinau case study to discuss the validity of each of the generalisations set out in the Background section (page 75).

3 The study concludes that the Melinau will take on an increasingly braided form. Carry out a library search to find out about:

   a the causes of braiding, and

   b the threshold which causes a river to change from a meandering to a braided mode, and vice versa.

CASE STUDY 4.2 *The Colorado River – a controlled system ... or is it?*

Background

Today, the River Colorado, draining 8% of the United States, is a cascading system controlled by a series of dams and reservoirs (resource 4.8). The lower basin lies within the arid zone of the American Southwest, and relies almost entirely upon the upper basin for its water inputs. In 1983, extensive stretches of the floodplain below the Davis and Parker Dams suffered severe flooding. Therefore the key question is: if such an expensive and sophisticated control network has been installed, how can disastrous floods still occur? This case study seeks an answer in the interaction of (i) the river regime; (ii) meteorological and forecasting uncertainties; (iii) the nature and capacity of the control system; (iv) the decision-making process for operating the system; (v) the pattern of settlement across the floodplain.

▶ *Before working through this case study you will need to check your understanding of these terms:*

input, cascade of stores, capacity, throughput, output, decision-making process.

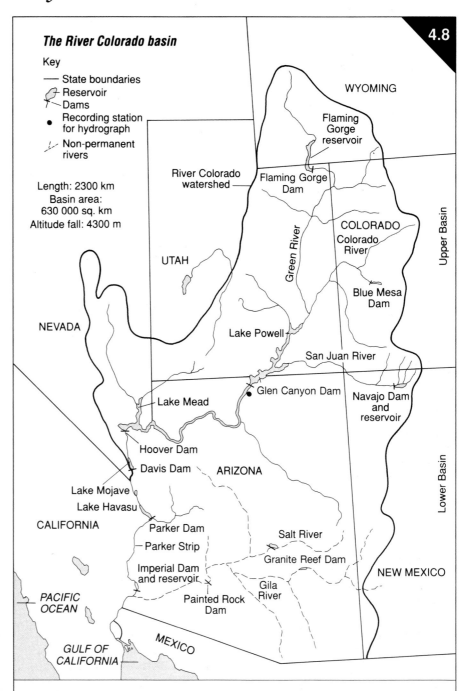

4.8

The River Colorado basin

Key
— State boundaries
⌇ Reservoir
⌐ Dams
● Recording station for hydrograph
⌁ Non-permanent rivers

Length: 2300 km
Basin area: 630 000 sq. km
Altitude fall: 4300 m

WYOMING
Flaming Gorge reservoir
River Colorado watershed
Flaming Gorge Dam
Upper Basin
COLORADO
Colorado River
UTAH
Green River
Blue Mesa Dam
NEVADA
Lake Powell
San Juan River
Glen Canyon Dam
Navajo Dam and reservoir
Lake Mead
Hoover Dam
Davis Dam
ARIZONA
Lower Basin
Lake Mojave
Lake Havasu
CALIFORNIA
Parker Dam
Parker Strip
Salt River
Granite Reef Dam
NEW MEXICO
Imperial Dam and reservoir
Gila River
PACIFIC OCEAN
Painted Rock Dam
MEXICO
GULF OF CALIFORNIA

The changing facts

'Since the completion of the first large dam in 1935, the wild Colorado Rover has been dramatically transformed into a tamed man-made system of placid desert lakes. Today, less than 1% of the river's virgin flow reaches its delta. Virtually all the sediment transported by the river is now stored within the reservoirs. This has eroded the channel, and lowered the stream bed, as the river seeks to replenish its sediment load. Reduced discharges and lower flood levels have caused new banks to build within the former, larger channel.'

(Source: W L Graf, Geographical Magazine, October 1987)

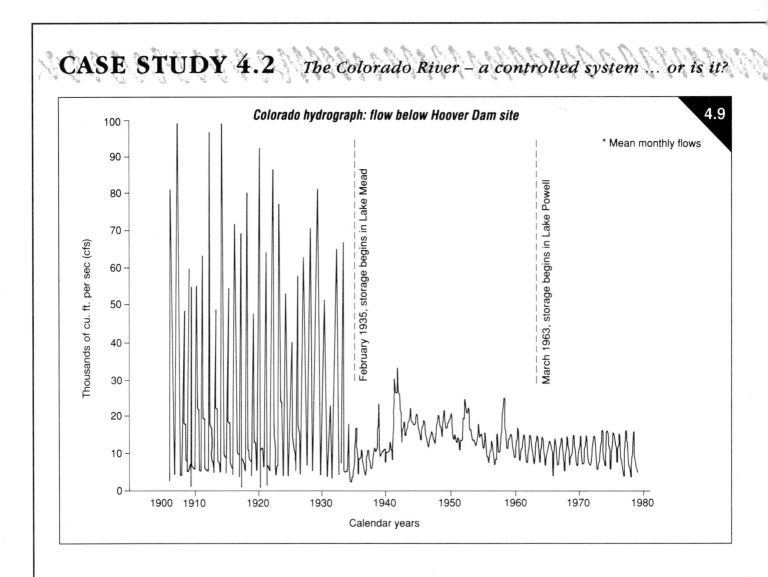

Colorado hydrograph: flow below Hoover Dam site

4.9

* Mean monthly flows

Thousands of cu. ft. per sec (cfs) (y-axis: 0, 10, 20, 30, 40, 50, 60, 70, 80, 90, 100)

February 1935, storage begins in Lake Mead

March 1963, storage begins in Lake Powell

Calendar years (x-axis: 1900, 1910, 1920, 1930, 1940, 1950, 1960, 1970, 1980)

Key understandings

◆ River basins work as systems, with inputs, throughputs and outputs.

◆ Humans have changed the Colorado River basin from a natural system to a control system, in order to turn an irregular and unpredictable discharge into a regulated flow.

◆ Water managers need accurate information of both the *demand* for the water, e.g. irrigation, cities, and the *supply*, e.g. spring meltwater from snowpacks in the upper catchments.

◆ The most crucial decision for water managers in the Colorado basin is how much reservoir storage to make available to hold the spring snow melt.

◆ Each reservoir has a finite capacity, and each river channel has a finite discharge capacity. Thus it takes time to organise a controlled flow of water through the system.

The system at work

In its 'free' state the Colorado was a genuinely wild river, with great seasonal fluctuations in discharge. The April–July spate season was caused by melting of the heavy snowpack in the headwater catchments of Wyoming, Colorado and Utah. These annual floods surged through the lower arid basin, spilling over floodplains, renewing the groundwater store and being steadily reduced in volume downstream as a result of infiltration and evaporation. Each year, fresh sediment would be added to the floodplain and channel. The hydrograph (resource 4.9) vividly illustrates these mighty flood surges, and their 'taming', first by the Hoover Dam and later by the Glen Canyon Dam.

The dam/reservoir system has a dual function: first to **conserve water** and distribute it for industrial, municipal, domestic and agricultural use, for power generation and for recreation; second to provide **flood control**. A complex set of regulations has been established by the US Bureau of Reclamation to provide empty storage space in the reservoirs for flood control. This requirement varies seasonally according to river flow forecasts made by the National Weather Service based largely on the snowpack volume in the headwater catchments. Each reservoir is a vessel with a certain capacity determined by the height of the dam, the nature of the topography and the amount of sediment infill behind the dam. In turn the total reservoir system has a finite storage capacity. Equally important, each section of channel between dams has a finite capacity, thereby constraining the rate of releases from the upstream dam, e.g. the maximum permitted release from the Hoover dam is 45 000 cubic feet/sec (cfs) (18 mill. gals./min).

Thus, it may take weeks to draw down a reservoir to create extra storage (resource 4.10). Each winter the essential decision for the Bureau of Reclamation engineers is how much space to make available for the spring snowmelt: if they overestimate, the reservoirs will not fill, and there will be a shortage later in the year for urban, agricultural and power users; if they underestimate, the snowmelt will exceed the capacity of the reservoirs. It was the latter scenario which occurred in 1983. At the beginning of each month a forecast is made of the expected runoff during the next April–July period. A release schedule is put into operation to provide sufficient storage space for this runoff. Resource 4.11 shows that the January–March forecasts for April–July runoff, based on snowpack and rainfall estimates suggested a 'normal' situation, with runoff around the 6.9 million acre-ft average. Planned releases were scheduled accordingly (extract A, resource 4.12).

It was from early April that the balance began to be lost. The usual pattern for the snowpack store is for a peak in April, with sharp decreases in May and June as the snow melts. In 1983, storms swept over the upper basin throughout May, together with unusually low temperatures, resulting in a larger snowpack at the end of May than at the beginning — an unprecedented situation. The last weekend in May turned very hot, causing very rapid snowmelt, the heatwave continuing into June. In late June, unusually heavy rainstorms added to the inputs and created record discharge levels above Lake Powell (extract B, resource 4.12). The result was the highest April–July runoff levels in the upper basin on record, causing steep escalation of runoff forecasts, accompanied by shrinkage and ultimate disappearance of available storage capacity (resource 4.11). Remember that the river channels below each dam can accept only a certain volume. Drawdown of a reservoir to create storage space, therefore, takes time — and this is just what the engineers did not have.

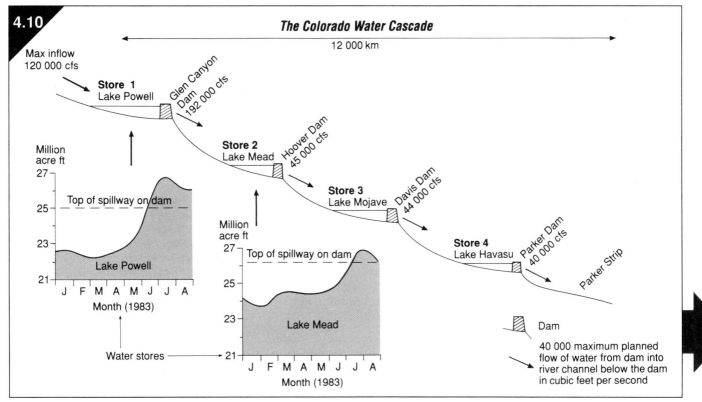

4.10

The Colorado Water Cascade

12 000 km

Max inflow 120 000 cfs

Store 1 Lake Powell

Glen Canyon Dam 192 000 cfs

Store 2 Lake Mead

Hoover Dam 45 000 cfs

Store 3 Lake Mojave

Davis Dam 44 000 cfs

Store 4 Lake Havasu

Parker Dam 40 000 cfs

Parker Strip

Million acre ft

Top of spillway on dam

Lake Powell

J F M A M J J A
Month (1983)

Water stores

Million acre ft

Top of spillway on dam

Lake Mead

J F M A M J J A
Month (1983)

Dam

40 000 maximum planned flow of water from dam into river channel below the dam in cubic feet per second

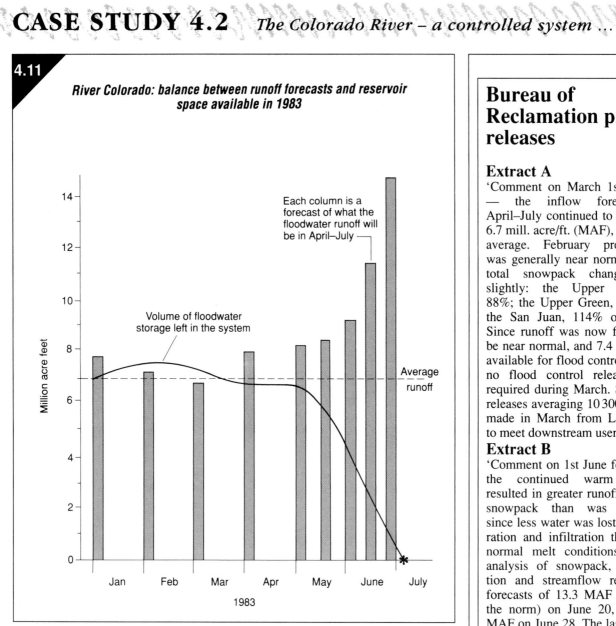

4.11

River Colorado: balance between runoff forecasts and reservoir space available in 1983

Each column is a forecast of what the floodwater runoff will be in April–July

Volume of floodwater storage left in the system

Million acre feet

Average runoff

Jan   Feb   Mar   Apr   May   June   July

1983

4.12

Bureau of Reclamation press releases

Extract A

'Comment on March 1st forecast — the inflow forecast for April–July continued to decline to 6.7 mill. acre/ft. (MAF), or 96% of average. February precipitation was generally near normal, ... the total snowpack changed only slightly: the Upper Colorado, 88%; the Upper Green, 80%; and the San Juan, 114% of normal. Since runoff was now forecast to be near normal, and 7.4 MAF was available for flood control storage, no flood control releases were required during March. Scheduled releases averaging 10 300 cfs were made in March from Lake Mead to meet downstream user needs'.

Extract B

'Comment on 1st June forecast — the continued warm weather resulted in greater runoff from the snowpack than was expected, since less water was lost to evaporation and infiltration than under normal melt conditions. Further analysis of snowpack, precipitation and streamflow resulted in forecasts of 13.3 MAF (190% of the norm) on June 20, and 14.6 MAF on June 28. The last revision was due primarily to heavy showers and thunderstorms on June 25–26 that resulted in a peak inflow to Lake Powell of 116 000 cfs on June 28.

The large increases in the forecast could have required increases in Lake Mead flood control releases up to 65 000 cfs. The main factor that enabled us to keep Lake Mead releases at the 40-45 000 cfs level was the use of surcharge storage at Lake Powell and Lake Mead by the addition of flashboards at the top of the spillway gates ... water began to flow over the Hoover spillway gates on 3 July'.

The two key reservoirs were literally filled to bursting (resource 4.10). This created planned and unplanned releases beyond the agreed capacities of the downstream channels. For example, the 40 000 cfs limit agreed in 1968 accepted that such release would involve inundation of sections of the floodplain below the Hoover Dam. At that time this was regarded as 'acceptable', for this had been the 'natural' way for the Colorado to unload its surplus, and there was little settlement on the lower Colorado floodplain. Thus, the 1968 management plan for the controlled water cascade included the use of the floodplain as an emergency overspill store. This would come into use should all the reservoir space become full. Despite public awareness of the plan, since 1968 there has been extensive agricultural and recreational development and flood impact is heavier in human terms (resource 4.13). It seems that floods become 'disasters' only when human life and property are involved!

Sudden and high releases have major impacts on channel form. In the stretch immediately below a dam there is likely to be deep channel scour as the energetic waters, carrying relatively little sediment as they leave the dam, accumulate their load. Downstream, lateral spreading across a floodplain and decline in gradient as the next reservoir (local base level) is approached, cause deposition and marked aggradation of the river channel. The result is an unstable longitudinal profile which may increase the likelihood of a lowering of the water-table along one stretch and flooding along others (resource 4.14).

Across a zone up to 50 km wide, well beyond the inundation zone, water-tables were raised to near-surface levels by the filling of the groundwater store. An emergency investigation by Yuma County, Arizona found the following impacts (resource 4.15).

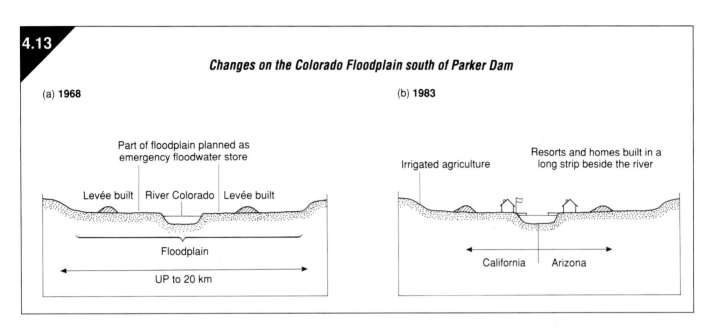

4.13

Changes on the Colorado Floodplain south of Parker Dam

(a) **1968**

Part of floodplain planned as emergency floodwater store

Levée built | River Colorado | Levée built

Floodplain

UP to 20 km

(b) **1983**

Irrigated agriculture

Resorts and homes built in a long strip beside the river

California | Arizona

4.14

Hoover Dam

Parker Dam and flooded Parker strip

4.15

Yuma Flood Control Task Force Report; Colorado River flood of 1983

'As groundwater inundates septic tanks and cesspools, the sewage mixes with the groundwater providing a source of pollution for adjacent domestic water wells. The situation could result in a serious health problem since it could affect an estimated population of 37 000 (in Yuma County, Arizona) ... agricultural crops are destroyed when their root zones remain standing in water ... approximately 60 000 acres of prime farm land are affected on the Arizona side alone. It could take several years for affected areas to return to pre-flood conditions'.

(Yuma, Arizona, September 1983).

The least expensive solution proposed by this Task Force was the sinking of a well field. This would be a long line of wells some distance from and parallel to the river, which would operate in high water periods to pump out the aquifers and prevent dangerous rises in the water-table.

4.16

Residents ignore flood warnings

Preparation for the flooding of the Colorado Rover continued Sunday as residents along the California-Arizona border sandbagged their homes and businesses and crossed their fingers in hopes of escaping major damage when the release of water from three dams sends the river to its highest levels in 40 years.

The amount of water flowing out of the dams will be increased from 26 000 cubic feet a second to 40 000 over several days and officials say the extra release could continue for three weeks.

The river already is running two feet higher than normal. The added water is expected to send it four feet higher in some area and up to eight feet in others.

The Bureau of Reclamation estimated potential damage at more than $1 million and local officials said it could go up to $5 million partly because the flooding will occur at the onset of the tourist season when thousands come to the river for recreation.

The anxiety over potential damage is mixed with anger that the government did not release more water from dams in the winter when the Colorado was lower, thereby preventing the current crisis.

'It's disgusting,' said Lois Wolterman, owner of the B & B Trailer Park in Parker. She fears she may lose a summer's worth of business if the river washes out her boat docks.

'Week to prepare'

'We just feel this could have been prevented', she said. 'They could have started releasing before. Instead, we had one week to prepare.'

La Paz County Supervisor Don Denton agreed that 'obviously there's been a mistake in calculation some place.' He said that local officials were not alerted to the situation until June 14.

'We had no idea this would happen,' he said. 'Unless you get feedback you don't know things are happening. We didn't know until last Tuesday. Then they said we're going to have problems.'

(Source: David Einstein, *Los Angeles Times,* 20 June 1983)

A river is supposed to be wet

As sad is it is that homes and businesses along the Colorado Rover in Arizona are flooded, it's a little difficult to sympathize with people who build in a river bottom, then complain when the river runs exactly where it's supposed to flow.

The property owners are complaining because the bureau did not make smaller releases earlier. Unfortunately nature conspired against such a precaution. The runoff into the Colorado surged suddenly when snowpacks in the Rockies were melted by an onset of hot weather, accompanied by heavy rains.

(Source: *Phoenix Gazette,* 21 June 1983)

A river reborn

The Parker Strip, an almost solid stretch of resorts and restaurants between Parker Dam and Parker, was all but closed last year during the man-caused flood on the river.

The Bureau of Reclamation miscalculated the amount of runoff from the melting snowpack in the river's Rocky Mountain watershed and delayed making large water releases from Lake Mead and Lake Powell until June 1983.

The releases, when they were started, were massive and caused widespred damage to resorts and marinas along the river. The floods cost local businessmen millions of dollars, both in damage and loss of revenue.

Critics claim that the Bureau of Reclamation tried to keep the reservoirs as full as possible to accommodate the Central Arizona Project, failing to realize that there was not enough room in the reservoirs to hold the sudden rise of water because of melting snow.

As a result, the Bureau was forced to make heavy water releases throughout the year, even when the danger of floodng was over, to prevent a repeat of the flooding this year.

Currently, the releases are at a 'high' 20 000 cubic feet a second (CFS) as the Bureau of Reclamation continues to make room in Mead and Powell lakes for the anticipated spring runoff.

'We can live with 30 000 CFS if the river goes no higher,' said Dottie Randall, executive director of the Parker Area Chamber of Commerce. 'At its peak flooding last year, the river was 42 000 cfs. Everyone along the river has since raised their docks and moved their cabanas back, so there is no problem if the river stays around 30 000 cfs.'

(Source: *Arizona Republic*, 12 April 1984)

BLM may have encouraged building in flood zone

An investigation by the Los Angeles Times shows that the Department of Interior through another of its agencies, the Bureau of Land Management, in fact encouraged resort operators to build and upgrade recreation facilities along the river. For nearly four years before the flood, the Bureau of Land Management approved detailed blueprints for hundreds of thousands of dollars worth of development in the flood plain.

The Bureau of Land Management approved large investments despite warnings that reservoirs were filling up – and that the river might overflow. The Bureau of Reclamation issued the warnings. The first came in March 1977 at a public meeting in Parker. One resort operator who did attend says now that he might as well have stayed at home. 'I took their advice and I raised my facilities two to four feet,' says Sammy Field, 59, who runs Castle Rock Shores resort. 'And now we've got about seven or eight feet of water.'

Darwin Snell, who heads the Yuma district of the Bureau of Land Management, which has jurisdiction over the Parker Strip, acknowledges that his agency allowed resort operators to build in the flood plain, on both the Arizona and California sides of the Colorado River. 'A lot of times we did not know exactly where the flood plain was,' Snell says. 'We found out as a result of these last few weeks,' he adds wryly.

(Source: *Reno Gazette Journal*, 1 August 1983)

Controlling the Colorado

The thrust of most of the media coverage and commentary on the lower Colorado River flooding is that it is the fault of the river's managers, the US Bureau of Reclamation (USBR). The available facts, briefly covred in this article, do not support this charge.

The Colorado River Basin is huge, covering about one-twelfth of contiguous United States. The river has extremely wide variations in flow, during any year, from year to year and from periods of mostly wet years to periods of mostly dry years. Congress authorized construction of major dams to provide the large reservoirs needed to control the river. These reservoirs provide flood control and enable many millions of people in seven states and Mexico to use water for municipal, industrial and irrigations purposes and provide power and recreation.

Flood control regulations at Hoover Dam, the key dam for the lower Colorado River, are established by the US Corps of Engineers. These regulations require the USBR to provide empty storage space throughout the year for flood control with the balance of the reservoir space used to conserve water. The space required for flood control varies depending upon the time of year and the river forecasts made by the National Weather Service River Forecast Center based largely on measurements of the depth of snow and its water content.

The Corps of Engineers regulations are designed to enable Hoover Dam to control floods by storing flows in Lake Mead and increasing releases as necessary but not exceeding 40 000 cubic feet per second.

In 1968 the Corps found that '... 40 000 cfs would have caused minimal damage in the downstream flood plain.' However, in 1981, the Corps stated that a release of 40 000 cfs would cause extensive property damage because of the development in the flood plain in the intervening years.

The USBR held public meetings in the communities along the Colorado River in the late 1970s explaining the forthcoming high flows. The communities were again notified at public meetings held in conjuction with the 1981 review of the Corps regulations. It should be noted that flood control is given as the highest priority in the operations of the Corps.

The usual pattern of the snowpack in the high mountains of the Colorado River Basin is for it to peak in April and then sharply decrease in May and June as the snow melts. This year, storms swept over the basin throughout May, together with unusually low temperatures, resulting in the unprecedented situation of the snowpack moisture content apparently being higher on June 1 than on May 1. The Memorial Day weekend turned very hot causing the snow to melt rapidly and the heat wave continued in June. The volume of water from the melting snow was increased by an extensive rainstorm in the latter part of June that caused a new peak in the river flow above Lake Powell. The net result is that the April-July runoff is expected to be the highest in recorded history.

The USBR increased its releases throughout this period but at no time did it exceed 40 000 cfs in the lower river below Parker Dam. The releases resulted in only a fraction of the damage that would have occurred without the flood control provided by the reservoirs.

The USBR has been criticised for not releasing water earlier in the season so that the reservoirs could have captured the flood flow. In February or March, with average or below average runoff being forecast, neither the USBR not anyone else could have predicted the high runoff of June and July. Investigation may reveal that the USBR operations or the National Weather Service forecasts could be improved. However, based upon the information the USBR had aviailable to it, they operated in a responsible manner in dealing with fast moving and unprecedented weather.

(Source: Myron B Holburt, *The Sacramento Union*, 10 August 1983)

Activities

1 Group discussion in role-play format. The extensive environmental impacts caused a public outcry, as the selection of newspaper extracts indicate (resource 4.16).

   a Using the extracts, make a list of the agencies, interest groups and individuals involved.

   b Members in your group then select a 'role' from your list.

   c Members prepare their role from the materials available — why they feel angry, why they took certain decisions, who they blame etc.

   d Finally set up a 'public enquiry' into the floods. Members will play out their roles — stating their views, defending their positions etc.

2 Draw two systems diagrams, i.e. using boxes and arrows, for stores, inputs, outputs, throughputs, to show:

   a the natural system,

   b the controlled system.

3 What are the key differences between the natural and the controlled hydrological systems?

CASE STUDY 4.3 *River regime, rocks and rainfall: the River Coln at Bibury*

Background

Discharge is the volume of water passing along a stream channel, usually expressed in units of time, e.g. cumecs = cubic metres/second. The discharge regime, or rhythm of flow is most commonly plotted as a **hydrograph,** to which is added a **rainfall histogram**. The purpose is to relate the response of a stream to the water input from precipitation and is often done for individual storms, as a 'storm hydrograph'. Thus, we say that some streams are 'flashy', i.e. their discharge responds rapidly to water inputs (see case study 6.1), while others may be less affected by individual storms. It is equally important to study and understand the broader rhythms of

stream discharge as the example of the River Colorado clearly shows (see case study 4.2).

Before you analyse the resources in this case study, it will be useful to discuss each of the variables set out in the key understandings with a partner, or in a small group. Focus your thinking firstly, on the alternative ways individual variables may affect a stream, and secondly, on the likely effects of combinations of variables. (You may find the systems diagram in resource 4.1 helpful in establishing the relationships between stores and pathways.)

The River Coln is a north bank tributary of the River Thames, to the east of Cirencester (resource 4.17). Most of its catchment is underlain by Jurassic Oolitic limestone, part of the dipslope of the Cotswold Hills, and an important aquifer. The discharge data (resources 4.18 and 4.19) were collected by the Thames Water Authority at their Bibury gauging station, while the rainfall figures (resources 4.20 and 4.21) are from a weather station nearby in the catchment. (Note that Water Authorities use a 'water year' from October to September. The reason for this is that stream discharges in Britain tend to be lowest in the autumn.)

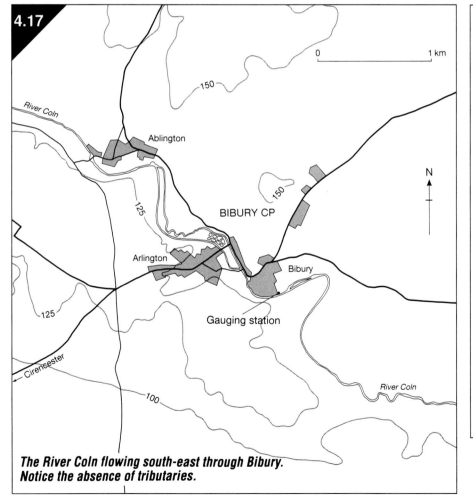

4.17

The River Coln flowing south-east through Bibury. Notice the absence of tributaries.

Key understandings

The volume of water delivered to a stream channel and the timescale of this delivery are dependent upon a number of variables:

◆ amount, character and intensity of precipitation

◆ nature of the stream catchment – relief, gradients, vegetation, size and shape

◆ drainage density – number of tributaries/unit area which feed the main channel

◆ underlying geology – permeability, porosity, water-holding capacity, the status of the groundwater store and the associated water-table

◆ atmospheric conditions – temperature, humidity, wind

◆ human activities and management of the catchment – agricultural rhythms, drainage, irrigation, dams and weirs.

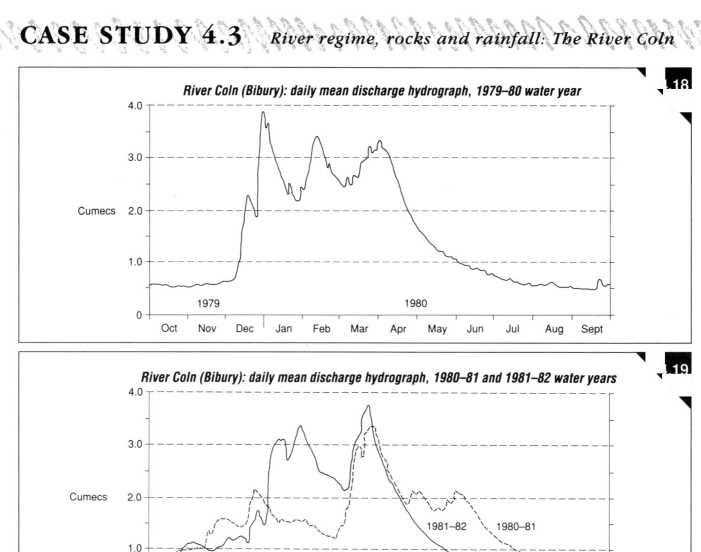

18

River Coln (Bibury): daily mean discharge hydrograph, 1979–80 water year

19

River Coln (Bibury): daily mean discharge hydrograph, 1980–81 and 1981–82 water years

20

Monthly rainfall totals, River Coln catchment, 1980–81 and 1930–81

	Oct	Nov	Dec	Jan	Feb	Mar	Apr	May	June	July	Aug	Sept	Yea
1980–81	82.3	55.7	56.7	36.9	32.6	134.0	52.1	97.2	34.5	39.1	47.4	148.2	816.8
1930–81 AV.	69.0	78.6	76.6	73.8	55.1	53.8	52.5	63.5	54.2	61.8	73.1	66.8	778.8

Activities

1 Resource 4.18 shows the discharge regime for 1979–80. It suggests that the River Coln has a two-season regime: a low-flow season from June to November, and a high-flow season from December to May.

a Give the dates and levels for (i) the highest and (ii) the lowest discharges.

b On how many days of the year is discharge more than 2.5 cumecs?

c Research indicates that the majority of the 'work' of a river, i.e. erosion and transportation, is done in brief surges, when the river possesses high energy. If this is true, then when would such activity have occurred along the River Coln in 1979–80? Is it likely that such intermittent activity applies to both physical and chemical weathering and erosion?

River Coln Catchment: Daily rainfall, 1979–80 (mm)　　**4.21**

Day	Oct	Nov	Dec	Jan	Feb	Mar	Apr	May	June	July	Aug	Sept
1.			0.1		3.5		9.0			0.1	0.1	
2.	0.6	7.1	1.3	2.7	3.6		0.9			0.6		
3.	2.0	5.9		13.1	3.2					5.2	1.3	
4.		2.4	0.6	0.4	11.6	0.4	0.5		1.0	0.5	5.5	5.6
5.		3.5	3.9	0.1	0.8	6.6			0.4		0.1	1.8
6.	5.5	7.6	6.7	0.2	6.6	10.2				1.5	0.6	0.2
7.	0.02	5.3	1.2	0.02	9.2	6.8			1.8	3.7	6.7	0.4
8.	4.3		3.3		3.1	1.3				1.5	1.9	1.7
9.	3.2	1.3	19.3		0.6	3.8				0.3		0.4
10.	4.0	0.3	15.1		0.1	0.2			0.04			0.8
11.	0.6	3.2	9.3		0.03	1.8			2.6	0.3	1.6	0.2
12.	0.1		6.7			9.2			5.9	1.3	16.5	
13.	1.7	4.1	20.0			0.1			6.4	20.1	1.7	
14.		2.4	7.2	7.0	2.3	0.6			5.8	0.02	21.9	0.2
15.		6.6	8.7	0.06	3.1				2.2			0.9
16.	0.1	0.1	0.1		0.9	0.03			11.1	0.1	1.0	6.2
17.	2.6	2.6	0.2		0.2	4.9			6.4	0.8	0.05	
18.		0.2	2.4			11.4			0.2	7.7	0.4	0.2
19.	0.8			1.6		0.4		2.6	1.6	1.6		7.2
20.		0.04		7.4	2.2			5.5	1.4	2.2	1.3	36.2
21.		0.4	0.6	4.0	9.7		0.2	0.06	4.0			2.7
22.		0.5	0.4	3.1	3.2	0.8	1.7		3.1			1.6
23.		0.4	0.5	2.5	0.05	7.5	2.1		3.4			0.8
24.	6.5	0.6	0.04	0.1	2.7	5.0	1.0		1.3			
25.	6.3	0.3	0.2	0.1		1.4	0.6		2.7	7.0		
26.	1.0	9.3	8.6			6.1	0.1		6.9	0.5		0.6
27.		0.02	48.7			2.0	0.3	1.3	13.1	0.3	0.3	7.5
28.	0.3		3.1			8.4		5.6	6.4		0.4	0.02
29.	0.5	0.7	0.6	2.8	0.1	0.4	2.3	0.4		4.9	16.4	
30.	3.9	0.6	2.6	11.8		0.6	5.9	7.1	5.8	0.02	0.2	
31.	0.1		5.6	5.6		7.0		5.5		1.0		

2 Define the term 'base flow' of a river, and suggest a base flow figure for the River Coln.

3 Use resource 4.21 to plot a rainfall graph for 1979–80. (Use the same horizontal scale as resource 4.17, and if available use graph tracing paper, to allow you to overlay your graph on resource 4.18).

a To what extent does the rainfall graph explain the stream discharge regime?

b Why is discharge far less responsive to rainfall inputs in the summer season than during the winter? (Check back through the variables affecting runoff, and through the stores and pathways of resource 4.1).

c What influence might evaporation have upon discharge? (Resource 4.21).

4 Resource 4.19 shows the discharge regimes for 1980–81 and 1981–82.

a To what extent do these graphs support the conclusions that you reached from the 1979–80 figures (resource 4.18)?

b Resource 4.20 gives the 1980–81 monthly rainfall tables. When compared with the discharge regime, do they suggest similar seasonal variations in responsiveness to rainfall as was evident in 1979–80? What problems are likely in using monthly figures rather than daily totals?

c Putting all three years together, write a summary of the discharge regime for the River Coln, e.g. seasonality, base flow, extremes, responsiveness, reliability, 'flashiness' etc. Your statement should include a description and an explanation.

5 From what you have learned about the River Coln regime, suggest the type of rainfall pattern which might have produced the 1981–82 hydrograph on resource 4.19.

6 The longest rainless spell in 1979–80 was nineteen days (resource 4.21). What happened to stream discharge during this spell, and why did the stream not dry up?

Background

One of the fundamental characteristics of environmental systems is their built-in resistance to disturbance. When faced by changed inputs or outputs, an environment attempts to absorb the change and to retain its character. The adjustments to re-establish the former state of equilibrium occur by the operation of **negative feedback mechanisms**. For example, a flood surge in a river means additional inputs of energy and water. This enables increased erosion, sediment entrainment, transport and deposition and leads to modifications to channel and valley form. The speed with which the channel form responds to the changed inputs, is called the **relaxation time** of the system. After the flood has subsided, the river sets about re-establishing its 'normal' equilibrium between discharge, sediment and channel form. This may take days, years or even centuries (if there are no further disturbances to interrupt the process), and is known as the **recovery time.**

One widely accepted model states that systems such as rivers enjoy relatively long periods of stability, interspersed with brief episodes of accelerated disturbance and change (resource 4.22). Environmental systems vary in their ability to absorb and recover from disturbance. Thus, some rivers are able to bring powerful negative feedback mechanisms into operation and re-establish an equilibrium (1 and 2 on resource 4.22). Others are more sensitive to changed inputs and outputs and **positive feedback mechanisms** take over. These 'runaway' mechanisms accelerate change rather than dampen it down, and there may be a prolonged relaxation and recovery period before a new equilibrium is established (3 on resource 4.22). In fluvial systems, a well-known example is when a river changes

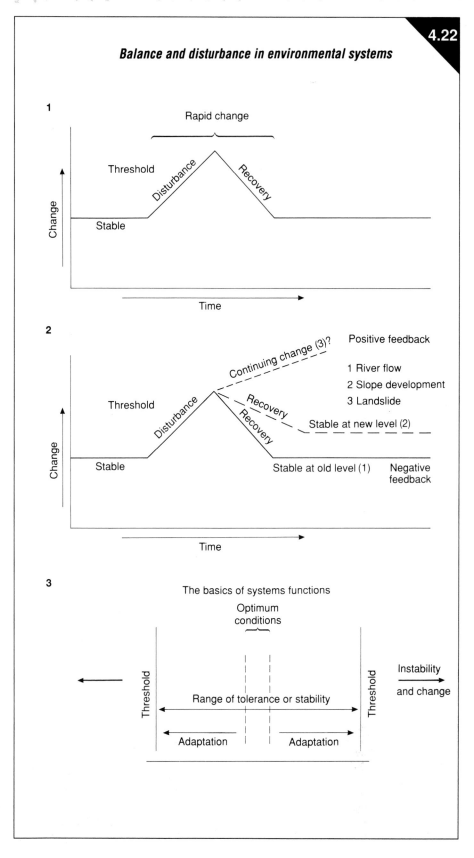

4.22

Balance and disturbance in environmental systems

1

Rapid change

Threshold

Disturbance   Recovery

Stable

Change

Time

2

Continuing change (3)?   Positive feedback

1 River flow
2 Slope development
3 Landslide

Threshold

Disturbance   Recovery
Recovery

Stable at new level (2)

Change

Stable

Stable at old level (1)   Negative feedback

Time

3

The basics of systems functions

Optimum conditions

Threshold   Threshold   Instability and change

Range of tolerance or stability

Adaptation   Adaptation

from a braided to a meandering form or vice versa.

The three examples which follow illustrate how the 'problem' faced by a river varies according to the type of disturbance, e.g. the rivers around Mount St. Helens were faced by a sudden, massive pulse of debris from the eruptions; the Waikaretaheke River in New Zealand was permanently altered by a major landslip; the River Ringarooma in Tasmania is still trying to recover from a century of mining activity. In each case, human activity has either instigated or been influenced by the disturbance. Thus, it is important that we understand the processes involved in a river's response, and whether there are general principles which will help in prediction and river management.

Part I: The 1980 Mount St. Helens eruption, and its impact upon the regional river system

The May 1980 eruption (See Chapter 1, case studies 1.3 and 1.4) has caused fundamental disturbance to the hydrological system radiating from Mount St. Helens. The massive and sudden input of water and material into the system, has left the rivers with adjustment problems which have serious implications for human activities in the region. This type of disturbance is known as a **pulse input** (resource 4.23). Notice, however, the difference between (a) the water surge, which passes through the system, creating the short-term impacts, and (b) the sediment input, which largely remains, and is giving the medium and long-term problems for the rivers and the population.

Resource 4.24 identifies three main impacts upon the fluvial system. The first is the damming of the upper Toutle valley and the creation of an enlarged Spirit Lake. The debris slide following the earthquake which triggered the eruptive episode,

blocked the Toutle valley at the point where the river emerged from Spirit Lake. On top of this layers of ash and volcanic debris were plastered, to build a natural dam which has raised the level of Spirit Lake by 100 m (see resource 4.24).

The second impact is the dumping of millions of tonnes of debris in the river valleys radiating from the mountain. When the mountain exploded, the upper slopes were coated with snow, and this snowpack was abruptly melted. At the same time, vast quantities of ash and debris were being spewed out of the volcano. The proportion which fell immediately around the mountain combined with the meltwater to form huge mudflows (Lahars), which roared down the valleys, gouging out valley floors and sides for up to 50 km. However, as the inputs of energy and water declined, the debris was deposited, infilling the valley floors to depths of up to 50 m, and changing the nature of the terrain (see the photos on resource 4.25). As the rivers have returned to their pre-event discharge regimes they have an available sediment load far greater than their available energy.

The third impact was on the river catchment by destruction of the forest cover and subsequent

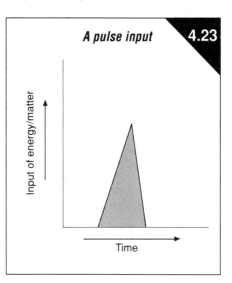

A pulse input 4.23

Graph with vertical axis labelled "Input of energy/matter" and horizontal axis labelled "Time", showing a single sharp triangular peak.

deposition of layers of ash (resources 1.10 and 1.11 in Chapter 1). In this mountainous region, the stripping of the steep slopes and the addition of unconsolidated debris, provide perfect conditions for rapid sheet and gully erosion, especially where lumber companies have been permitted to remove the dead timber (resource 4.25). Inevitably, the supply of sediment to the stream channels has been growing — and remember, these streams are already trying to adjust to the sediment dumped across the valley floors. The recovery of equilibrium by the fluvial system may be dependent upon the recovery of the ecosystem.

4.24

The debris slide blocking the Toutle Valley and damming back Spirit Lake

Extract A

Flood watch: volcano-formed dam worries residents near St. Helens

Flood insurance has become a big seller among many of the 45 000 residents in the southwest Washington area near Mount St. Helens. They are afraid an unstable dam formed at Spitit Lake by volcanic debris at the base of the peak will breach, releasing 274 000 acre-feet of water.

Just as ominously, debris from the mountain's 18 May, 1980, eruption, which spewed out a cubic mile of ash and rock, is settling in the beds of the Toutle and Cowlitz rivers, reducing the capacity of river channels.

To lessen the possibility of the dam breaking and sending a wall of mud and water over the dikes protecting the area, the US Army Corps of Engineers has twenty pumps roaring around the clock on a one-year, $7 million project to keep water pressure from building up on the dam.

'What we're trying to do is maintain the lake at its current level,' said Ed Daugherty, the engineer coordinating the project. 'We're confident that what we're doing up there will preclude a breach of that dam – and that's (without) another eruption taking place.'

The National Weather Service believes if Spirit Lake were to breach, the dikes along the populated areas could be topped.

'It could be worse than May 18th,' when the swollen Toutle turned into a killer, said Chuck Orwig, a weather service hydrologist. 'There is more water involved now in storage in the lake.

'There are all sorts of scenarios in between as to how the water will release, but if the worst should happen, and if it were to pick up the water in Cold Water Lake, the present levy system downstream could be overtopped.'

The bailout is aimed at gaining time while an extensive study is done to see what long-term measures should be taken on Spirit Lake.

But more of the concern in the towns in the flood plain of the Toutle and Cowlitz rivers, including Longview, Kelso and Castle Rock, centers on sediment buildup in the river system.

'We figure of the cubic mile of material up there, that about a third of that will eventually come down the rivers.' Daughterty said. 'And we estimate that about 40 per cent of that will settle in the river system.'

'Some $4 million in dike work along the system is aimed at offsetting that problem', he said.

In addition, 21 sirens have been purchased by Cowlitz County at a cost of $750 000 to provide an early warning of a flood. The alarms will give residents in the tiny logging community of Toutle, closest to the peak, two hours notice of a flood and as much as eight hours notice to residents of Longview.

'It's a very serious threat,' said Ben Bena, Cowlitz County coordinator of emergency services. 'As far as the Cowlitz is concerned, sedimentation has caused infilling. It's not that we'll be receiving more water, it's that the bottom of the river has come up (cutting down on river capacity).'

(Source: *San Francisco Sunday Examiner & Chronicle*, 12 December, 1982

Extract B

Toutle begins cleaning itself

The Toutle River is cleansing itself. Technical measurements of mud and suspended solids in the Toutle, taken by the Washington Department of Ecology, show the river is not much muddier than during one of nature's heavy rainstorms.

Measured in Jackson Turbidity Units, a nationwide standard, the Toutle had a tentative reading of 325 JTU on Monday. On 21 May, three days after the volcanic mudflows and flooding, the Toutle measured 2 500 JTU at its mouth.

Before the eruption, the highest reading ever taken in the Toutle was 220 JTU.

Bill Yake, a turbidity expert for the stage DOE, said 'There are a lot of sources left, from the sediment on the bottom to what is being washed out of Spirit Lake. But my guess is it's leveled off at this point, and will stay here for some period.'

Two samples are taken, one for turbidity and one for total suspended solids.

Since the turbidity sampling began in 1971, the Toutle's lowest measurement was 1 JTU. That's nearly crystal pure. The highest, during an autumn rainstorm, was 220 JTU. The average for the nine years, Yake said; was 11 JTU.

On the morning of 21 May, the reading at the bridge was 2 500 JTU and dropped to 2 200 JTU that afternoon. On 27 May, the reading had dropped to 1 600 JTU, and to 260 on June 23.

The sampling for total suspended solid measures the weight of material that can be filtered out of the water. These samples started in 1978, and averaged 37 milligrams per liter. The measurements ranged between an all-time low of 2 milligrams per liter to an all-time high of 480 mg per liter. That is, an all-time high before the volcano exploded.

On 21 May, the TSS weighed 9 800 mg per liter in the morning and 8 200 mg per litre in the afternoon. On 27 May, the reading was down to 7 100 mg per liter and was to 3 100 mg per liter on June 23. The DOE lab isn't finished with the TSS sample taken Monday.

(Source: Lew Pumphrey *The Daily News,* Longview, Washington, 17 July, 1980)

4.25

Extract C

Volcano's effects less than feared

There was near panic on the Portland waterfront in the days immediately following the 18 May blast which left 65 people dead or missing. Millions of tons of ash, mud and debris washed down the Toutle River, into the Cowlitz River and then into the Comumbia River.

More than 22 million cubic yards of material formed a massive shoal that choked the river — the economic lifeline between Portland and the Pacific ocean 100 miles to the northwest.

The depth of the main river channel was reduced from 40 feet to as shallow as 15 feet along a nine-mile stretch both above and below the confluence of the Cowlitz and the Columbia, about 45 miles north of Portland.

When a ship ran aground in the muck less than 24 hours after the eruption, ocean-going ship traffic was halted for four days. The development sent nervous tremors through an industry which accounts for an estimated $4 million a day in business in the Portland metropolitan area.

Since then, a fleet of dredges working 24 hours a day has reopened a 300-foot wide and 35-foot deep channel which will accommodate most of the ships calling on the Port of Portland.

The US Army Corps of Engineers, which is supervising the dredging operations, predicts the normal channel of 40 feet deep and 600 feet wide will be restored by the end of September at a cost of $44 million.

(Source: *Associated Press,* 2 July, 1980)

Mount St. Helens: gullying and erosion in the blast zone.

Extract D

Plans being made to control future flooding

Castle rock – If two usually uncontrollable forces cooperate, the U.S. Army Corps of Engineers has a plan to save the Cowlitz River Valley from extensive flooding this fall.

Those forces are Mother Nature and the federal government.

Mother Nature must cooperate by not sending too much rain in one dose. And the federal government must appropriate money to improve flood protection near the river.

The Corps is designing anti-flood measures around the Cowlitz which lost 85 percent of its water capacity when Mount St. Helens erupted 18 May. About 25 million cubic yards of mud, silt and other debris washed into the river channel.

The work will cost an estimated $219 million and will include dredging parts of the Cowlitz, building five dams to trap sediment in the Toutle River, and permanently evacuating parts of the area's flood plain.

Engineers and Jim Bauman, a hydrologist from the National Weather Service, agree the area probably is safe from flooding now. The ground is dry enough to absorb water, slowing the runoff, Bauman said.

'If the eruption had happened in the fall, this area could have been devastated by floods over and over again,' he said, but it would take five to six inches of sustained rain to cause floods now.

'Usually what we're planning for would take four years of study. We're trying to do it in a couple of weeks.'

If it receives the required $38 million, the Corps will build five sediment dams on the Toutle River. The largest – 39 feet high – would be on the north fork about two miles upstream of Camp Baker.

The dams would trap silt and mud before it enters the Cowlitz, and could be built by the next flood season.

Without the dams, Bauman said, 'We could dredge the Cowlitz channel out by November and have a gully washer (heavy storm) bring down all that silt and have the same problems.'

The area behind the dams, on Weyerhaeuser Co. property, would have to be dredged yearly at a cost of $1 million. As much as 1 billion cubic meters of mud and silt may lie in the Toutle River Valley.

(Source: Andre Stepankowsky *The Daily News*, Longview, Washington, 4 June, 1980)

Activities

Using extract A (resource 4.25) and the photos on resource 4.25, answer the following questions:

1 In what ways has the eruption changed the throughput of water and sediment down the River Toutle basin?

2 Why are local people worried about the new natural dam?

3 What has been the human response to the hazard?

4 Using extract B on resource 4.25:

a Construct a table of suspended load and turbidity levels in the River Toutle after the eruption.

b How do these levels compare with 'normal' conditions along the Toutle?

c What do these figures tell us about a river's capacity to adjust to the discharge – energy – load equation?

5 a How did the changed channel form threaten economic activities? (Extract C).

b Who should pay for the costs and losses caused by such natural disasters?

6 Using extract D on resource 4.25:

a What were the effects upon the channel capacity of the River Cowlitz?

b Much of the rain in the Toutle – Cowlitz catchment falls as heavy summer storms. Suggest how this helps to explain the hydrologist's claim that an eruption in the autumn (fall) would have been more serious.

c Describe and explain the methods being used to re-organise the throughput of water and sediment along the Toutle – Cowlitz basin.

7 **Group research and discussion:** If the Toutle and Cowlitz rivers were left to natural processes to operate (i.e. there were no engineering works), what channel form is likely to evolve in the medium-term: meandering; braided; incised?

Use standard texts and your understanding of fluvial processes to make your selection and validate your choice. Note: Base your thinking on (a) the conditions necessary for the development of each channel type; (b) the present conditions in the Toutle – Cowlitz valleys in terms of the discharge – energy – sediment equation.

Part II: Natural dams can be useful: Lake Waikaremoana, New Zealand

Not all natural dams across valleys are hazards like the Toutle Valley landslip at Spirit Lake (pages 91 – 92). The Waikaretaheke River rises in the mountains of Urewera National Park, in North Island, New Zealand, and flows South East in a sharply cut valley. This is a tectonically active region. About 2200 years ago an earthquake triggered a huge landslip in the steeply dipping succession of sandstones, limestones and shales (resources 4.26 and 4.27). The landslip blocked the river valley, creating Lake Waikaremoana. This

natural dam is a jumble of massive blocks – one sandstone block is 3 km long and 1 km across – and therefore, is not watertight. Apart from the main river exit channel, a large number of 'leaks' in the base of the dam emerged as springs below the landslip. These outlets, plus the strength of the interlocked jumble of blocks, have given considerable stability to the dam, so much so, that it is today the site of the Kaitawa HEP scheme (resource 4.28). Most of the leaks have been sealed by a concrete blanket and an artificial channel has been built to the turbines — but there has been no need to build an expensive dam.

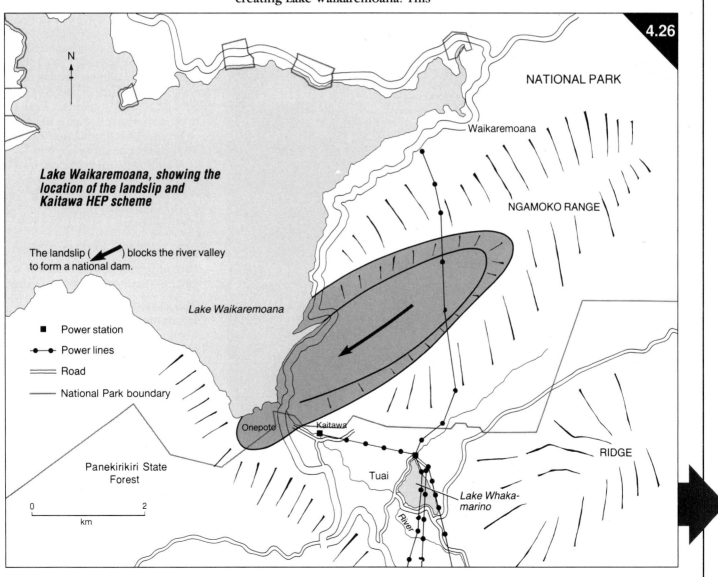

Lake Waikaremoana, showing the location of the landslip and Kaitawa HEP scheme

The landslip ( ) blocks the river valley to form a national dam.

- ■ Power station
- ●—● Power lines
- ═══ Road
- —— National Park boundary

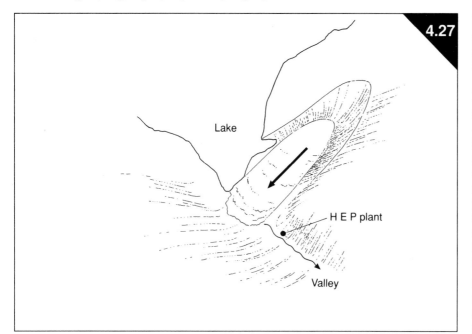

The Waikaremoana landslip

The Kaitawa HEP scheme

Part III: How channels adjust to load changes – River Ringarooma, Tasmania

Tackling a problem

Suppose that the discharge – energy – sediment relationship in a stream is in balance, i.e. that the stream has sufficient energy to work on the available sediment so that the channel is relatively stable over a period of years. We could claim that this stream system is in a state of dynamic equilibrium, with negative feedback mechanisms sustaining this overall balance.

Now suppose that additional sediment is supplied to the channel along a stretch near the stream source. This may occur either from natural processes, e.g. slope failure, or from human activities, e.g. mining wastes, and is a common aspect in the work of streams. Is there a model or general statement which allows us to predict what is likely to happen to this sediment and hence to the stream channel over time? This is an important question as more people settle in river valleys and human activities increasingly modify catchments, thereby altering sediment supply.

We clearly need information on:

1 The sediment added: Where? How much? What type? For how long?

2 The stream: Discharge regime; fluctuations in regime; existing channel form and bed/bank characteristics; energy available.

Seeking an answer

The type of information required has been collected and analysed for the River Ringarooma, a 75 km long stream in North East Tasmania, a humid temperate environment and a generally wooded catchment. Alluvial tin mining began in 1875, peaked in 1900–1920, and finally ended in 1982. Both of the methods used – hydraulic sluicing with power hoses, and dredging – released large volumes of spoil, and a total of 40 million m³ entered the river. There were a number of mining locations, but most of the sediment entered the stream in a stretch between Branxholm, Derby and Pioneer (resource 4.29). The fact that sediment entered the stream channel at more than one location makes understanding the stream response difficult, but the graphs on resource 4.30 tell us that mining began in the upper reaches and moved downstream. The discharge histograms indicate that the stream has fluctuated significantly in its capacity to sort and transport the sediment inputs.

The story of the mine spoil sediment is told in resource 4.30, which is based on a combination of field evidence and computer modelling. Each line represents the distribution of the spoil along the channel in a given year, with the zero deposition axis representing the channel with no mine spoil sediment. The graphs also allow us to follow the story of a particular stretch of stream channel through time, e.g. for the stretch 10-20 km from the source, we can quantify the amount of spoil present at each five year interval. Finally, by locating the peaks of each line we can trace movements of the bulk of the sediment through time.

As an illustration, we can analyse the upper channel section, upstream of kilometre 28 (these are kilometres from the source): in 1890, when most of the sediment entered from the Briseis Mine, the stream was capable of transporting the added sediment fairly efficiently. This is indicated by the lack of 'peaking' in the graph and the even spread far downstream. Between 1890 and 1905, stream discharges were relatively low (resource 4.29), but inputs from the upper mines increased. The result was a rapid build-up of sediment upstream of kilometre 28. In systems terms, sediment inputs to the channel store exceeded outputs from the store by stream transportation. The sediment store in this upper channel section

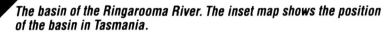

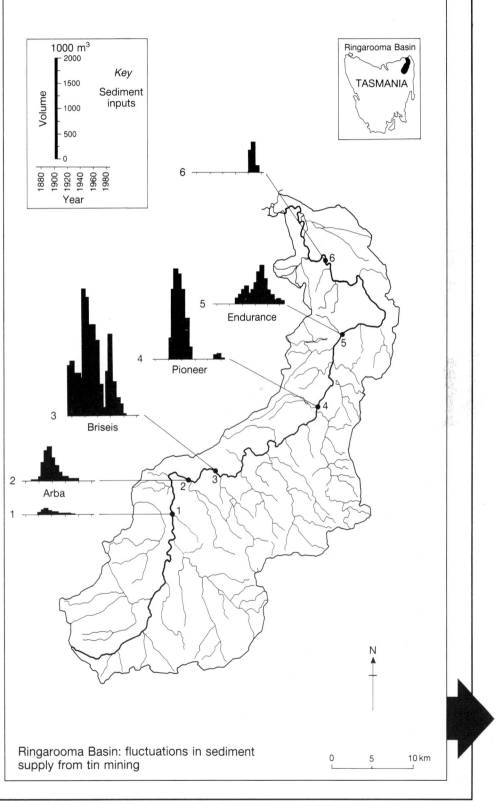

4.29

The basin of the Ringarooma River. The inset map shows the position of the basin in Tasmania.

Ringarooma Basin: fluctuations in sediment supply from tin mining

peaked around 1920, since which date sediment outputs from the channel store have exceeded inputs.

This sequence suggests that the stream uses its available energy to remove the extra sediment and so restore the discharge – energy – sediment balance. The time taken to achieve this equilibrium is the **stream recovery time**. Resource

4.30 predicts that in the stream channel upstream of kilometre 28, the recovery will be complete by the year 2000, i.e. all the mine-generated sediment will have been removed from the channel store. Remember, most sediment will be slowly translocated downstream in a series of entrainments, i.e. it will be picked up and dropped a number of times in its journey to the sea.

(Source: adapted from A D Knighton, 'River adjustment to changes in sediment loads the effects of tin mining on the Ringarooma River, Tasmania, 1875–1984; *Earth surface processes and landforms,* 14(4), June 1989, pages 333–360).

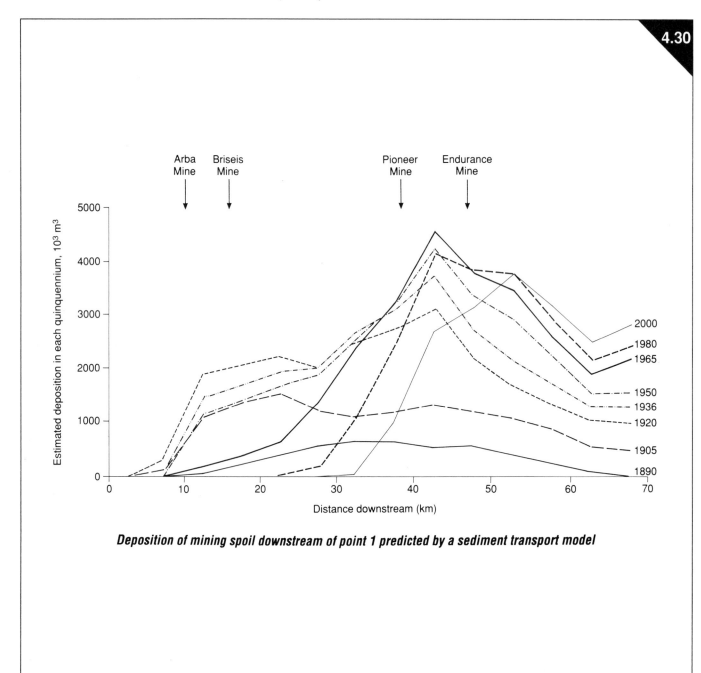

4.30

Deposition of mining spoil downstream of point 1 predicted by a sediment transport model

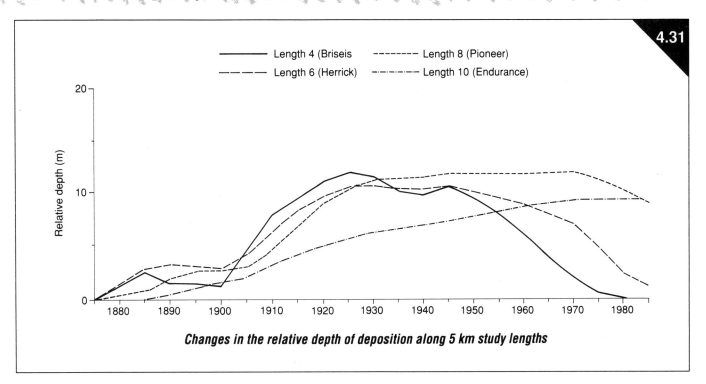

4.31

Changes in the relative depth of deposition along 5 km study lengths

Activities

1 Using resources 4.29–4.31, analyse the sequence of events along the middle channel section, between kilometres 28 and 50. Note: Consider the two sources of sediment: the mines along this section and the entrained sediment from the upper section.

2 a Construct a table showing the location of maximum mine spoil for each year in terms of distance from stream source.

   b Resource 4.31 shows the volume of sediment at four locations along the stream over time (resource 4.29 gives these locations). From your table and these graphs, make a summary statement about how the River Ringarooma has responded to the added sediment load.

3 From the study of a number of streams which have endured major sediment inputs, this general statement has been made: That the sediment mass moves in a wave downstream over time as the stream works to re-establish the discharge – energy – sediment equilibrium. To what extent does the story of the Ringarooma River support this statement?

4 Group project or discussion: As the hydrologist in charge of river management, you are asked to respond to this query from a planner in a city along the lower course of your river:

'As mining spoil is to be put into the river 50 km upstream for the next twenty years, will this increase the chances of channel changes and flooding in the city? We have been told that river sections undergoing channel aggradation are more likely to flood and to develop braiding and anastomosing channels. Is this so, and how and when will this affect our city?'

Give a brief response to this query. (Include graphs and diagrams as relevant.)

Background

Water is a focal resource in all economic and social development. Consequently, the form and functioning of hydrological systems are easily and crucially modified by human activities. This case study illustrates how such changes affect the quantity and quality of water moving through and stored in a system, and also the 'knock on' effects through the rest of an environmental system.

▶ *Before reading the case study, check your understanding of the following terms:*

oligotrophy, eutrophication, photosynthesis, role of nitrogen and phosphorus in water bodies, primary productivity.

Key understandings

◆ We should try to anticipate impacts caused by changed inputs to a system, rather than simply responding once they have happened.

◆ Development should involve integrated management of land and water resources across the whole drainage basin.

There are more than 3500 natural and man-made lakes in the Japanese islands, and as industry and population grow, they are an intensely used resource. Since the mid 1970s the major water management problem has been the eutrophication of these lakes. The tropic status of a lake is measured by the concentrations of nitrogen and phosphorus, and the change from oligotrophy to eutrophy is shown by a marked increase in the concentration of these nutrients. The most obvious sign of eutrophication is increased primary production, manifested by an explosive growth of photosynthetic micro-organisms during the summer months, e.g. algal 'blooms'. Eutrophication of freshwaters is becoming a worldwide phenomenon, coinciding with rapid population growth, intensification of agriculture, and industrial expansion, all of which accelerate the inputs of nitrogen and phosphorus into the waters.

Lake Biwa

Lake Biwa is the largest freshwater lake in Japan, with a surface area of 674 sq km and a maximum depth of over 100 m., and is situated in the centre of Shiga Prefecture on the main island, Honshu (resource 4.32). The catchment area is 3227 sq km and the high mean annual precipitation of 2000 mm produces an average annual inflow of 5109 cu.m. It takes about 19 years for the hydrological cycle to exchange the whole water body.

Lake Biwa today sustains a population of 13 million, plus about 29 million visitors annually to the Lake Biwa Park. Even today, 52 per cent of the catchment basin remains forested, and most of the farmland is still wet rice paddies. The urban area comprises 17.3 per cent of the catchment area and is concentrated around the southern part of the lake. Textile and chemical industries are particularly important.

As Lake Biwa has become the major water resource in Japan, so the quality of the lake has deteriorated rapidly. This is a result not only of changing agricultural technology, e.g. adding nitrate and phosphate fertilisers, and industrial growth, but also of the failure to manage domestic wastes. After 1945 the installation of modern service water systems in most villages replaced local water supply systems. However,

---

Annual nutrient inputs to Lake Biwa					**4.32**
	Industrial	**Domestic**	**Agricultural**	**Natural**	**Total**
Total nitrogen (t yr $^{-1}$)					
1960	405.5	1021.3	2047.7	1986.9	5461.4
1970	1281.4	1821.3	1804.0	2033.9	6940.6
1980	2089.2	3248.0	1726.9	2131.9	9196.0
Total phosphorus (t yr $^{-1}$)					
1960	110.3	88.4	98.4	70.4	367.5
1970	372.0	348.7	119.6	72.2	912.5
1980	371.1	497.4	120.7	75.8	1065.0
Source: Lake Biwa Research Institute, Otsu, japan					

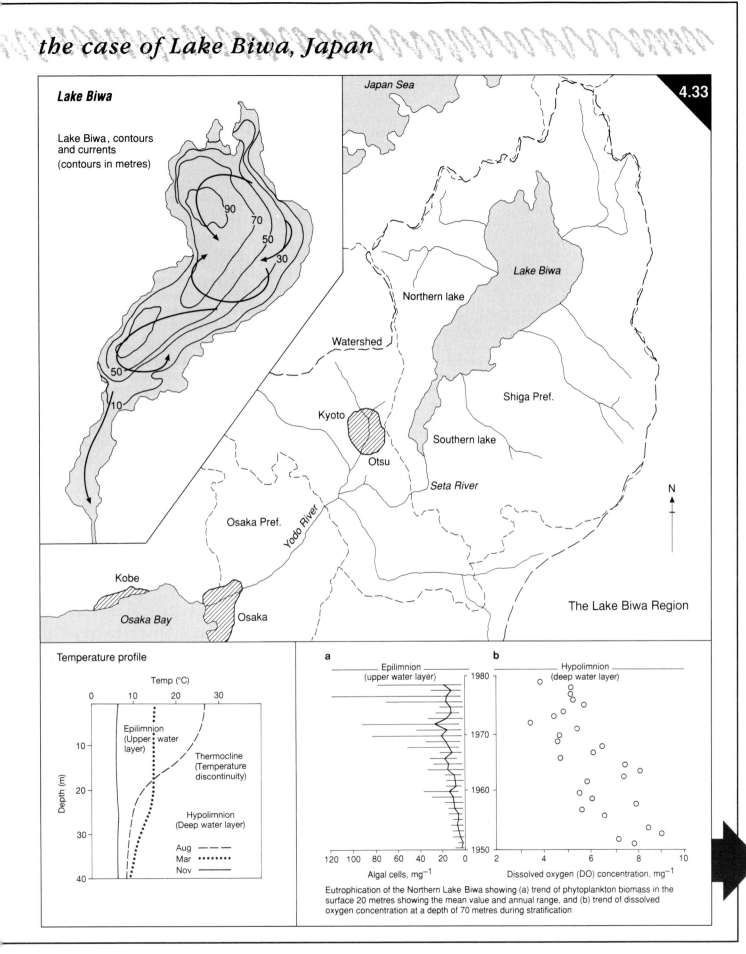

Lake Biwa

Lake Biwa, contours and currents (contours in metres)

90 70 50 30

50

10

The Lake Biwa Region

Japan Sea

Lake Biwa

Northern lake

Watershed

Shiga Pref.

Kyoto

Otsu

Southern lake

Seta River

Osaka Pref.

Yodo River

N

Kobe

Osaka Bay

Osaka

Temperature profile

Temp (°C)

Epilimnion (Upper water layer)

Thermocline (Temperature discontinuity)

Hypolimnion (Deep water layer)

Aug
Mar
Nov

Depth (m)

a ——— Epilimnion ———
(upper water layer)

b ——— Hypolimnion ———
(deep water layer)

Algal cells, mg⁻¹

Dissolved oxygen (DO) concentration, mg⁻¹

Eutrophication of the Northern Lake Biwa showing (a) trend of phytoplankton biomass in the surface 20 metres showing the mean value and annual range, and (b) trend of dissolved oxygen concentration at a depth of 70 metres during stratification

4.33

CASE STUDY 4.5   *Changes in a hydrological system – the case of Lake Biwa, Japan.*

little attention was paid to managing the water once it had been used, e.g. by 1981 only 4 per cent of village households were on public sewage and less than 19 per cent had septic tanks.

Eutrophication of Lake Biwa

Since 1950 the lake has changed from oligotrophic to eutrophic status, e.g. by the early 1970s the transparency had halved from 10 to 5 metres. Plankton increased remarkably. This was due to an increase in annual inputs of nitrogen and phosphorus. Between 1965 and 1975 for example, inputs of nitrogen and phosphorus increased by 1.35 and 1.5 times respectively. The first algal 'bloom' occurred in 1959, and every year since 1977 there have been outbreaks of the so-called 'red tide' caused by explosive developments of algae which turn the lake colour to reddish brown and give off a pungent odour. Oxygen levels have halved, fish and shellfish catches are down tenfold and the lake bed habitats have changed. Resource 4.32 quantifies the inputs and their sources.

Water quality management

The fundamental approach to reducing freshwater eutrophication is to control the inputs of nutrients to the lake. Even if these inputs can be reduced, nutrient release from the lake sediments by bacterial activity will be sufficient to maintain high rates of micro-organic growth for many years. Clearly then, policy for prevention of eutrophication

requires anticipatory controls and this must be concerned with integrated land and water management throughout the catchment.

Local residents' movements began in the late 1960s, demanding controls on industrial pollutant discharges. They produced positive results: national and local governments set up environmental affairs departments. Later, laws were passed, e.g. the national Basic Law of Pollution Control (1967); the Shiga Prefecture, Lake Biwa Environment Conservation Program (1972). Controlling domestic effluents has proved more difficult because the sources are so dispersed and are often without main sewers. Again, the people themselves responded by questioning their own life-styles. For instance, there was a spontaneous campaign to abandon the use of synthetic phosphorus detergents which were responsible for 18 per cent of the phosphorus input in 1975. The citizens' 'Use soap' campaign encouraged 70 per cent of the families to use soap exclusively and resulted in the Shiga government passing the Prevention of Eutrophication of Lake Biwa Act in 1980. This bans the sale of detergents using phosphate stabiliser and controls the use of nitrates and phosphorus fertilisers by farmers, and in factory effluents. By 1986, the nutrients in streams flowing to the lake were down by 20 per cent. In the shallower southern part of the lake, phosphorus levels are today down by 30 per cent.

Conclusions

1 The case of Lake Biwa illustrates the current view that the goals of economic development and ecological balance are not conflicts but are inevitably interrelated and mutually reinforcing.

2 The current responsive attitude to environmental problems must be replaced by an anticipatory approach which stresses awareness of the sensitivity of ecosystems to human interference.

3 Human-induced changes are often slow to become apparent, but once they do, the effects may be irreversible. Again, we must anticipate impacts, not simply respond to them.

4 Water management cannot be separated from land use, and vice versa.

(Source: G E Petts, 'Water Management: The Case of Lake Biwa, Japan.' *Geographical Journal*, 154(3), Nov. 1988, pp. 367–376.)

Activity

Discuss with a partner or in a group:

If the management policy for the Lake Biwa basin had been anticipatory rather than responsive, what form could such a policy have taken?

CHAPTER 5

The work of ice and associated meltwaters

Introduction

'Since human beings emerged as a species Homo Sapiens, half a million years ago, the biggest natural changes in climate have been the switches into, and out of, ice ages. During that time (and for several million years before) the earth has been slightly colder than today ... There has been a regular rhythm of changes in temperature in which an ice age roughly 100 000 years long is succeeded by a slightly warmer interval, called an interglacial, which lasts between 10 000 and 20 000 years. The pattern has repeated ten times in a little more than a million years ... Today, we are living near the end of a natural warm spell, an interglacial which began a little over 10 000 years ago' (resource 5.1).

These rhythms of the Pleistocene period over the past three million years or

so are caused by (a) minor changes in the earth's orbit around the sun and (b) fluctuations in the amount of atmospheric carbon dioxide, i.e. the natural 'greenhouse effect'. Mean global temperatures may drop by 5°C, and at their maximum, the icesheets have advanced to cover 30 per cent of the earth's surface, e.g. across the British Isles, ice reached roughly as far south as the Bristol Channel – Thames Estuary line, and in North America the icesheets pushed as far as 40°N. As we are now enjoying the probable peak of an interglacial, extensive land surfaces are exposed which have been glaciated within the past 20 000 years. Remember, however, that as water is progressively released from the ice store, so sea-level rises to inundate low-lying coastal zones.

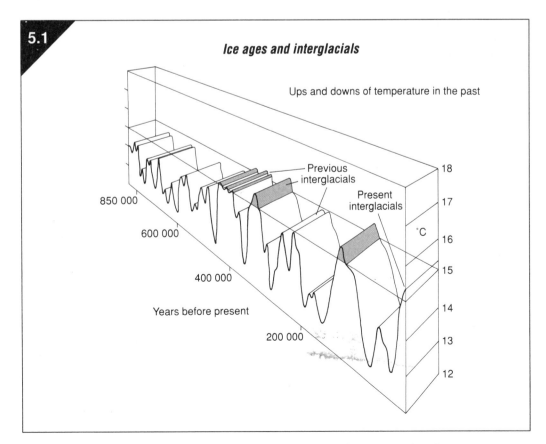

5.1

Ice ages and interglacials

Ups and downs of temperature in the past

Previous interglacials

Present interglacials

°C

850 000

600 000

400 000

Years before present

200 000

18

17

16

15

14

13

12

The following case studies demonstrate key erosional and depositional processes and the interactive role of ice, water and debris. Notice in particular, how they illustrate various time-scales and spatial scales. For instance, while major glacial–interglacial rhythms may be thought of in millennia, many northern hemisphere glaciers have shrunk significantly within the last century (case studies 5.1 and 5.2). Case studies 5.3, 5.4 and 5.5 encourage you to ask questions about popular generalisations. First, do the set of features found in front of a retreating glacier-snout always fit the diagrams shown in textbooks? (Case study 5.3, from Iceland.) Second, just because a glacier carries load, does this mean it erodes? (Case study 5.4.) Third, are all meltwater channels the result of stream systems beneath the ice? (Case study 5.5.)

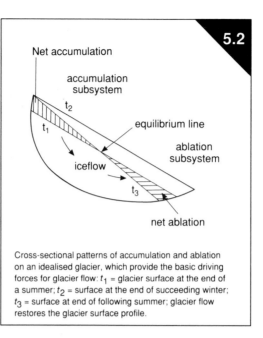

5.2

Cross-sectional patterns of accumulation and ablation on an idealised glacier, which provide the basic driving forces for glacier flow: t_1 = glacier surface at the end of a summer; t_2 = surface at the end of succeeding winter; t_3 = surface at end of following summer; glacier flow restores the glacier surface profile.

Processes and landforms 5.3

	Erosion	Deposition
Ice	e.g. U-shaped trough	e.g. Moraine
Meltwater	e.g. Meltwater channel	e.g. Esker

Note:

1 Individual features may have been influenced by more than one agent and process.
2 Glaciated landscapes are made up of landform assemblages combining the four categories.
3 Present-day landforms may be the result of repeated ice advances and retreats, but most are determined by the most recent cycle.
4 Individual landforms may represent different phases in a glaciation-deglaciation cycle.

Key understandings

◆ A glacier, icesheet or ice-cap 'is a body of ice, consisting largely of recrystallised snow, that shows evidence of downslope or outward movement due to the pull of gravity'. In terms of its influence upon the land, we can think of a glacier 'as a sedimentary system that is involved with the accumulation, transfer and deposition of mass (snow, ice, water, rock debris) in response to additions and losses of mass and energy'.

◆ Thus, glaciers and the landforms they create can be described and interpreted in systems terms: inputs – stores – throughput – outputs of matter and energy. Whether a glacier is growing, shrinking or stable depends upon the input – output relationship between accumulation and ablation during a certain time-span. This relationship is called the **mass**

balance of the glacier. Resource 5.2 sums up how ice bodies work. Before you continue, you should discuss these diagrams carefully with a partner, to clarify your understanding.

◆ Meltwater from the ice is as important an agent as the ice itself in shaping the land.

◆ There are three aspects to the place of rock debris – where it comes from (input to the ice), how it moves through the glacier (store and throughput) and how it leaves the ice (output). Understanding the interactions between the ice, water and rock debris provides the key to interpreting landscapes which have been glaciated. Resource 5.3 structures the fundamental outcomes.

Background

Films or photographs of the Greenland ice-cap or New Zealand glaciers give an impression of permanence, of masses as constant as a mountain. This impression is misleading, for although such ice masses have persisted for perhaps 3 million years, they are constantly changing. Like many physical features, they tend to exist in a relatively stable condition for long periods, interspersed by shorter episodes or more rapid change. With a glacier, the most visible evidence of stability or change is the position of the ice front over time.

Let us regard a glacier as an environmental system, with the ice mass as the **store**. The volume of this store depends upon the ice budget: the balance between the **input** of snow in the upper accumulation zone, and the **output** of meltwater and icebergs in the lower, ablation zone. Remember too, that the ice moves through the store **(throughput)**. In colder periods, more snow enters the store than is being ablated (melted or evaporated) or lost by iceberg 'calving', and thus the ice front will advance, i.e. there is an ice budget surplus. In warmer periods, the ablation/calving output exceeds the snowfall input, there is an ice budget deficit, the ice store shrinks and the ice front retreats.

This case study shows clearly that glaciers can respond quickly to changes in ice budget balances triggered by short-term climate fluctuations, and that such glacier activity can create hazards as well as attractions for human activities.

A moving experience

The major marketing feature of ocean cruises to Alaska is Glacier Bay (resource 5.4). The cruise ships move slowly up a spectacular fiord and past the great ice cliffs of the glacier snout at the head of the bay. If they are lucky, the tourists see 'the

5.4

Cruise ship in Glacier Bay, Alaska

calving process' as massive icebergs detach themselves and collapse into the water with a mighty roar and splash. As resources 5.5 and 5.6 indicate, the tourists are having an experience quite different from the one they would have enjoyed 250 years ago.

Warning signs

Changes in glacier behaviour can cause hazards and create disastrous knock-on effects through the environment. Resource 5.7 was published in 1987. In March 1989, the tanker Exxon Valdez ran aground, causing Alaska's worst oil pollution disaster (resource 5.8).

Key understandings

◆ Icesheets and glaciers are systems, with inputs of snow, stores of ice, throughputs of moving ice and outputs of meltwater and icebergs.

◆ Icesheet and glacier stores fluctuate constantly in response to budget-balance changes between inputs and outputs.

◆ Glacier activity can create both attractions and hazards for human activity.

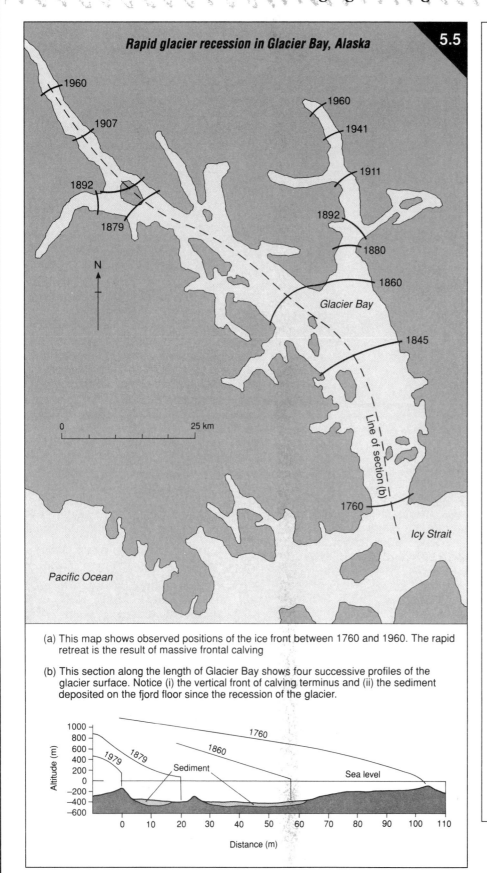

Rapid glacier recession in Glacier Bay, Alaska

1960
1907
1892
1879

1960
1941
1911
1892
1880
1860

Glacier Bay

1845

Line of section (b)

1760

Icy Strait

N

0   25 km

Pacific Ocean

(a) This map shows observed positions of the ice front between 1760 and 1960. The rapid retreat is the result of massive frontal calving

(b) This section along the length of Glacier Bay shows four successive profiles of the glacier surface. Notice (i) the vertical front of calving terminus and (ii) the sediment deposited on the fjord floor since the recession of the glacier.

1760
1860
1879
1979
Sediment
Sea level

Altitude (m): 1000, 800, 600, 400, 200, 0, −200, −400, −600

Distance (m): 0, 10, 20, 30, 40, 50, 60, 70, 80, 90, 100, 110

When Captain George Vancouver sailed up the coast of southeastern Alaska in the late eighteenth century he plotted on his charts the positions of a number of large ice streams that issued from the high coastal mountains and terminated near the rocky shore. Today, in their place, one finds long open fjords. Such deep glacially carved valleys submerged by the sea extend many tens of kilometres back into the mountains. The dramatic recession of these fjord glaciers during the past century and a half at rates far in excess of typical glacier retreat rates on land is due to frontal calving, a process that involves the progressive breaking off of icebergs from a glacier that terminates in deep water. Although the base of a fjord glacier may lie far below sea level along much of its length, its terminus can remain stable as long as it is 'grounded' against a shoal. However, if the glacier's mass balance becomes negative, the front will recede into deeper water and calving can proceed. Once it commences, calving may continue rapidly and irreversibly until the glacier front once again becomes grounded, generally near the head of the fjord.

(Source: Skinner and Porter, *Physical Geology*, Wiley, 1987)

5.7

A 1987 warning

While most of the large fjord glaciers of coastal Alaska have retreated well back into their source regions during recent decades, an exception is Columbia Glacier which has remained relatively stationary with its terminus near the point of its greatest recent advance. During the early 1980s, signs of imminent retreat were detected along its front as calving increased and the terminus began to recede into deeper water.

Calculations indicate that the rate of recession is likely to increase dramatically as the terminus calves, releasing a vast number of icebergs. Many of the bergs are likely to drift across nearby shipping lanes where large oil tankers enter and leave the port of Valdez at the southern end of the Alaska Pipeline, thereby creating potential hazards to navigation."

(Source: Skinner and Porter, *Physical Geology,* Wiley, 1987, p.348)

5.8

Giant oil spill hits Alaska

The worst oil spill in American waters spread an ominous dark stain across the ice floes and fragile Alaskan ecology of Prince William Sound yesterday, after a giant oil tanker ran aground near the Valdez oil terminal.

The 1100ft Exxon Valdez, loaded with more than 1.2 million barrels of crude oil valued at nearly £15 million, was taking an unauthorised route through the sound to avoid ice floes from the Columbia Glacier when it hit a charted reef 25 miles from the port of Valdez.

(Source: Martin Walker, *The Guardian,* 25 March 1989)

America's worst spill covers 100 square miles

The tanker, supposedly incorporating the latest safety designs, had moved down the channel but veered considerably to the left about 25 miles out to avoid small icebergs 'calved' from the nearby Columbia glacier.

(Source: *The Guardian,* 28 March 1989)

Activities

Resource 5.5 gives the position of the ice front and the ice height in different years. Notice in resource 5.5(b), the irregular long profile of the fjord floor and how sedimentation is changing this profile now that the glacier front has retreated, i.e. ablation and calving have exceeded accumulation.

1 a How far has the ice front retreated up the fjord?

  b What has been the average annual distance of retreat since 1760?

2 a Why does calving and ice-front retreat occur more rapidly when the glacier is not 'grounded'?

  b What factors other than calving could be influencing the retreat?

3 Why is it likely that the ice-front may be about to enter a stable period, where calving is less common?

4 Using resources 5.7 and 5.8 say what the connection was between the behaviour of the Columbia Glacier and the environmental pollution?

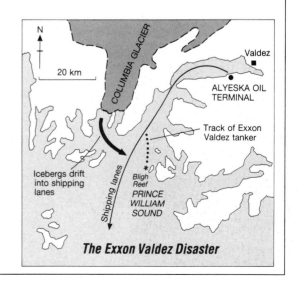

The Exxon Valdez Disaster

Background

Glaciers and thick snowpacks occur on all the major mountain ranges of the world, even near the equator (resource 5.9). Locating, measuring and understanding how these huge stores work is important for two main reasons:

(i) runoff of meltwaters feeds river basins and hence influences irrigation, power generation, settlement, flood hazard etc. (See case study 4.2);

(ii) the behaviour of glaciers provides crucial evidence in estimating 'the greenhouse effect', i.e. the global warming forecast as a result of the accelerating release of carbon dioxide into the atmosphere. If temperature are rising, then glaciers will be shrinking.

Key understandings

◆ Glaciers are sensitive indicators of climatic change.

◆ During the twentieth century there has been no clearly defined pattern.

◆ A mixed pattern of mass balance change.

◆ Three key elements in measuring mass balance changes in a glacier store are the position of the equilibrium line, the size of the accumulation and ablation zones and the rate of ice movement

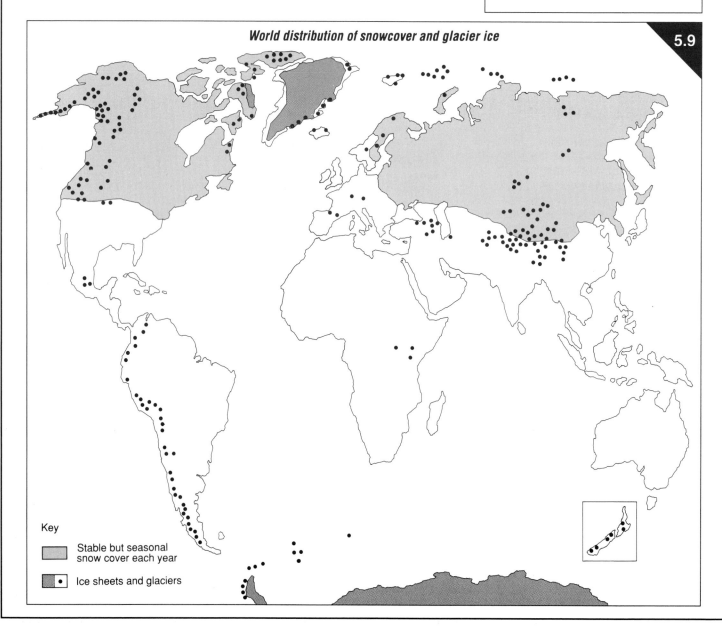

World distribution of snowcover and glacier ice

5.9

Key

▨ Stable but seasonal snow cover each year

▪ Ice sheets and glaciers

Typically, high-altitude terrain receives more precipitation than the lower areas because of the orographic effect. Evapotranspiration and other water losses are also usually lower. And, of course, in the higher regions much of the precipitation is in the form of snow. Thus the amount of runoff per unit area is larger than in low-lying areas, time of peak runoff is delayed until the warmer weather sets in.

The rugged topography of the mountains causes a thin snow cover to be blown away from some areas and concentrated in other areas as deep accumulations in hollows or basins. This causes sustained snowmelt to occur over a longer period of time. The spring or summer melt peak thus being subdued, floods are uncommon.

The storage of precipitation in the form of mountain glacier ice over a several-year period can make a large amount of water potentially available, and change the annual distribution of that water. For example, in contrast to a basin fed only by rainfall or seasonal snow, the runoff from a glacier basin in any one year can be much less or much more than that year's precipitation. The reason for this lies in the importance of the heat balance at the snow/ice surface especially on the amount of solar radiation and the reflectivity (albedo) of the surface. Hot summers normally imply higher incoming radiation which, together with the heat transferred directly from the air, causes increased melting and runoff; cool summers produce decreased runoff.

Surprisingly, the amount of precipitation in the form of snow has an inverse effect on the amount of runoff. Precipitation strongly affects the reflectivity; new snow is highly reflective so that it absorbs less heat and therefore melts more slowly. Old snow, firn and glacier ice have a low reflectivity. Thus, the greater the precipitation in the form of snow, the longer the glacier is covered by a highly reflective material, and the less the runoff. A decreased amount of snowfall leads to a low-reflectivity surface being exposed longer than usual, producing greater melt and increased runoff. Thus runoff from mountain glaciers is naturally buffered or regulated in a way beneficial to man, producing increased runoff at times of high temperature or deficient precipitation, and storing water when the need for it is lower. This effect can be illustrated by contrasting data from two abnormal years at one glacier station (resource 5.10).

The two most common methods used to measure changes in the ice store are the position of the ice front, and the net balance of the glacier. The ice front position depends upon the reaction of the motion in a glacier to a change in the net mass balance. The annual change in the mass of a glacier (store) depends upon the difference between total snow accumulation (inputs) and total loss of snow by melting and evaporation (outputs). Resource 5.11, shows that there is a consistent relationship between the net balance and the altitude of the equilibrium line, i.e. the line separating the area of new snow/ice accumulation or loss. The simplest way of estimating this is by aerial or satellite photography, as illustrated in resource 5.12.

The first part of the case study examines evidence at the global scale, of recent ice front and ice-mass fluctuations. The second and third parts focus on individual examples from the USSR.

5.10 Snow pack and water runoff from South Cascade Glacier, Washington, in two contrasting years				
Water year	Spring snowpack (water equivalent)		Ice and snow melt runoff	
	mm	% of average	mm	% of average
1971/72	4270	150	2840	89
1978/79	2180	77	3740	118

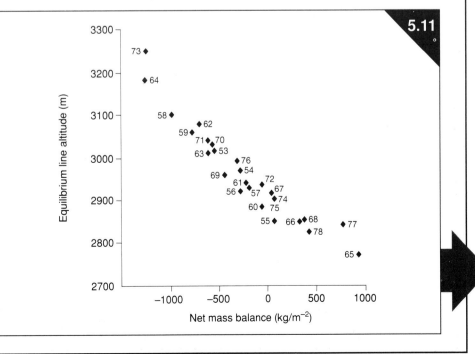

5.11

CASE STUDY 5.2   *Ice budgets and climatic change*

South Cascade Glacier, Washington

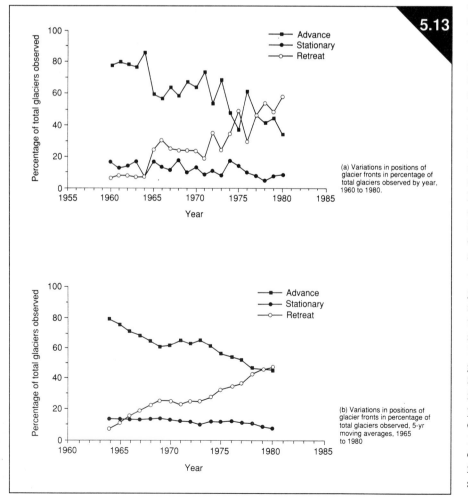

(a) Variations in positions of glacier fronts in percentage of total glaciers observed by year, 1960 to 1980.

(b) Variations in positions of glacier fronts in percentage of total glaciers observed, 5-yr moving averages, 1965 to 1980

Are the world's glaciers growing or shrinking?

Part 1: Changes in the Alps

Alpine glaciers, the collective name for valley glaciers and small ice sheets in mountainous regions, are thought to be sensitive indicators of climatic change. Thus, if global warming is indeed taking place, these alpine glaciers should be shrinking. Analysis of data for 450 glaciers collected by the World Glacier Monitoring Service between 1960 and 1980, however, gives no clear support to this idea. (Note: The glaciers studied are only 1 per cent of the world total.)

There is little doubt that from at least the early twentieth century, most alpine glaciers, especially in the northern hemisphere, had been shrinking. Thus, in 1960, only 6 per cent of the observed glaciers showed advancing ice fronts. Yet by 1980, 55 per cent were recording advance (resource 5.13). The second measure of change, mass balance, also indicated significant growth: during the 1960–80 period, 57 per cent of observed glaciers in the European Alps and 40 per cent in other parts of the world, increased in mass (resource 5.14). Even as late as 1985, the mixed trends continued, but globally, the 1980s have been called 'the warmest decade of the century', and certainly in the European Alps the decade ended with several years of low snowfalls (resource 5.15).

'In general, over the last 200 years, glaciers in the Alps were most advanced during the early 1800s, then retreated until the early 1900s, a period of partial readvance. For the 1926 to 1960 period, most observed glaciers in Austria, Italy, and Switzerland (70 to 95 per cent) were in recession and only a few (5 to 20 per cent) were advancing. In this context, the shift in the Alps over the 1960 to 1980 period to a regime dominated by advancing glacier fronts appears to be even more significant. Data for 1981 to 1985 suggest some reversal of this trend in the Alps and a reduction in the percentage of advancing glaciers that appears to have stabilized at about 50 per cent. Long-term data for Icelandic glaciers also suggest a shift in glacial regime'.

We must be careful in inferring climate change from these short-term fluctuations, because of the time lag between snow inputs and glacier response: 'For example, the Aletsch Glacier in the Alps has steadily retreated in length over the 1920 to 1980 period but has significantly increased in mass balance since the 1960s, suggesting that changes in length can lag behind changes in mass balance by up to decades'

(Source: adapted from: F B Wood, 'Global Alpine Glacier Trends, 1960s to 1980s', *Arctic and Alpine Research* 20(4), 1988, pp. 404–413.)

Part II: The global picture

Globally, the picture was much more confused:

'Outside of the European Alps, mass balances remained negative, but not overwhelmingly so, with about 40 per cent of glaciers showing positive balances on the average. Likewise, in addition to the Alps, for the United States, China, Iceland, and Norway by 1980 more than half of the observed glaciers were advancing and/or stationary. On the other hand, more than half of the observed glaciers in Antarctica, the Soviet Union, North America, Peru, Sweden, and Kenya were retreating (resource 5.16 overleaf). As noted earlier, the limited overall data on glacier area and volume were mixed'.

'It is not easy to assess what these fluctuations tell us about world climate. Interpreting the climatic implications of glacier changes is difficult. For example, there appear to be several climatic conditions under which glacial growth can occur. One is a decrease in summer temperature (and thus reduced summer melt), all other things being

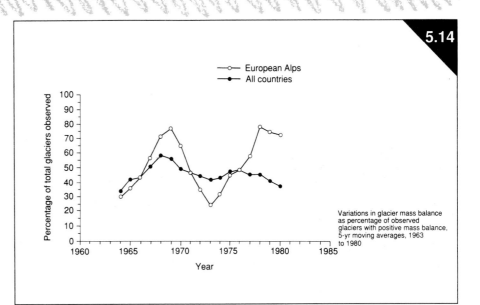

5.14

Variations in glacier mass balance as percentage of observed glaciers with positive mass balance, 5-yr moving averages, 1963 to 1980

5.15

The warmest decade

For scientists, the evidence is that worldwide temperatures show the 1980s to have been warmest decade of the century. Widespread opinion among meteorologists is that this is not a chance happening.

Although historical recordings and descriptions are not altogether reliable, this seems to have been the warmest decade for several centuries.

This raises the question of why it was warmer in Norman and, indeed, Roman and prehistoric times than in, say, the 17th century. If we cannot fully explain these fluctuations in the past, then our greenhouse predictions could look short on credibility.

(Source: *The Guardian*, 15 December 1989)

Skiers scratch around for snow

Skiers departing this weekend to spend a new year holiday on the slopes face a week of clear blue skies and sunshine - but no fresh snow.

For the third successive year, mild weather has brought disappointment for more than 70 000 British holidaymakers. In most European resorts snow on the pistes is already a week old and there are long lift queues for the higher slopes.

Weathermen say poor snow at the turn of the year is becoming the norm, ending a run of good ski conditions during the 1970s and early 1980s.

Meanwhile the United States ski resorts continue to enjoy near-perfect conditions. One operator said business had tripled over the last year in spite of prices of £1,000 per person or more.

(Source: *The Sunday Times*, 31 December 1989)

equal. A second is an increase in winter snowfall. A third is a combination of reduced summer temperature and increased winter snowfall. This is the combination that is thought to explain the generally positive mass balances and advancing glacial fronts during the 1960s and 1970s in the Swiss and Austrian Alps. Conversely, an increase in summer temperature and decrease in winter precipitation is thought to explain the declining percentage of advancing Swiss and Austrian glaciers during the early 1980s.

A fourth possibility is increased winter temperature accompanied by increased precipitation that falls as snow, not rain. Research evidence from the Wolverine Glacier in southern Alaska for 1967 to 1985 indicates that, contrary to common perception, rising temperature can lead to glacier growth so long as it is still cold enough for snowfall'.

(Source: adapted from F B Wood, 'Global Alpine Glacier Trends, 1960's to 1980's, *Arctic and Alpine Research* 20(4), 1988, pp. 404 – 413.)

Part III: The local scale: mass balance on Victoriya Island, Soviet Arctic

Victoriya Island lies in the northern Barents Sea, between Franz Josef Land and Svalbard (80°N, 86°E). It is a small island, 5 km long, 3 km width and 11 km in area. Some 98 per cent is covered by a glacier dome 110 m high (resource 5.19).

Measurements taken from 1953 to 1972 show continuous ice front retreat and reduction in mass. Over almost the entire surface of the dome the snow from the previous winter melts during the short summers, leading to the exposure of progressively deeper horizons of old glacier ice. Between 1953 and 1961 the glacier margin retreated at least 320 m. What is more significant, however, is the variation from year to year. Between 1961 and 1972, the ice margin retreat ranged from 0.25 m in the warmest year to 13 m in the

5.16

Portage Glacier, Alaska, 1991. The snout can be seen three miles away beyond the lake. One hundred years ago, the snout lay against the terminal moraines where this photo was taken. The small icebergs were calved from the glacier.

5.17

Mass balance during a cold year, 1965

	Height Above Sea Level (m)			
	25	50	75	110
Snow depth at the end of the winter accumulation season i.e. the depth of snow lying on the ice (cm)	77	71	63	62
Melting of snow during summer ablation season (cm)	77	62	43	24
Balance	0	9	20	38

coldest year. In the warm years of 1961, 1964, 1966, 1968, 1972, up to 40 gr/cm² ablated.

Resource 5.17 shows the balance in 1965, a particularly cold year, when ice front retreat averaged only 0.25 m, and not all the previous winter snow was melted.

The relationships between mass balance and air temperatures and the variations from year to year are set out in resource 5.18. In the summit area of the island dome in some years a mass increase is recorded, but this increase occurs over a restricted area. During average ablation seasons after complete melting of the snow pack from the previous winter, an overall lowering of the ice surface is occurring.

Surface mass balance and air temperatures

	Change in height of surface during summer ablation season (cm) i.e. amount of snow and ice melting.				Mean air temp (°C)				Ice Margin retreat (m)
					Month Alt(m)				
	25	50	75	110	J	J	A	S/O	
1966	−74	−27	−17	−11	−2.5	0.3	−0.9	−1.0	5–7
1969	−9	−7	−4	+5	−3.4	0.3	−1.1	−1.4	1–2
1970	−21	−14	−2	+9	−1.6	−0.2	−0.0	−0.6	<0.6
1971	−4	+11	+8	+18	−2.0	−0.2	−0.7	−1.0	0.5–2.5
1972	−61	−52	−45	−39	−0.8	−0.1	0.4	−0.2	9–13

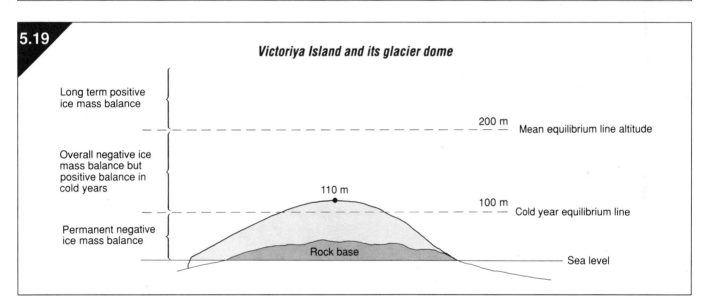

Victoriya Island and its glacier dome

Long term positive ice mass balance

200 m — Mean equilibrium line altitude

Overall negative ice mass balance but positive balance in cold years

110 m

100 m — Cold year equilibrium line

Permanent negative ice mass balance

Rock base

Sea level

The climatic equilibrium line in this region is 200 – 300 m above sea level, but descends to 100 m in cold years. As the peak of the Victoriya Island ice dome is 110 m, it is below the mean equilibrium line and so has an overall negative ice mass balance. However, in cold years, when the equilibrium line sinks below 110 m, accumulation may exceed ablation (resource 5.19).

(Source: adapted from: L S Govorukha, 'The present state of ice cap islands in the Soviet Arctic' *Polar Geography and Geology* 12(4), Oct–Dec 1988, pp. 312-316.)

Part IV: A cirque glacier in the Ural Mountains, USSR

The Obruchev Glacier lies on the eastern flank of the Ural Mountains, north of the Arctic Circle, about 150 km from the Arctic Ocean coast. It is a classic example of a cirque glacier (resource 5.20). The 'winter' snow accumulation season lasts approximately 240 days, late September to mid-May, although one of the outstanding features of the region is the variability of weather conditions from year to year.

Snow accumulation on the glacier is determined by a combination of weather conditions and local topography. The winters are dominated by intense depressions moving eastwards along the North Atlantic branch of the Arctic Front. These depressions bring strong winds, heavy precipitation and abrupt temperature changes. Blizzards are recorded for up to 30 per cent of the time and winds of more than 10 m/second occur on an average of 90 days. The strong winds and steep headwalls of the cirque create air turbulence. As a result, about 50 per cent of the snow accumulating on the glacier is from drifting and avalanches, rather than from direct snowfall.

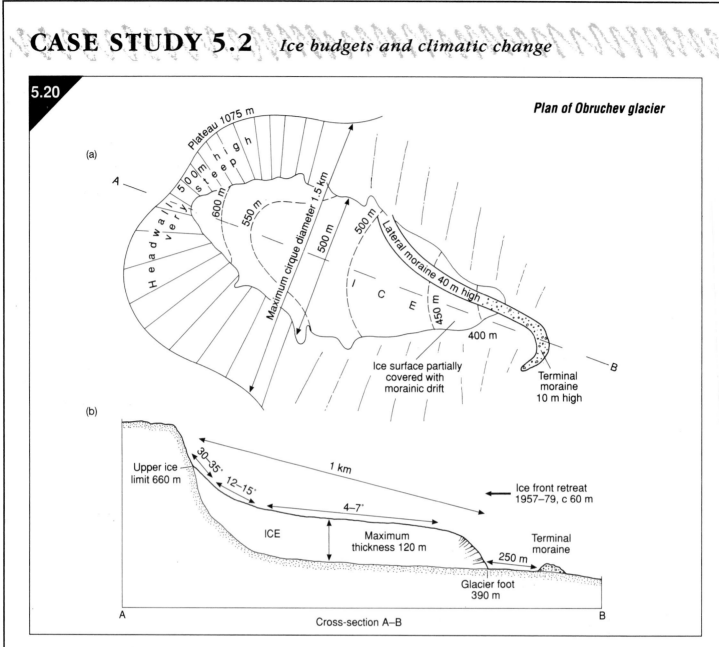

5.20

Plan of Obruchev glacier

(a)

Plateau 1075 m

Headwall very steep high

500 m

600 m

550 m

500 m

Maximum cirque diameter 1.5 km

500 m

500 m

Lateral moraine 40 m high

I C E

450

400 m

Ice surface partially covered with morainic drift

Terminal moraine 10 m high

A

B

(b)

Upper ice limit 660 m

30–35°

12–15°

4–7°

1 km

Ice front retreat 1957–79, c 60 m

ICE

Maximum thickness 120 m

Terminal moraine

250 m

Glacier foot 390 m

A

B

Cross-section A–B

The short summers are influenced by weaker depressions giving frequent overcast and drizzle conditions. Ablation is greatest when warm air drifts in from the south, raising temperatures by as much as 15°C. Sections of the glacier with a south-facing aspect experience most severe summer melting.

The variable weather conditions cause strong annual fluctuations in the mass balance of the glacier (resource 5.21). During the 1959–79 period, winter snow accumulation ranged from 110 (1963–64) to 376 gr./cm² (1966–67), and the summer ablation loss from 160 to 499 gr./cm². Mass balance was positive in

8 out of the 20 years, i.e. the glacier mass increased in size during a year. In the coldest year, 1967–68, the equilibrium line dropped to 471 m altitude leaving 88 per cent of the surface of the glacier covered by snow all year, and resulting in a positive mass balance of 181 gr./cm². This is where the idea of the equilibrium line becomes important: above this altitude, at least some of the previous winter's snow remains unmelted through the summer, and the glacier mass increases. Below the line all of the snow is removed, allowing melting of surface ice, thereby reducing the glacier mass.

Resource 5.22 illustrates these balance characteristics over the

20-year period, during which the mean equilibrium line was around 550 m altitude. Notice that the maximum surface area occurs just below the equilibrium line, where the mass of the glacier is greatest (550–500 m). As the glacier begins to taper, the greatest rate of loss is achieved (500–450 m). Despite the lower altitude, the melting rate declines near the foot of the glacier because morainic debris covers much of the ice surface. Overall, the Obruchev Glacier has been declining, with the loss of 21 gr./cm² over the 1959–79 period, and an ice-front retreat of 60 m since 1957 (resource 15.20(b)).

(Source: adapted from: A P Voloshina, 'Some results of glacier mass balance research on the glaciers of the polar Urals' *Polar Geography and Geology*, 12, July–September 1988, pp. 200–212)

Activities

1   Using columns (b) and (c) of resource 5.21, construct line graphs of the mass balance. Shade in red, the periods with a negative mass balance, and in black, the periods with a positive mass balance.

2   Construct two scattergraphs to indicate the relationship between:

   a   annual mass balance (column (d)) and the altitude of the equilibrium line (column (e)),

   b   mass balance (column (d)), and the proportion of the glacier above the equilibrium line (column (f)).

3   Use your graphs and the tables to interpret the behaviour of the Obruchev Glacier.

4   Use resource 5.22 to explain how the equilibrium line concept helps us to understand the glacier as a system.

Mass Balance components for the Obruchev Glacier, USSR, 1959–79   **5.21**

Year (a)	Winter accumulation (gr/cm²) (b)	Summer loss (gr/cm²) (c)	Annual balance (gr/cm²) (d)	Height of equilibrium line (m) (e)	% Of glacier above equilibrium line (f)
1959–60	175	225	−50	530	48
1960–61	280	301	−21	552	51
1961–62	350	365	−15	516	56
1962–63	250	323	−73	562	19
1963–64	110	240	−130	566	15
1964–65	242	278	−36	540	40
1965–66	203	175	28	507	65
1966–67	376	356	20	497	69
1967–68	341	160	181	471	88
1968–69	148	203	−55	556	23
1969–70	220	186	34	490	71
1970–71	226	247	−21	517	48
1971–72	365	280	85	483	73
1972–73	308	290	18	520	62
1973–74	262	330	−68	581	30
1974–75	275	258	17	502	68
1975–76	352	487	−135	574	20
1976–77	335	499	−164	584	16
1977–78	376	220	156	484	81
1978–79	298	299	−1	543	44

Mean annual mass balance variations by altitude, Obruchev Glacier, USSR, 1959–79   **5.22**

Height (m)	% of Glacier Area	Winter Accumulation (gr/cm²)	Summer Loss (gr./cm²)	Annual Balance (gr/cm²)
660–650	0.3	400	242	158
650–600	6.7	389	253	136
600–550	26.3	341	272	69
550–500	40.7	249	286	−37
500–450	17.0	190	321	−131
450–400	8.7	184	310	−126
400–390	0.3	204	295	−91
Overall	100.0	268	289	−21

CASE STUDY 5.3 *Relationships between ice, water,*

Background

Block diagrams in textbooks suggest an orderly sequence of landforms resulting from the advance, halt and retreat of ice-fronts (resource 5.23). At maximum advance, ablation at the glacier snout deposits a terminal moraine as a ridge of unsorted debris. Beyond this moraine, a stratified outwash plain evolves, which is criss-crossed by shallow channels, as meltwaters erode, transport and re-distribute the morainic debris. As the ice-front retreats, a till plain of ground moraine laid down beneath the ice is progressively exposed behind the terminal moraine. Superimposed on this till are sinuous esker ridges, deposited by subglacial meltwater streams, and kames or kame terraces laid down by meltwaters marginal to the ice or channels cut in the ice. There are also drumlin fields which are mounds of morainic debris streamlined by the earlier advance of the ice. Kettleholes are dotted about, indicating where lumps of ice within the till have melted, causing the overlying debris to collapse. Suites of subglacial, ice-marginal and proglacial meltwater channels are incised into the till and the bedrock beneath. Finally, patches of hummocky drift occur where stagnant ice masses have ablated in situ, dumping their englacial and supraglacial load.

This model of a landform assemblage has a logic to it which is based on the relationships between the agency (ice/water), the process (erosion/ transportation/deposition), the energy availability (glacier budget balance), and the debris supply (bedrock and surrounding terrain character), operating over time. In the reality of fieldwork, however, things rarely seem so straightforward: there are modifications to the landscape since deglaciation; geomorphic processes around the glacier fringes make the environment highly dynamic; not all the features are necessarily present; sets of 'real' features are put together more confusedly than the textbook models suggest. This case study illustrates the problems and allows a testing of the model by a close study of a small area in Iceland recently exposed by ice-front retreat.

◆ *You should check your understanding of the following terms before working on the case study:*

moraine, outwash plain, till/ground moraine, esker, kame, kettle, meltwater, meltwater channels.

Key understandings

◆ The fundamental importance of glacier budget balance, as it determines ice-front location and trend, and meltwater supply.

◆ The complexity of topography produced by the erosive and depositional processes of ice and water in combination.

◆ Landform assemblages associated with glaciation can change rapidly.

◆ Stagnant ice melting in situ is a significant process in landscapes of deglaciation.

◆ A sequence of landforms resulting from glacier fluctuation is identifiable over time and space.

Features along the edge of the Breidamerkurjökull Glacier, Iceland

Ice front changes

The Breidamerkurjökull glacier is one of the ice tongues which descends southwards from the Vatnajökull icefield in South East Iceland. In its descent it is confined between ridges of volcanic rocks which deliver a copious debris supply to medial and lateral moraines. Since 1890 the ice-front has retreated rapidly (resource 5.24). Compare resources 5.23 and 5.25, and you will see that the Breidamerkurjökull topography does support several characteristics of the model, e.g. the extensive sandar in front of the main (1890) terminal moraine; till, eskers and meltwater channels across the zone between the 1890 moraine and the 1965 ice front.

Detailed fieldwork, supported by map and aerial photograph analysis, for the rectangular area marked on resource 5.25 has been completed by staff and students of the Geography Department, University of Glasgow. Their results are summarised in resources 5.26 and 5.27. From resource 5.24 'it can be seen that the rate of frontal retreat was very slow between 1890 and 1937, very rapid between 1937 and 1945 and continuous but steady from 1945 to 1965. The frontal retreat was of course accompanied by a general thinning of the glacier. The rate of down-wastage on the ice surface in the frontal zone for the period 1945 to 1965 ranged between 5.0 and 7.5m/year'.

Morainic features

The pulsating retreat of the ice front has left a suite of four moraine ridges (resource 5.26), which vary between 1 and 10 m in height. Apart from the main 1890 moraine, which is a complex feature of a major ridge with smaller ridges superimposed, the stage moraines are simple linear, often crescentic, ridges indicating a short-lived halt in the glacier retreat. The materials are mainly gravels with some finer, rather weak matrix and occasional boulders. Close examination of these materials produced two problems: morainic debris should be (a) angular and (b) unsorted, but the particles in these moraines are mostly rounded and with their long axes oriented at right-angles to the direction of ice movement.

Landforms developed by continental glaciers commonly are related to the position of the ice margins or the direction of the flow

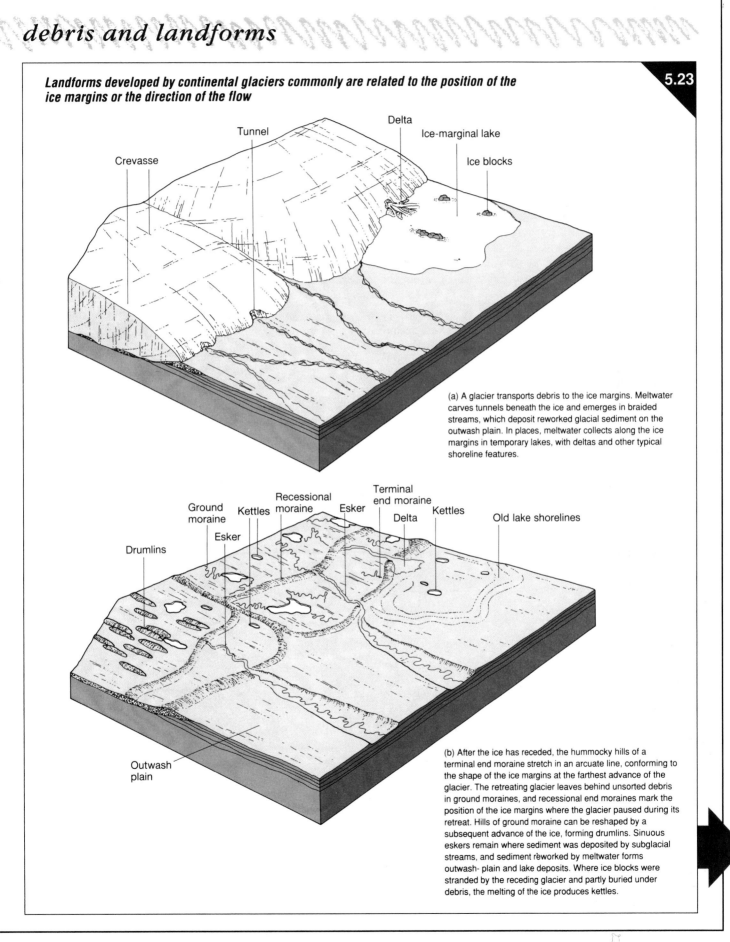

(a) A glacier transports debris to the ice margins. Meltwater carves tunnels beneath the ice and emerges in braided streams, which deposit reworked glacial sediment on the outwash plain. In places, meltwater collects along the ice margins in temporary lakes, with deltas and other typical shoreline features.

(b) After the ice has receded, the hummocky hills of a terminal end moraine stretch in an arcuate line, conforming to the shape of the ice margins at the farthest advance of the glacier. The retreating glacier leaves behind unsorted debris in ground moraines, and recessional end moraines mark the position of the ice margins where the glacier paused during its retreat. Hills of ground moraine can be reshaped by a subsequent advance of the ice, forming drumlins. Sinuous eskers remain where sediment was deposited by subglacial streams, and sediment reworked by meltwater forms outwash- plain and lake deposits. Where ice blocks were stranded by the receding glacier and partly buried under debris, the melting of the ice produces kettles.

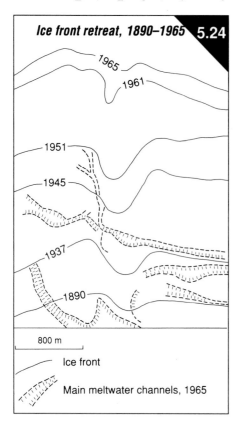

Ice front retreat, 1890–1965 5.24

1965
1961
1951
1945
1937
1890

800 m

— Ice front

Main meltwater channels, 1965

The study proposes an answer: 'The strong orientation of the particles in these moraines clearly indicates that they were not dumped or bulldozed by the ice. One possible mechanism of formation ... would be the squeezing of water-saturated till from beneath the ice to form ridges, the crest-lines of which would be parallel to the ice front.' The squeezing would cause the alignment while the till source would explain the rounding as the particles could have been moved by water before incorporation into the till.

Despite the very recent exposure of the study area from beneath the ice, only one-third of the surface is covered with ground moraine. 'It consists of till in the form of a gently undulating surface of low relief (1 – 2 m). ... It only occupies those areas not affected by fluvioglacial erosion and deposition and was presumably much more extensive prior to the modification of the area by numerous meltwater streams

which developed as the glacier retreated. The surface expression of the material is dull and monotonous. Frequently the surface is scattered with large blocks of rock up to 5 m across which were just dumped by the glacier as it melted away. The surface material appears to be similar to fluvioglacial material except that it shows no signs of size sorting.' Beneath the surface the till consists of mainly pebbles set into a compact clay matrix. The source of at least some of this till may have been the fluvioglacial gravels lying across the area as a result of an earlier ice retreat and incorporated into the bed load as the ice readvanced to its 1890 position.

Fluvio-glacial features

More than 60 per cent of the study area is covered by fluvioglacial deposits, mostly sandar (outwash sheets) and kames. The stratified deposits of sands, gravels, cobbles and boulders are derived from the local volcanic rocks. 'The high

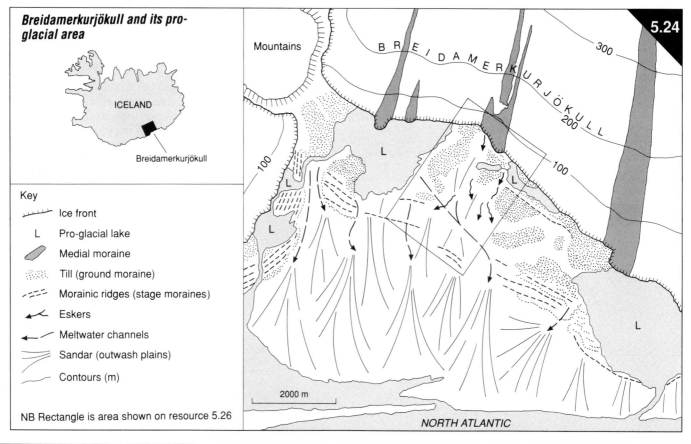

Breidamerkurjökull and its pro-glacial area

ICELAND

Breidamerkurjökull

Key

- Ice front
- L   Pro-glacial lake
- Medial moraine
- Till (ground moraine)
- Morainic ridges (stage moraines)
- Eskers
- Meltwater channels
- Sandar (outwash plains)
- Contours (m)

NB Rectangle is area shown on resource 5.26

Mountains

BREIDAMERKURJÖKULL

300
200
100

2000 m

NORTH ATLANTIC

5.24

degree of rounding exhibited by the rock particles may well be caused by the fact that, although the distance travelled by individual particles may not have been great (probably less than 5 km) during the most recent cycle of erosion, transport and deposition, these same rock fragments have probably been subjected to several cycles of transport by water.' These repeated advances and retreats, plus the copious supply from medial and lateral moraines explain the enormous volumes of fluvioglacial debris, which is up to 100 m thick in places. The sandar have been and are being deposited by **anastomosing** proglacial streams, many of which originated from supraglacial, englacial or subglacial channels.

One of the outstanding features of resource 5.26 is the extensive occurrence of kettleholes across the sandar surfaces. 'The origin of these kettleholes is related to the development of sandar across areas of stagnant ice. ... The fact that sandar developed on top of a sheet of ice is supported by the fact that, in some areas, little or nothing of the original sandur surface survived after the melting-out of the buried ice. The development of these extensively pitted areas must have been related to the emergence near the ice front of either englacial or

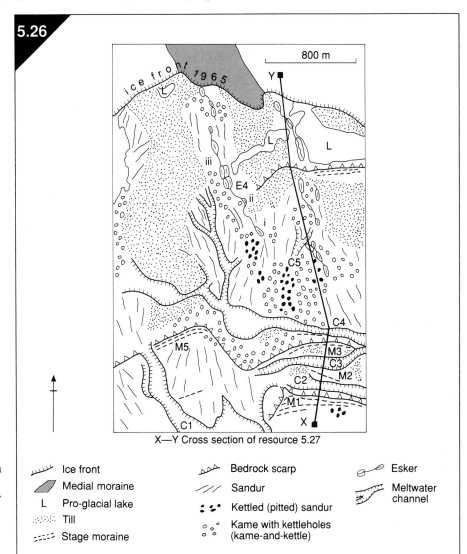

5.26

800 m

X—Y Cross section of resource 5.27

ᴗᴗᴗ Ice front	ᴧᴧᴧ Bedrock scarp	⬯⬯ Esker
▨ Medial moraine	⫽⫽ Sandur	⚏ Meltwater channel
L Pro-glacial lake	∶∶∙ Kettled (pitted) sandur	
⋰ Till		
⫶⫶⫶ Stage moraine	∘∘∘ Kame with kettleholes (kame-and-kettle)	

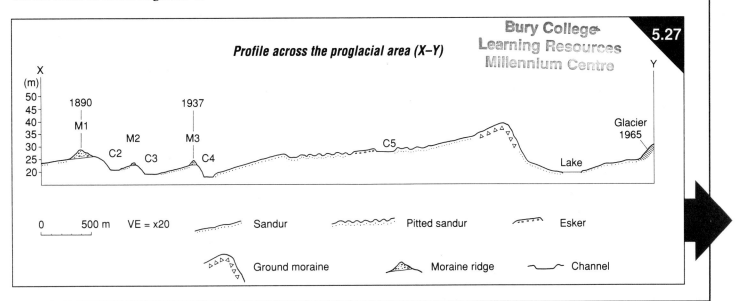

Profile across the proglacial area (X–Y)

Bury College
Learning Resources
Millennium Centre

5.27

X
(m)
50
45
40
35
30
25
20

1890
M1

M2

1937
M3

C2

C3

C4

C5

⬠⬠⬠⬠

Glacier
1965

Lake

Y

0 500 m VE = x20	⌢⌢ Sandur	⟳⟳⟳ Pitted sandur	⌒∘∘ Esker
	⟁⟁⟁ Ground moraine	⌂ Moraine ridge	⌒ Channel

supraglacial streams which carried sediments on to a sheet of stagnant ice.' This process is summarised in resource 5.28. Notice the terminology associated with the progression: sandur with isolated kettles – kettled sandur – kame and kettle topography (the last being applied to areas where the original sandur surface has effectively disappeared).

The area is crossed by over 5 km of eskers: sharp-crested, steep-sided sand and gravel ridges which 'represent the former courses of meltwater streams either in tunnels under or in the ice or in channels on the ice surface'. Resource 5.26 shows that they originate from the main source of debris supply — the medial moraine. Resource 5.29 is a long profile of one of the best developed eskers in the study area (E4 on resource 5.26). Notice that sections of the profile run 'uphill'. This is a common feature of eskers and is normally explained by the sediment having been deposited in a tunnel beneath the ice where hydrostatic pressure allows the water to flow upslope. In the case of the Breidamerkurjökull eskers, an alternative is proposed: 'It may be that some parts of an esker ridge were deposited subglacially while others were subsequently let down by the melting-out of ice which once formed the floors and sides of englacial tunnels or supraglacial channels.' Thus, sections of the tunnels were in or on the ice, and were let down on to the bedrock surface only after the ice melted. This accounts for the highly irregular long profile.

Finally, there are the main meltwater channels shown on resource 5.26. Look carefully, and you will see that they collect water from the numerous anastomosing streams and then are forced to turn laterally across the regional slope. This is caused by the barriers of the stage moraines. They are cut into, and hence post-date the sandar sheets.

Except for perhaps their upper courses, they have thus evolved as ice-marginal rather than sub-ice features.

Resource 5.27 is the cross-section X – Y on resource 5.26, and summarises the landform sequence from the sandar beyond the 1890 moraine to the 1965 ice-front. Note the set of scarps facing upslope towards the ice front, which influence the location of the glacial and fluvioglacial features. These are caused by the tilted igneous succession of lava and ash beds.

(Source: adapted from: R J Price 'Moraines, sandar, kames and eskers near Breidamerkurjökull, Iceland,', *Trans. IBG.*, 46, March 1969, pp.17-43.)

Activities

In groups or pairs:

1   Use the cross-section of resource 5.27 as a basis for a summary of the sequence in which this landform assemblage has evolved.

2   For each of the main landform elements, outline the processes involved.

3   Determine the extent to which the Breidamerkurjökull study area supports the model of landform assemblage shown in the block diagram (resource 5.23).

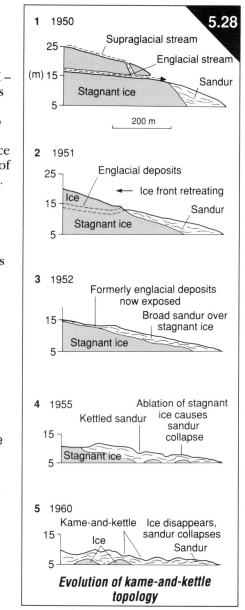

1   1950
25 (m) 15 5
200 m
Supraglacial stream
Englacial stream
Stagnant ice
Sandur

2   1951
25 15 5
Englacial deposits
← Ice front retreating
Ice
Stagnant ice
Sandur

3   1952
15 5
Formerly englacial deposits now exposed
Broad sandur over stagnant ice
Stagnant ice

4   1955
15 5
Kettled sandur
Ablation of stagnant ice causes sandur collapse
Stagnant ice

5   1960
15 5
Kame-and-kettle
Ice
Ice disappears, sandur collapses
Sandur

Evolution of kame-and-kettle topology

5.28

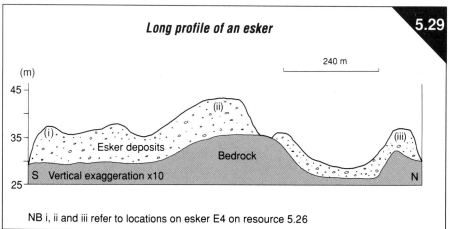

Long profile of an esker   5.29

240 m

(m)
45
35
25
(i)   (ii)   (iii)
Esker deposits
Bedrock
S   Vertical exaggeration x10   N

NB i, ii and iii refer to locations on esker E4 on resource 5.26

CASE STUDY 5.4   *Do glaciers really erode? The moraines of the Glacier de Tsidjiore Nouve, Switzerland*

Background

Glaciers are regarded as powerful erosional agents. In an article published in 1982, Professor John Small wrote: 'We tend to ask ... A-level geographers not to doubt glacial erosion, but to select from the abundant evidence of its great efficiency'. He then gives three examples:

1 **U-shaped valleys**: In western Norway 'Sognefjord may have been overdeepended by some 1400 m'. But – 'V-shaped valleys are by no means unusual in heavily glaciated uplands', and what about the erosive power of vigorous subglacial streams?

2 **The processes of plucking and abrasion**: But – 'How can glacial abrasion occur beneath a 'cold' glacier at –10°C, when the ice will be firmly frozen to bedrock and basal sliding ... cannot take place?'

3 **The huge volume of morainic debris** which is so typical of valley glaciers. He calculates that for the Glacier de Tsidjiore Nouve, in Switzerland 'the volume of the lateral moraines ... is approximately 9 000 000 m³, assuming the period of formation to be 5000 years, the average annual debris increment to these moraines is ... 1800 m³'[3, 9]. But are these huge volumes really the product of glacial plucking and abrasion, or are other mechanisms involved?'

Professor Small is not denying the erosive power of glaciers, he is asking us to think critically and to avoid simplistic answers. The case study below shows how he does this, using the evidence of moraines on the Glacier de Tsidjiore Nouve.

1 Medial moraines

'My observations of Alpine glaciers have revealed two main types of medial moraine (and several sub-types): moraines resulting from the junction of individual ice-streams bearing marginal debris accumulations (this is the type depicted in geomorphological textbooks): and moraines, without any obvious debris source, that appear to 'grow out' from the surface, frequently on glaciers beneath ice-falls. The former type, developed below the firn-line of the glacier, are nourished by debris falls from above the ice; the latter are supplied by englacial debris which melts out on the ablation zone of the glacier.

Two medial moraines, emerging from Glacier de Tsidjiore Nouve at the base of the Pigne d'Arolla ice-fall, have been studied in detail, (resource 5.30). In the 'zone of emergence' the moraines comprise surface debris patches, aligned across the glacier; downglacier, as debris becomes more plentiful, the patches merge to give continuous moraine ridges, which eventually rise to heights of 30 m and 10 m respectively. On close examination the individual debris patches are seen to mark the outcrops of steeply dipping englacial debris bands. These are orientated transversely to glacier flow, are a few metres in length, are up to 30 cm or more in thickness, and contain many sharply angular rock fragments set in a matrix of gravel and coarse sand. As the glacier surface is lowered by ablation the debris is released and contributes to moraine formation.

The question is: are these debris bands composed of subglacial debris, folded or sheared up in the zone of compression at the base of the ice-fall? The debris itself shows no obvious signs of rounding or striation; moreover the glacier base lies here at a depth of 180 – 200 m. Samples of sediment from 24 bands were analysed in the laboratory and grain-size distributions were found to resemble typical supraglacial debris. It was therefore concluded that the debris had entered the ice from above, not from below. Likely sources in the form of rock-faces some 2 km upglacier, high on the accumulation zone of Glacier de Tsidjiore Nouve, were identified. Frost-shattered debris from these faces falls into crevasses, which become closed and compressed downglacier and also buried beneath ice (from winter snow) forming on the lower part of the accumulation zone. The resulting debris bands pass through the ice-fall and in time are exposed by ablation on the glacier tongue.

Medial moraines emerging at the base of Pigne d'Arolla ice-fall

---

Key understandings

◆ Not all the load transported and deposited by a glacier may have been eroded by it.

◆ The debris load to the ice store of a glacier may be an input from processes and sources external to the glacier.

---

2 Lateral moraines

Those of Glacier de Tsidjiore Nouve are of exceptional size, comprising huge debris embankments (each with a number of constituent ridges) up to 80 m in height; in effect, the moraines confine the glacier-like massive levées (resource 5.31). The embankments are largely 'fossil' features, in the sense that they accumulated during glacial advances over the last 5000 or so years. However, the moraine on the northern glacier flank is currently being overtopped by marginal ice and debris is sliding off the glacier and being dumped on the outer slope of the ridge. The debris actually on the ice-surface is derived either from rock-walls above the ice, or from the melting out of englacial debris bands similar to those of the medial moraines. Samples from surface debris and bands are predominantly supraglacial in character, with an abundance of coarse angular fragments and a relative lack of fines. Debris from the various individual ridges of the moraine embankment is also evidently supraglacial, showing that present processes of deposition are similar to those of the past.

The purpose of this discussion has been to show that, on the evidence available, most debris on and within Glacier de Tsidjiore Nouve is of supraglacial origin. In the light of this it is possible now to make some interesting, and possibly significant,

calculations. If the annual increment of debris to the lateral moraines (1800m^3) is distributed over the rock-faces within the glacier catchment, an annual slope recession rate of 0.75 mm is implied. If the debris being shed at the glacier snout (that is, not onto the lateral moraines) is also taken into account, the slope recession rate rises to nearer 1 mm/annum. However, when the suspended sediment – the product of glacial abrasion – being washed out from beneath the glacier is calculated, and distributed over the subglacial surface area, an erosion rate of only 0.25 mm/annum is indicated. If this is adjusted to allow for bedload (not actually measured), the rate would probably rise to 0.3 mm/annum. Thus there are reasons to suspect that, at the present time, Glacier de Tsidjiore Nouve is more active in the transport and deposition of debris from above the ice than in glacial erosion in the strict sense of the term.

Conclusions

It hardly needs saying that the study of one glacier does not prove that glacial erosion is everywhere a relatively ineffective process in the Swiss Alps. Nevertheless, there are good grounds for supposing that, in Post-Glacial times, Alpine glaciers have undergone something of a change in role. As the glaciers have retreated and thinned, their powers of plucking and abrasion must have

diminished – for despite theoretical arguments to the contrary the field evidence suggests that erosion by thick glaciers is greater than that achieved by thin glaciers. Equally important, as the glaciers have shrunk, the rock-faces above them have been increasingly exposed to frost action; and slopes oversteepened by glacial erosion have become prone to collapse onto the ice-surfaces as physical support has been removed.

Perhaps the major conclusion to be drawn is that it is manifestly incorrect to regard all glaciers, at all times, and in all areas as powerful eroding agents. There are many controlling factors to be considered, quite apart from the climatic change – with all its repercussions – of the Post-Glacial period. A fundamental distinction can be drawn between (i) a 'warm' glacier, receiving large increments of winter snowfall, occupying a steep valley, experiencing rapid motion (mainly in the form of basal sliding) and existing within a region of unresistant rocks, and (ii) a 'cold' glacier, receiving little winter snow, occupying a gentle valley, flowing very slowly (without any basal sliding component) and existing within an area of very durable rocks. The former will erode effectively, the latter will not. Under some circumstances there is, after all, something to be said for glacial protection!'

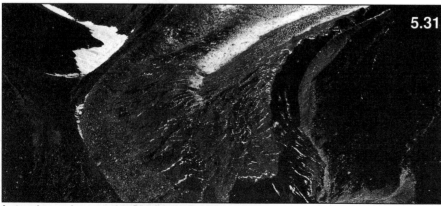

5.31

Lateral moraines on the Glacier de Tsidjiore Nouve

Activities

As a group discuss the following:

1   What evidence is there that the Glacier de Tsidjiore Nouve does erode?

2   What processes and sources other than glacial erosion deliver debris to the glacier?

3   What factors are important in causing variations in the source of supply of morainic debris to a glacier?

CASE STUDY 5.5 *Subglacial origins of meltwater channels – the Appleby district, Cumbria*

Background

Earlier case studies have shown that the copious meltwaters associated with glacier ablation and with snowmelt running on to a glacier, are able to cut channels marginal to and in front of the ice. Many deglaciated districts, however, are scarred with channels which do not seem to be explainable as ice-marginal, nor are they directly related to the post-glacial stream system. Indeed, many are now stream-less although they have been undoubtedly cut by water. They fall into two main types: **cross-spur channels** (resource 5.32) and **valley networks** (resource 5.33), plus several sub-types e.g. **'in-and-out' channels**, **benches** across the hill faces. The majority are easily identifiable by three features: (i) they are cut abruptly into a slope or valley floor; (ii) they have steep, even sides; (iii) their floors are flat, although this may be due partly to deposition occurring after formation. Some have a fourth feature – a hump-backed long profile. Individual channels vary widely in size from 1 to 20 m deep, up to 50 m wide and 2 km long (resource 5.33). It is generally accepted that many are subglacial in

Cross-spur channels, Knock Pike

origin, and associated with a deglaciation phase.

An explanation lies in three understandings: The first is that water can flow englacially and subglacially under hydrostatic pressure. The second is that as ablation proceeds, the ice mass thins, i.e. the surface downwastes. The third involves the physical properties of ice: estimates vary, but

it is thought that meltwater can penetrate to a depth of 100 – 150 m into the ice mass. This basal plane conforms to the boundary between the brittle and plastic layers of the ice. Above this boundary, englacial tunnels can persist, while below it, the plastic properties of the ice tend to deform and destroy such passageways. This boundary layer acts as an englacial water-table, and

Cocklock Scar showing valley networks

Key understandings

- Meltwaters flow supraglacially, englacially and subglacially.

- During deglaciation, as an ice mass thins, the englacial water-table is lowered, eventually reaching the underlying surface.

- As ice-thinning progresses, englacial stream systems may be superimposed partly or wholly on the underlying land surface as subglacial channels.

- As the available energy of these streams may be high, such sub-glacial channels may be cut rapidly.

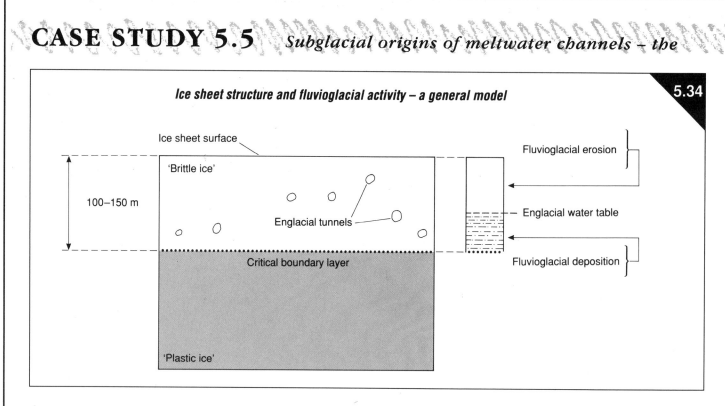

Ice sheet structure and fluvioglacial activity – a general model

5.34

as the ice thins, so this water-table is lowered (resource 5.34). Eventually, it may reach the underlying rock or debris surface. The englacial tunnel can then become subglacial and a channel can be cut.

Meltwater channels in the Appleby District, Cumbria

The geology and topography of the Vale of Eden and Cross Fell Pennines have already been outlined in case study 2.1. We now return to the area as it exhibits a number of classic features of glaciation. The best known of these is perhaps the extensive drumlin field surrounding the town of Appleby. Etched into the eastern margins of this drumlin field and across the scarp face of the Pennines is a fine series of fluvioglacial meltwater channels (resource 5.35).

During the last main episode of glacial advance, the major ice source for the Vale of Eden ice sheet was the Lake District massif, with a minor ice-cap forming over the Cross Fell Pennines. The two ice masses met across the Pennine scarp, and at maximum glaciation, the more powerful Lake District ice seems to

have overridden the Pennines and pushed on eastwards into Teesdale. After this glacial maximum, the Cross Fell ice source was able to push tongues of ice westwards down the valleys towards the Vale of Eden, causing further deepening e.g. High Cup trough, and accentuating the spur–valley–spur profile of the scarp. This strong spur development was important in the occurrence of the cross-spur meltwater channels.

Resource 5.35 identifies three main types of channel, the first consisting of two sub-types:

1 High level North West trending channels

a 'In-and-out' channels (resource 5.36). These are horse-shoe shaped gashes into steeply inclined hillsides, and quite discordant from existing drainage or local gradients. Several have hump-backed long profiles, suggesting a subglacial origin by a stream under hydrostatic pressure.

b Cross-spur channels (resource 5.32). These cut directly across spur crest-lines, and several spurs have a suite or sequence, each at decreasing heights. The suites on several spurs can be matched up,

the oldest channels at highest level, followed down-spur by younger channels as the ice level declined. (1, 2, 3 on resource 5.35). They are generally straight or slightly sinuous, and the larger examples are fault guided, i.e. following lines of weakness across a spur.

2 Low level dendritic systems, trending North West

On resource 5.35, the Flakebridge and Ousby systems stand out clearly. They cut into the drumlins, across till plains and into solid rock, and follow gently sinuous courses until they veer towards the present River Eden floodplain and disappear. Notice that not all the channels are continuous, or linked to a main network, a feature suggestive of sub-glacial origins.

3 Fell drainer channels

These channels follow the regional gradient, i.e. to the West and South West, and cut sharply across the North West alignment of the dendritic channels. Today they form the basis of the current stream network and have been much modified by post-glacial fluvial processes. However, they intersect

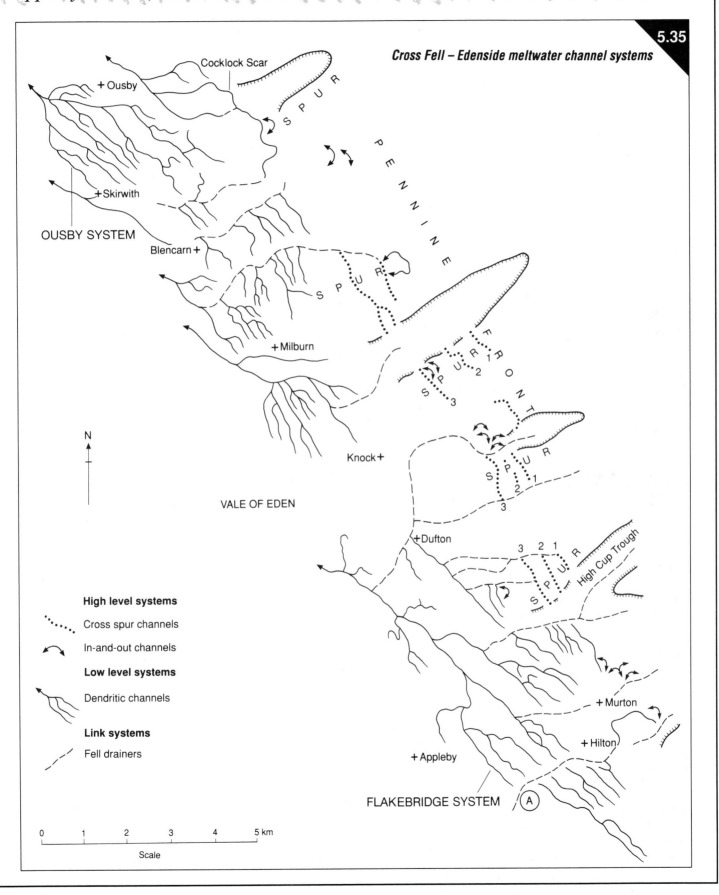

5.35

Cross Fell – Edenside meltwater channel systems

Cocklock Scar

+ Ousby

S P U R

P E N N I N E

OUSBY SYSTEM

+ Skirwith

Blencarn +

S P U R

+ Milburn

F R O N T

S P U R 1
2
3

Knock +

S P U R 1
2
3

N

VALE OF EDEN

+ Dufton

3 2 1
S P U R

High Cup Trough

High level systems

······· Cross spur channels

In-and-out channels

Low level systems

Dendritic channels

+ Murton

Link systems

Fell drainers

+ Hilton

+ Appleby

FLAKEBRIDGE SYSTEM (A)

0   1   2   3   4   5 km

Scale

5.36

In-and-out channels, Murton Pike

the dendritic channels, at times acting as links between them, and so appear to be younger. For example, the Hilton Beck fell-drainer (A on resource 5.35) cuts sharply across the Flakebridge channels and clearly post-dates them. It is likely that they belong to a late stage in the deglaciation when their upper courses drained exposed rock surfaces. On reaching the largely stagnant ice across the lower slopes, the waters would seek out crevasse systems and continue downslope as subglacial chutes.

A suggested explanation for the cross-spur, in-and-out, and low-level channels is as follows (resource 5.37): During ice downwasting processes, the critical boundary layer between brittle and plastic ice, i.e. the englacial water-table, intersects the spur crests. At the points in their courses where the englacial streams

touch rock, cross-spur and in-and-out channels are superimposed. As the boundary layer strikes successively lower points along the inclined spur crest, so a suite of channels develops. The ice level declines further and the upper channels are abandoned and exposed. Eventually, the boundary layer reaches the lowland floor, with its drift veneer, and the well developed englacial channel systems are superimposed into the drift and bedrock forming subglacial meltwater channels. The North West orientation of the cross-spur and the low-level channels is accounted for by the ice gradient which declined in that direction.

Activities

1   Explain briefly:

   a why the highest channels cut into the spur crests are likely to be the oldest,

   b how channels on neighbouring spurs could have been incised by the same stream,

   c why several of the cross-spur channels have hump-backed profiles.

2   In pairs or in groups use labelled block diagrams and notes to suggest situations in which cross-spur channels could be ice-marginal rather than subglacial in origin. You may find enlarged versions of resource 5.38 useful as a basis. You then need to add ice masses and stream networks.

5.37

Model of channel development

(a) Formation of high level system of channels

Englacial tunnels

Brittle ice

SPUR

Critical boundary layer

Plastic ice

Subglacial channels

W

E

Low-lying undulating Vale of Eden

Steep-sided high-level spurs of the Inlier and the Pennine Front

(b) Formation of low level system of channels

Former ice sheet surface

Downwasting

Later ice surface

Oldest

Abandoned channels

Youngest

ICE

Channels superimposed from englacial tunnels

W

E

Low level system of dendritic channels

High level system of cross-spur and 'in-and-out' channels

5.38

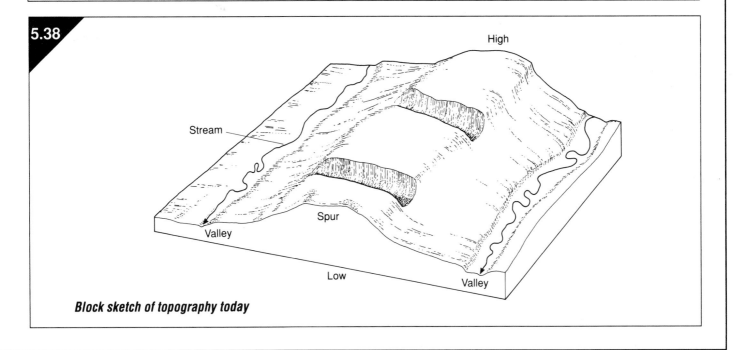

High

Stream

Spur

Valley

Low

Valley

Block sketch of topography today

Background

From some textbooks, it is easy to get the impression that glaciers slowly and steadily grind their way over the landscape, eventually depositing their loads in some orderly fashion in various mounds, ridges and fans. In reality, glacial environments may be highly dynamic, almost chaotic in the way they behave. This is especially true in mountain environments, and this case study, from the Karakorum, illustrates vividly the bewildering and sometimes disastrous changes triggered by the complex interactions between ice, water and wind.

The report summarised some of the work of the International Karakorum Project (IKP), a research project into the geomorphology of this mountain region (resource 5.39). The author uses the concept of the environment as an 'economy'. By this he means that a glacier, river, moraine etc., each has a 'budget', with income or gains (inputs), bank accounts (stores) and outgoings or losses (outputs). Each system then works according to the varying balance of

---

Key understandings

- ◆ The difference between 'warm' and 'cold' glaciers.
- ◆ The complex interaction between ice, water and debris.
- ◆ The highly dynamic nature of glaciated mountain environments.

Note: A number of key understandings from Chapter 4 and the rest of this chapter.

Decay in the Karakorum

Above the snow-line (about 5000 m) the disintegration of rock becomes bound up with the snow and ice economy. The glaciers surrounding most of the main Karakorum ridges are fed by snow avalances – the longest of the glaciers, like the Hispar, run for more than 50 km before ending in the midst of desert valleys. Their contribution to the landscape is to rip out great valleys and turn the quarried debris into a vast wasteland of spoil tips. The glaciers in the Karakorum are particularly dirty and destructive – towards the snout of each glacier the ice becomes entirely hidden under a moving landscape of rubble. Above all, in the erosional economy a glacier overproduces – and the means by which it over-produces is largely concentrated at the base.

The behaviour of glaciers depends fundamentally on their temperature: 'warm' glaciers are those at 0°C that contain both water and ice; 'cold' glaciers are well below freezing and are all ice. Cold glaciers are largely cold, temperate ones largely warm. Cold glaciers tend to stick to the underlying rock, moving only by plastic flow; warm glaciers can glide on basal water. The ice was found to be warm even 20 km up the glacier, and unlike the ice-caps of Iceland, Greenland or Antarctica, the surface of the glacier was strewn with rock from the valley sides, set in an ice-scape of great rivers and lakes formed from rapid surface melting.

It is quiet out on the glacier – a silence broken only by the chatter of small stones rattling down some raw ice face, the occasional thump of a distant ice-quake, and the gurgle of water deep below the surface. The movement of water through, under and over the glacier – the glacial plumbing – is of interest in a warm glacier because it is very much part of the mechanics of the glacier. Investigating the pattern of surface channels and buried piping reveals only the rapid flow of meltwater – more details of the inaccessible basal water system can be discovered through studying the varying chemistry of the stream discharged by the glacier.

Meltwater that comes direct from ice warmed by the Sun is relatively pure, and increases in quantity during daylight – high-tide coming at 6 pm. The water flowing slowly at the base of the glacier becomes enriched in soluble ions dissolved out of the neighbouring rocks, and flows much more regularly. A continuous record of the solutes contained in the water can be obtained by measuring electrical conductivity. A simple glacial system shows an increase in conductivity at night as the flow-rate decreases and the basal water becomes proportionally more significant. Some glaciers reveal that part of the meltwater released during the day is stored in internal reservoirs before being released during the night.

Such information could contribute towards an understanding of 'surging glaciers'. These are glaciers that fairly regularly set off on forays down the valley at speeds as high as 5 metres an hour, for up to six years, before entering into stagnation and retreat for periods of 15 to more than 100 years, by which time the ice reservoir will have been sufficiently replenished to provoke a new surge. The advance is the result of a wave of overthickening that travels down the glacier far faster than the actual ice movement – a wave not much different from a wave of water.

The material dumped at the snout of the glacier is highly varied and includes rocks gently put down as the underlying ice melts away, material carried for a short distance within the outwash stream, and even silts from temporary lakes – all labelled 'fluvial-glacial' material. Such material is found plastered along the sides of the Hunza valleys; in places there are layers of such sediments hundreds of metres thick. Add about 10 per cent water to this material and it will start to flow in slides of thick mud and debris. After a summer storm perhaps 10 such flows, each a metre or two in height, will have cut across the Karakorum Highway (resource 5.39). Far larger flows of debris originate from below the glaciers where, after a sudden surge of water, moraines (mounds of material dumped by the glacier) further down the valley may be undercut by the flood and so collapse to generate the most enormous debris flows. Two members of the IKP project came across such a debris flow in action, emerging from a side-valley about 100 km west of Gilgit. Every 20 minutes, over a period of 36 hours, 10m high waves of debris burst out of the side-valley at speeds of up to 25 m/s, breaking high into the air before spreading out to form a million-tonne dam across the main valley river – the Ghizar. The flow of debris had been generated by a reservoir of glacial water which broke, disrupting moraines.

The flow of the main rivers of the Karakorum e.g. the Indus, the Hunza, – does not always run smooth. Above altitudes of 3000 m, major glaciers move across the paths of rivers; and at all heights, huge rock-falls from the bulging oversteepened mountain sides, and from flows of debris moving down the side-valleys, can interfere with the progress of rivers. The lakes, formed as such debris dams the rivers, may be more than 100 m deep and may extend back from the dams for tens of kilometres; but they are often extremely temporary. After an earthquake around New Year 1840/41 a sizeable part of a western spur of Nanga Parbat (8126 m) fell into the Indus, creating a dam 300m high that took five months to fill, before bursting to send a wall of water that swept away an entire Sikh army (reputedly 100 000 strong) encamped on the river bank 200 km downstream. Within the Karakorum region such dam-bursts take place every two or three years. They are a demonstration that the river cannot cope with the amount of sediment it is expected to transport. But the relationship between the sediment load and the rate of flow means that the river can carry far more if it operates in bursts, than if it flows regularly over the same period. The greatest concentrations of sediment are often found just as the flow-rate is increasing; a prolonged high rate of flow merely dilutes the concentration because the extra sediment that the river could transport is not available.

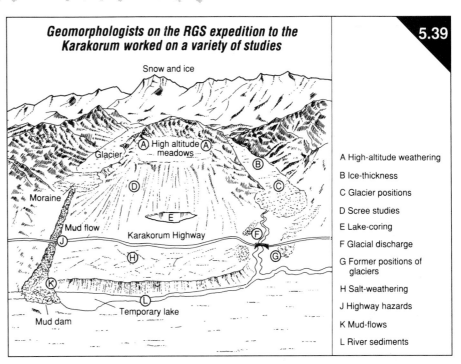

Geomorphologists on the RGS expedition to the Karakorum worked on a variety of studies

5.39

Snow and ice
High altitude meadows
Glacier
Moraine
Mud flow
Karakorum Highway
Temporary lake
Mud dam

A High-altitude weathering
B Ice-thickness
C Glacier positions
D Scree studies
E Lake-coring
F Glacial discharge
G Former positions of glaciers
H Salt-weathering
J Highway hazards
K Mud-flows
L River sediments

The advance of the glaciers disrupts and destroys earlier evidence of glaciation. At the furthest extent of their advance, through their bulldozing and melting, glaciers deposit barren stony moraine hills. As they pause or readvance a little within their retreat, glaciers will similarly deposit moraines. The history the moraines contain is like that of high-tide marks on a beach – a succession of furthest advances since a higher advance. Thus we can learn a lot about the retreat of the Karakorum glaciers but little of their advance.

The glacier's position is a 'barometer' which measures a collection of climatic details. Glaciers do most of their melting on sunny days, between the disappearance of the spring snow-cover and the first snowfall of autumn. The Batura Glacier lost 19 m through melting at the surface in one year (1974). When snow blankets the ice the glacier is effectively switched off. A glacier's mass also depends on input from snow. With rainfall in the Karakorum Valley of only 12 cm/year it was once thought, that such glaciers were a relict from the most recent ice age. More recent measurements of snowfall along the ridges reveal that

above 5000 m there is almost 20 times the valley's precipitation, most of it arriving with a westerly airstream in winter; the summer monsoon that fattens up the Himalayan glaciers breaks through into the Karakorum only about once in every 50 years. A glacial advance is therefore an indication of 'worse' weather, perhaps both colder and cloudier, but other information is needed to put it in context. The most recent glacial advance came about 1900 – at present there still appears to be a surplus of ice despite recent climatic warming, which has boosted the supply of the Indus river.

(Source: R Muir Wood, 'Decay in the Karakorum', *New Scientist*, 89(1246), 26 March 1981., pp. 820-823)

Activities

1 List the differences between 'warm' and 'cold' glaciers.

2 Summarise the diurnal and seasonal rhythms of glacier ice melting, and their effects.

3 Give **three** examples of what can happen when meltwater is added to glacial debris.

CHAPTER 6

Water in arid environments

Introduction

A 1977 United Nations report defines 'deserts' as areas with less than 100 mm mean annual rainfall, and the 'arid zone' as 'those areas lying between the 100 and 400 mm isohyets ... characterised by vegetation distributed on a diffuse pattern.' It is important to distinguish between **aridity,** which refers to permanently low absolute levels of moisture, and **drought,** which is an unexpected shortage of available moisture sufficient to cause severe stress to flora and fauna, including the human population. Arid environments exist in a state of permanent water budget deficit (resource 6.1). Even normally humid environments experience episodes of water deficiency, i.e. the 1990 drought in Britain.

In any system each component has a function, yet certain components control the fundamental nature and functioning of that system. In hot, arid environments the critical component is water in any one of its four modes and the balance between them (resource 6.2). In one sense it is the non-availability of moisture which is the determining factor. For example, the groundwater store assumes a crucial importance; mechanical weathering and erosion rather than chemical weathering processes dominate geomorphological evolution; ecosystem components exhibit strong adaptations to withstand protracted water deficits (See case study 11.4, on the Namibian dune ecosystem,); low humidity levels and cloud amounts, with resultant high insolation rates dominate climatic and meteorological conditions. However, do not under-estimate the significance of temperatures. The low cloud amounts and intense insolation result in the world's highest surface temperatures (Azizia, Libya, 58°C; Death Valley, USA, 56.7°C), and exceptionally wide diurnal ranges – up to 55°C in the Sahara. These extremes reduce the effectiveness of the already scanty moisture supply through high evaporation rates, and apply severe stress to living organisms.

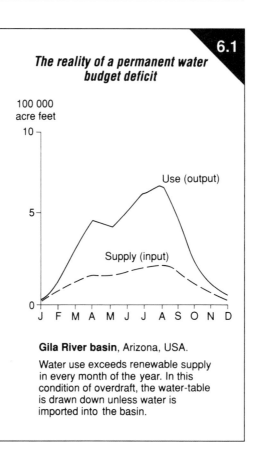

6.1

The reality of a permanent water budget deficit

100 000 acre feet

Gila River basin, Arizona, USA.

Water use exceeds renewable supply in every month of the year. In this condition of overdraft, the water-table is drawn down unless water is imported into the basin.

6.2

Modes of water occurrence

	Surface	*Ground*
PERMANENT	Rivers, lakes, reservoirs	Aquifers (a) living (b) fossil
EPHEMERAL	Non-permanent streams, lakes, reservoirs e.g. flash floods	Post rainstorm regolith and bedrock store

Remember, too, that there are cool and cold arid environments. As well as continental interior deserts such as the Gobi, extensive areas of the tundra and polar environments are 'semi-arid' or 'arid' in terms of mean precipitation totals. The extremely low temperatures during much of the year reduce the capacity of the atmosphere to store and hence to release moisture.

A first-time visitor is likely to be struck by the 'visibility' of an arid landscape. Vegetation cover is often less than 20 per cent, light is strong, and landforms are set out starkly. A second striking feature is the rarity or absence of surface water, unless of course, the visitor arrives at the same time as one of the infrequent storms (resource 6.3). Yet a careful look soon reveals that water has a significant geomorphological role, although such work is highly episodic (resource 6.4).

All desert-dwelling species have realised that the keys to survival are firstly, gaining access to as much of the available water as possible, secondly, making the most efficient use of it, and thirdly, developing the ability to do without water for varying periods. Humans have very limited capacity for the third option and so have adopted three main strategies in terms of water supply: create surface water stores (dams and reservoirs); tap groundwater stores (wells); transfer water from regions of surplus to budget deficit areas (canals). As these strategies extend geographically and grow in scale, their environmental impacts are becoming apparent. Although arid environments are 'hardened' to withstand extremes and disturbances, the water balance is very sensitive, Thus, modification and manipulation of the inputs, stores and throughputs of water can trigger rapid change and instability, as the following case studies show. The first case study uses a small water basin in Southern California to demonstrate how arid land hydrology works, and the sensitivity of the water balance. The second focuses upon river channel instability and groundwater store sensitivity, giving examples from Arizona where dams, well-pumping and irrigation have disrupted surface water throughputs and groundwater stores. The third moves the water throughput and transfer strategies to a much larger scale. Alternative perspectives of the massive development projects in the Aral and Caspian Sea basins of the USSR are given, which illustrate the complexity of water-management issues (compare with the Colorado River issue in case study 4.2)

▶ *In addition to providing further experience of the understandings and processes illustrated in Chapter 4, the materials explore in particular, the following concepts:*

balance, threshold, disturbance, extremity, periodicity, reliability, sensitivity, stability, resilience, adaptation and adaptability, capacity.

Armagosa River in flood, Death Valley, USA

Fans and washes show the effect of water on the desert, Anza Borrego, Southern California

Background

The arid and semi-arid lands of southwestern USA provide many fine examples of arid environment hydrology and of the increasing human impacts upon the throughput and storage of water in these systems. This is partly because of the geological framework in the southern section of the Basin and Range Province, which segments the region into a series of structural basins with sedimentary infill, surrounded by mountain ranges, i.e. systems with well defined boundaries and structures. Vegetation cover, especially on the mountains, is sparse, rainfall arrives in sudden, irregular storms, there is a permanent water budget deficit, and the sedimentary basins contain thick aquiferous beds. All these features are significant to the hydrology of arid environments.

This case study focuses on a small water basin in Southern California, some 150 km inland from San Diego and just north of the Mexican border, in what is known as the Anza Borrego Desert. It illustrates firstly, how an abrupt pulse of water passes through the system, secondly the relationships between such pulses and human activities, and thirdly how resource demands by humans are adversely affecting both the quantity and quality of the water store.

The Ocotillo hydrological basin is 35 km long and 20 km wide. There is a total absence of permanent surface water, little groundwater enters from

Key understandings

◆ In arid environments, water inputs tend to arrive in irregular, intense pulses.

◆ The environmental components are adjusted to these irregular inputs/throughputs.

◆ The groundwater store is all-important.

◆ Demands made on the water store (outputs) must not exceed the supplies (inputs) to the store.

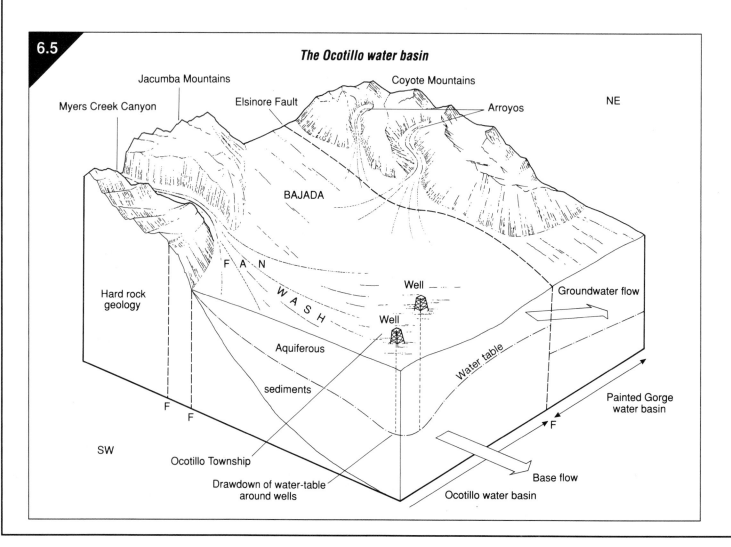

6.5

The Ocotillo water basin

Myers Creek Canyon

Jacumba Mountains

Elsinore Fault

Coyote Mountains

Arroyos

NE

BAJADA

F A N

W A S H

Well

Well

Groundwater flow

Hard rock geology

Aquiferous

sediments

Water table

Painted Gorge water basin

F

F

F

SW

Ocotillo Township

Drawdown of water-table around wells

Base flow

Ocotillo water basin

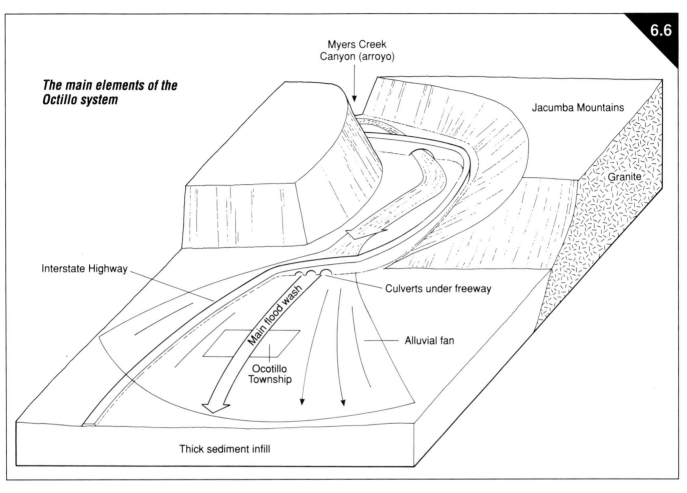

The main elements of the Octillo system

Myers Creek Canyon (arroyo)

Jacumba Mountains

Granite

Interstate Highway

Main flood wash

Culverts under freeway

Alluvial fan

Ocotillo Township

Thick sediment infill

6.6

other basins, and almost the entire water input is from occasional storms. Rain occurs on fewer than five days a year and the mean annual total is less than 100 mm. Although this basin is outside the Tropics, this is a genuine hot desert area, with maximum daily temperatures of more than 34°C from April to September and frost is unknown. (The all year irrigated agribusiness region of the Imperial – Coachella Valley lies 30 km to the east.)

Resources 6.5 and 6.6 show the main components of the basin:

(i) the Jacumba Mountains, a rugged granitic mass, with little vegetation;

(ii) a series of arroyos (gorges) cut into the mountains;

(iii) a bajada of alluvial fans built out from the mouth of each arroyo;

(iv) a playa (dry lake flat) at the lower end of the basin;

(v) the Elsinore Fault along the foot of the Coyote Mountains, marking the eastern margin of the basin. On to this natural system have been added: (a) the small settlement of Ocotillo across the middle of the Myers Creek fan, and (b) a major freeway (Interstate Highway 8) which runs along the Myers Creek arroyo and swings across its mouth at the apex of the fan over a series of culverts designed to carry floodwaters beneath the carriageway.

Getting too much water

Most of the water is received from infrequent storms across the Jacumba Mountains during the winter months. Occasionally,

however, a more intense downpour arrives: 'The main threat to Southern California and the Southwest is not from hurricanes but rather from their remnants. In late summer and early fall (autumn) it is not unusual for copious moisture from the remains of an eastern Pacific hurricane or tropical storm to enter the southwest US. This moisture feeds large thunderstorms, and torrential rains cause many washouts and flash floods'. This is precisely what happened on 9–10 September 1976. Hurricane 'Kathleen', having curved back northeastwards from the Pacific, crossed into California and dumped up to 200 mm of rain on to the Jacumba Mountains in less than ten hours. Resource 6.7 is a description by a local resident.

The Ocotillo Flood

'Rain began falling heavily about midnight on the 9th and continued all morning. By 9.00 a.m., tropical storm Kathleen was still pouring her wrath along the mountain peaks just above the desert floor. 'Water was pouring off the canyon slopes like waterfalls' said California Highway Patrolman Bob Grossett, 'but what was most alarming were the rocks and boulders falling on the road.'

Myers Creek, normally a dry wash, had soon swollen into a raging river. The first of the four 14 x 21 ft arch culverts, which pass the creek beneath the freeway, had surging water backed up 20 ft above the arch. The water raced across the road, halting a dozen motorists going down the grade. One couple were waiting in their van on the shoulder of the roadway. Suddenly, water raced over the second arch culvert and smashed into their van, spinning and pushing it towards the raging creek. The couple were trapped for twenty minutes, as water continually battered against them.

The third and fourth arch culverts suffered the same fate as the first two. At culvert number four, water raced 2 to 4 ft deep down the freeway, gnawing at the shoulders and slopes. Before long, large sections of the asphalt pavement crumbled and joined the boiling waters in the race toward the desert floor. Never before in recorded history had this much water raced down Myers Canyon: 10–15 ft deep, 20–40 ft wide. The water's velocity was up to 25–30 mph, forcing huge boulders to tumble along, and the noise was deafening. Amidst the rumbling and cracking of rocks bumping in the creek, a huge section of roadway gave way: 'I couldn't believe it! That 50 ft high fill and road bed just slipped into the creek," said one maintenance worker.

In the desert town of Ocotillo, two miles downstream, no one was really aware of what was about to happen. The community had gradually grown over the years and consisted of small retirement houses and mobile homes. There was a depression across the middle of town, but folks there never thought of it as a major wash. In actuality, it was the downstream portion of Myers Creek and was sitting right smack in the path of the racing flash flood.

When Kathleen's assault hit Ocotillo, the waters had joined to form a front of 5 ft deep and a half mile wide. Houses and trailers were torn off their foundations; vehicles relentlessly overturned. 'After the wave went by," said grocery store owner Richard Bell, 'you could see household paraphernalia, refrigerators, trash barrels, furniture and propane tanks and all kinds of things floating by.'

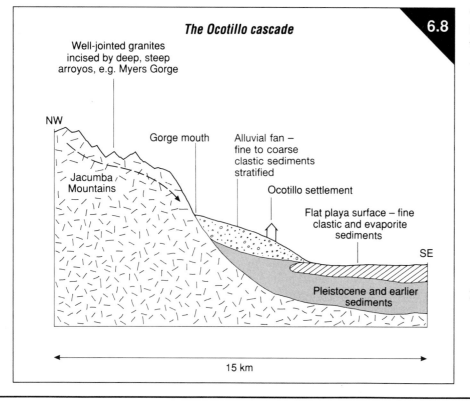

The Ocotillo cascade 6.8

Well-jointed granites incised by deep, steep arroyos, e.g. Myers Gorge

NW

Jacumba Mountains

Gorge mouth

Alluvial fan – fine to coarse clastic sediments stratified

Ocotillo settlement

Flat playa surface – fine clastic and evaporite sediments

SE

Pleistocene and earlier sediments

15 km

This account provides two useful insights into the workings of the water basin (resource 6.8).

1 The water filled the Myers Creek canyon very quickly. This indicates rapid runoff from the mountains, as shown in the comment 'Water was pouring over the canyon slopes like waterfalls'. This was the result of (a) steep slopes, (b) impermeable rocks, (c) bare, unvegetated surfaces, giving little opportunity for interception or infiltration of the rainwater. The storm hydrograph reflects the speed of the build-up in the channel (resource 6.9).

2 There is high energy available, and therefore the ability to transport the copious debris supply from the weathered granite surfaces. This is evident in the reference to 'rocks and boulders falling on to the road.'

6.9 The Ocotillo storm hydrograph

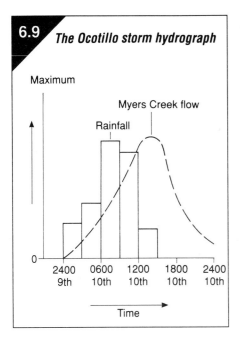

Arroyos such as Myers Creek generally have steep gradients and act as efficient funnels for the high energy waters and abundant debris of the flash floods. Beyond the mouth of the arroyo, however, the hydraulic geometry changes, energy is diffused and local carrying capacity diminishes. Conditions do change however, during different phases of the flood (resource 6.10). The Ocotillo fan behaves in this way, with the thick layers of permeable and aquiferous sediments facilitating infiltration and groundwater storage. Flash floods are, therefore, part of the normal functioning of the system, and indeed are essential to the construction of extensive fans and bajadas.

In 1976, however, conditions are different (resource 6.6). The freeway has partially occupied the canyon floor reducing its capacity, and by crossing the canyon mouth, has created a dam. The design capacity of the culverts built to carry floodwaters under the road proves inadequate to deal with this exceptional storm. As the account tells us, the culverts are overwhelmed one after another, causing flood surges downstream. When sections of the road finally collapse, a wall of water roars towards Ocotillo township. Thus, human activities – reducing the capacity in the canyon and causing ponding back at the canyon mouth – alter the characteristics of the flood

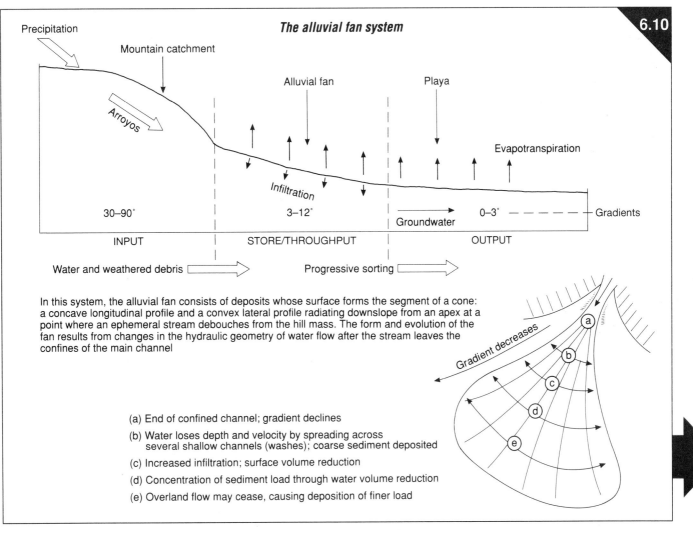

The alluvial fan system 6.10

In this system, the alluvial fan consists of deposits whose surface forms the segment of a cone: a concave longitudinal profile and a convex lateral profile radiating downslope from an apex at a point where an ephemeral stream debouches from the hill mass. The form and evolution of the fan results from changes in the hydraulic geometry of water flow after the stream leaves the confines of the main channel

(a) End of confined channel; gradient declines

(b) Water loses depth and velocity by spreading across several shallow channels (washes); coarse sediment deposited

(c) Increased infiltration; surface volume reduction

(d) Concentration of sediment load through water volume reduction

(e) Overland flow may cease, causing deposition of finer load

by concentrating the energy available and hence increasing the destructive capacity. This, in turn, places Ocotillo township in greater hazard.

Looking for enough water

The account of the flood states that 'there was a depression across the middle of town, but folks there never thought of it as a major wash.' In fact, the managers of the town's water company are well aware that the settlement is along the main wash. In the drylands of the American West access to water and water rights have always been crucial issues. On alluvial fans and bajadas this means where the water-table is nearest the surface and wells can be shallowest. This is normally along the major washes because it is these washes which carry most of the floodwaters and so supply the groundwater store. The settlers of Ocotillo have followed this principle – they have sunk their wells along the wash and built their township (resource 6.5). They have avoided building in the wash depression, and

in this way, shallow floods have passed through without causing problems, while the natural system was at work. Since the completion of the freeway in the early 1970s however, the pattern of the flooding has changed. Despite rebuilding and redesigning of the road, there have been further floods causing damage in 1980, 1982 and 1985, suggesting that the human and natural components in this environmental system have yet to reach a balance.

The people of Ocotillo rely entirely upon the groundwater store of the hydrological basin. They realise that in the long-term, they cannot extract more from this store than is being replaced by annual recharge, i.e. they must live within a balanced water budget. Yet demands for this precious resource have been growing (resource 6.11). In 1925, immediately before the first wells were sunk, the water budget was balanced (resource 6.12). The three components of output were balanced by the 2600 acre feet recharge (input). (One acre foot =

the volume of water required to cover 1 acre to a depth of 1 foot. It is a unit in common use in USA.) By 1980, the basin was operating at a significant budget deficit, i.e. outputs exceeded recharge inputs (resource 6.13).

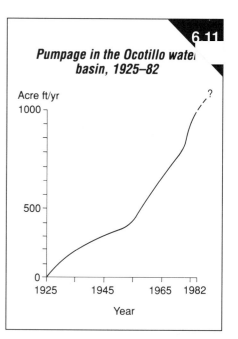

6.11

Pumpage in the Ocotillo water basin, 1925–82

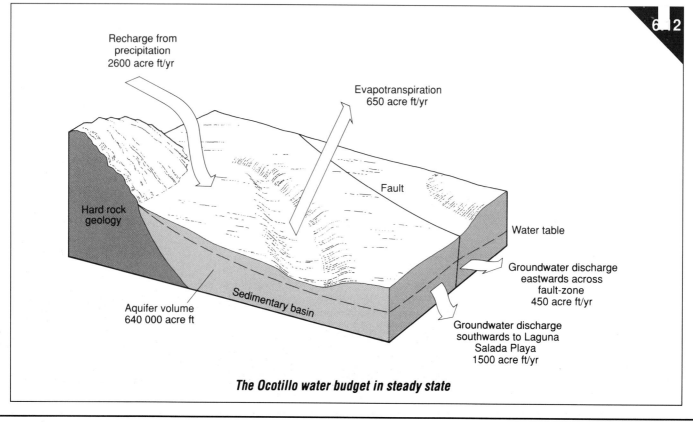

The Ocotillo water budget in steady state

6.13 Changes in the Ocotillo basin water budget, 1925–1995

	(a) 1925 (system in steady state)	(b) 1935	(c) 1982	(d) 1995: (projection for pumpage of 2000 acre ft./yr)
INPUT (Basin recharge through infiltration of precipitation) (acre. ft/yr)	2600	2600	2600	2600
OUTPUT (Discharge components from Basin) (acre ft./yr)				
Pumpage	0	900	1200	2000
Evapotranspiration	650	300	300	300
Throughflow to Mexico	1500	1450	1450	1450
Throughflow E. across Elsinore fault	450	450	450	450
TOTAL	2600	3100	3400	4200
Water budget balance (acre ft./yr)	0	–500	–800	–1600
Store (acre.ft.)	640 000	635 000	632 000	617 000
Drawdown from previous date (metres)		1–4 (3)	0.5–1.0 (3)	1–5 (3)
Height of Ocotillo water table in relation to that of Painted Gorge (metres)	+6	+4	+3.5	0 (1)

(1) If the annual pumpage were to remain at 1000 acre ft./yr, then the relationship would be +2.5m.
(2) Residential use 1480; US Gypsum 600; Export 250. These totals assume; therefore, (a) a continuance of the commercial water export, and (b) a ten-fold increase in population and hence domestic demand over present levels, a projection which seems improbable.
(3) Drawdown is particularly severe around Ocotillo settlement.

The township relies on two wells. Pumping from these has produced a cone of depression or drawdown of the water-table, reaching 4 m around the wells and currently falling by 10–15 cm a year (resources 6.5 and 6.13). Yet despite the localised cone of depression, the domestic consumers are not the main culprits for the overall drawdown of the water-table and the water budget deficit (resource 6.15). The US Gypsum Company has bought rights to pump water to its huge plaster board plant at Plaster City, some 12 km to the east, and outside the Ocotillo water basin. The McDougal company owns property in Ocotillo and hence has the rights to water which it sends by road tanker and sells to the Mexican town of Mexicali

(resource 6.14). Fears for the long-term security of their water supply have forced the Ocotillo residents to go to court. By 1984 they had an agreement with US Gypsum that the company would seek its water during the 1990s from the large

water projects of the Imperial Valley to the east. The McDougal case has proved more difficult, going all the way to the US Supreme Court in 1982 and only in 1986 did the company sell up and cease pumping.

6.14

McDougal pumping station, Ocotillo Basin

CASE STUDY 6.1 *A desert water basin at work – the Ocotillo Basin, Southern California*

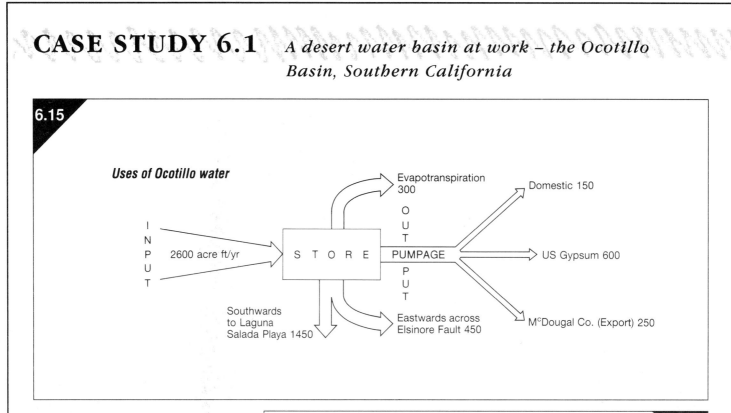

6.15

Uses of Ocotillo water

INPUT 2600 acre ft/yr → STORE

OUTPUT — PUMPAGE

Evapotranspiration 300

Domestic 150

US Gypsum 600

McDougal Co. (Export) 250

Eastwards across Elsinore Fault 450

Southwards to Laguna Salada Playa 1450

Never mind the quantity — what about the quality?

In the longer term, the Ocotillo residents fear more for the quality of their water supply than its quantity. A close look at resource 6.5 shows that the Elsinore Fault acts as the eastern boundary of the Ocotillo basin. By interrupting the aquifer and reducing the transmissivity, i.e. rate of throughput, it sustains the Ocotillo water-table at least 4 m above that of the Painted Gorge basin. Because of the nature of the rocks in its catchment, the Painted Gorge water is highly contaminated by salts and hence is unusable (resource 6.16). (The US Gypsum plaster board plant is in the Painted Gorge basin but cannot use the water.) The danger is that if the drawdown of the Ocotillo water-table continues then it will eventually sink below that of Painted Gorge and seepage will be reversed: Painted Gorge water would contaminate the Ocotillo supply. If the 1980 pumping rates continue, this will begin some time during the 1990s. By 1986, the Ocotillo water table was only 3 m above that of the Painted Gorge basin. If increased residential and farming development goes ahead as proposed in the 1982

Imperial County Development Plan then the reversed flow may begin in 1995.

6.16

Analyses of ground-water samples from Ocotillo and Painted Gorge water basins (Milligrams per litre except pH)

Constituents	Ocotillo	Painted Gorge
Silica	36	11
Calcium	18	410
Magnesium	5.1	150
Potassium	4.8	15
Sodium	74	4300
Bicarbonate	130	110
Sulfate	40	8100
Chloride	56	2200
Fluoride	0.7	0.6
Dissolved solids	307	15200
pH	7.1	7.7
Hardness	66	1600

Activities

1 Define the term 'balanced water budget' and illustrate its meaning by the use of data from resources 6.12 and 6.13.

2 Use resources 6.12 and 6.15 to list the similarities and differences between the water basin in 1925 and 1980.

CASE STUDY 6.2   *Relationships between water and people in an arid environment – the Gila River Basin, Arizona, USA*

Background

The Gila River, its tributary the Salt River, plus a series of tributary basins make up the major Arizona contribution to the Colorado (page 79). They are non-permanent surface phenomena, both in their traditional 'free' and their current 'controlled' states. As is common with such streams crossing gentle alluvial landscapes they produce wide, shallow, poorly defined valleys and channels. Channel/floodplain characteristics and relationships are unstable and highly dynamic, a consequence of the irregular, sudden pulses and surges of energy and material (water and sediment) inputs. There is frequent alternation from degradational to aggradational conditions, and from braiding to meandering patterns.

Two components of the Gila basin system are used:

(i)   the lower Salt River as it passes through Phoenix, exhibiting modifications to a migratory, braided channel caused by the construction of a dam;

(ii)   the Gila Bend section of the Gila River which illustrates the impact of irrigation activities and periodic reservoirs upon groundwater conditions.

Part I: Channel changes along the Lower Salt River

Channel evolution: Rivers, or more precisely, drainage basins, appear to be good examples of continuously operating cascading systems working towards a condition of dynamic equilibrium (see the case studies in Chapter 4). However, this concept of long-term equilibrium poses problems when we study arid region rivers which:

(a) operate discontinuously, and

(b) have high ratios of flood discharge to mean discharge.

Channel configuration is determined by intense, infrequent flood events,

6.17

Dry river bed: the Gila River, Arizona

6.18

Precipitation and runoff on the upper Salt River basin, Arizona, 1902–1936

		SUMMER				WINTER							Av. Ann.
	J	J	A	S	O	N	D	J	F	M	A	M	
AVERAGE PPT. (ins)	0.47	2.85	2.93	1.66	1.23	1.56	2.04	1.95	2.24	1.78	1.07	0.48	20.26
% of annual ppt.	2.3	14.0	14.5	8.2	6.1	7.7	10.1	9.6	11.0	8.8	5.3	2.4	
RIVER FLOW (cfs)	440	540	880	700	420	620	950	1350	2400	2700	2500	1100	1500
% of annual flow	3.0	3.7	6.0	4.8	2.9	4.2	6.4	9.2	16.3	19.0	17.5	7.4	
EXTREMES Max(cfs)	1400	3650	4000	2450	1500	6400	6000	17000	11450	15300	12550	4600	4500
Min(cfs)	80	80	270	200	130	160	170	190	200	200	150	130	300

Causes of reduced runoff impacts of summer rains:

(a) Character of storms: summer storms are sudden, intense and localised, therefore there is rapid, local runoff in ephemeral streams which is absorbed by infiltration before reaching main Salt River channel.

(b) Consumptive use is higher in summer: higher evaporation; rapid plant growth and high water intake/transpiration rates.

(c) Watershed peculiarities: winter rainfall is steadier, over broader areas; lower evaporation/transpiration rates.

with channels likely to be dry for varying periods (resource 6.17).

Between the Granite Reef Dam (completed in the 1920s) and its junction with the Gila River, the lower Salt River Valley runs for 48 km through the Phoenix urban sprawl. This periodic river rises in the White Mountains of eastern Arizona but for much of its length the shallow, broad channel cuts across the thick alluvial infill (which is more than 3000 m thick) of the Basin and Range province. Mean annual precipitation is approximately 150 mm but with high variability. Intense summer thunderstorms, produced in moist air masses which drift North West from the Gulf of Mexico, are localised sufficiently to restrict flooding. The main flood discharges result from winter rains brought by depressions moving east from the Pacific or from melting snows (resource 6.18). The basin is genuinely hot with daytime maxima regularly attaining 39°C April–September, but the mountain catchment may accumulate a significant snowpack.

The channel, now dry except for flood events, (e.g. no flow 1941–1965), has poorly defined banks, varies in width from 150–1500 m and is built of a mixture of coarse sands and large cobbles. It is braided and unstable but has a well-defined main-flow channel from 66 to 330 m wide. Over the past century this main-flow channel has migrated laterally across the valley floor by up to 1.6 km (resource 6.19). Zones of relative channel stability alternate, however, with stretches of rapid migration. Channel stability is caused by

(a) outcrops of solid rock, e.g. Precambrian rocks at Tempe Butte;

(b) engineering works such as bridges ((b) on resource 6.19);

(c) consistent sinuosity which sustains meander length and hence cross-points below constrictions, e.g. C on resource 6.19(a).

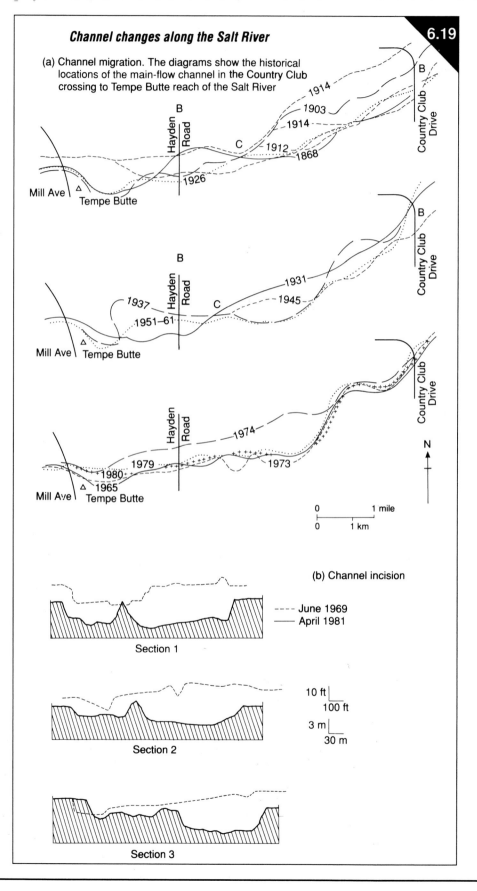

6.19

Channel changes along the Salt River

(a) Channel migration. The diagrams show the historical locations of the main-flow channel in the Country Club crossing to Tempe Butte reach of the Salt River

(b) Channel incision

- - - - June 1969
——— April 1981

Section 1

Section 2

Section 3

It is clear that this broad, shallow, shifting channel characteristic predates the building of the Granite Reef Dam. Common sense might suggest that under 'free' conditions the sudden surge of high energy floodwaters across unconsolidated alluvial material would lead to rapid incision by entrainment of debris and abrasion of bedrock. More careful thought tells us that while in the phase up to maximum spate, there may be scour and incision, during the latter stages of the flood episode the deceleration of the debris-laden waters across the low-gradient basin floor causes deposition, lateral swinging and ultimate braiding of the channel. This results from load exceeding the energy available for transportation.

The Granite Reef dam has altered this situation: firstly, most of the sedimentation takes place behind the dam, which has dramatically reduced its storage capacity and the sediment load below the dam; secondly, the discharges released from the dam or which spill over it tend to be less frequent but more abrupt and initially relatively free from sediment load. This seems to have created conditions of accelerated incision (resource 6.19(b)) with a lowering of the main-flow channel by 6 m, from 1965 to 1980, and reduced channel migration (resource 6.19(a)). Yet once the floodwaters spill over the main-flow channel their lateral energy seems to have increased, for the width of the high-flow flood channel has been increased markedly by the powerful 1978 and 1983 floods.

A flood episode has a degradational phase followed by an aggradational phase producing a broad, choked valley floor. This succession illustrates the threshold concept: at a critical discharge, i.e. energy level, materials of specific mass and shape become entrained. this is the **threshold discharge of instability**. Below this threshold value there is no downcutting or channel migration; above this value there is

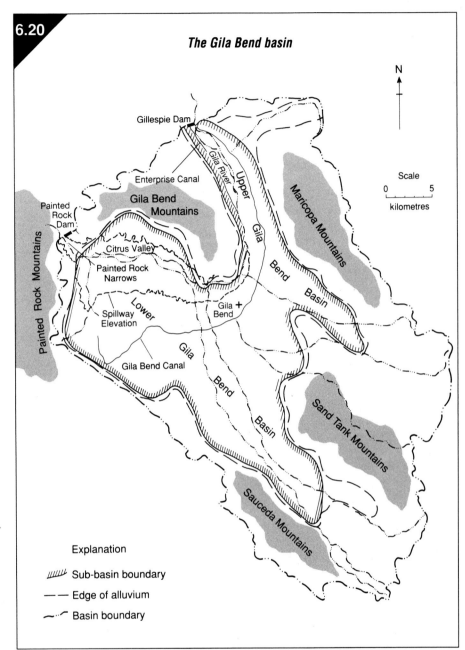

6.20

The Gila Bend basin

N

Gillespie Dam

Enterprise Canal

Painted Rock Dam

Gila Bend Mountains

Upper Gila River

Maricopa Mountains

Citrus Valley

Painted Rock Narrows

Lower Gila

Gila Bend Basin

Gila + Bend

Spillway Elevation

Painted Rock Mountains

Gila Bend Canal

Lower Gila Bend Basin

Sand Tank Mountains

Sauceda Mountains

Scale
0 — 5
kilometres

Explanation

�III Sub-basin boundary

— — Edge of alluvium

—··⌐ Basin boundary

sudden and progressive channel destabilisation. The threshold is based upon the recognised relationships between discharge (Q), channel dimensions – width (W), depth (D), velocity (V), i.e. Q=WDV1, and the characteristics of the bedload.

For arid region rivers the threshold of instability roughly equals the threshold for initiating the transport of coarse bedload, but this is less likely to be applicable for humid

region streams where suspended load is dominant. In the Salt River the threshold value is 560 cfs, above which bank and bed materials become unstable, with channel depth fluctuating more rapidly than width. Thus, for non-permanent streams in arid regions, when long periods without discharge are interspersed with episodes of abrupt high energy flood, equilibrium concepts of balance between water, sediment and channel dimensions are of limited use.

Part II: The Gila River – the impact of dams, reservoirs and canals

Water table form

The Gila Bend stretch of the Gila River takes the human manipulation of basin hydrology one stage further, with the presence of dams at both ends of the basin (resource 6.20). At the upper end, Gillespie Dam is a diversionary structure from which two irrigation canals distribute water (resource 6.21), while at the lower end the Painted Rock dam is for flood control and flow regulation, and impounds a reservoir (resource 6.22).

The alluvial basin contains an upper, fine-grained unit and a lower, coarse aquifer which before the building of the Painted Rock dam and the development of well pumping, produced a groundwater store and water-table sloping steadily in accord with the topography (resource 6.23(a)). Today the pattern is quite different, with three notable changes (resource 6.23 (b)):

1 Two cones of depression of the water-table along the middle and lower sections of the Gila Bend Canal, the result of pumping to augment the supply to the canal (resource 6.24).

2 A groundwater mound in the central basin where application of irrigation water to 8000 ha has created a perched water-table.

Gila Bend Basin – canal and pumping

3 A raising of the water-table in the lower basin by seepage from the reservoir.

Can you suggest why all three should fluctuate constantly and how the fluctuations can be controlled?

Reservoir impact

As resource 6.20 shows, the reservoir behind the Painted Rock dam when at its maximum height, floods some 21 600 ha, much of which is normally used for agriculture. However, there have been only six

Gillespie Dam, Gila River

Painted Rock Dam, Gila River

SR =	$(IGR+IP+IGW+IIR+IT)$ $-(OER+OPR+OGW)$
SR =	Change in reservoir storage
IGR =	Inflow from Gila River
IP =	Precipitation on reservoir surface
IGW =	Groundwater discharge into reservoir, i.e. bank storage return
IIR =	Inflow from irrigation water
IT =	Inflow from tributary washes
OER =	Evaporation from reservoir surface
OPR =	Gila River outflow below Painted Rock dam
OGW =	Groundwater recharge from reservoir, i.e. Bank storage losses

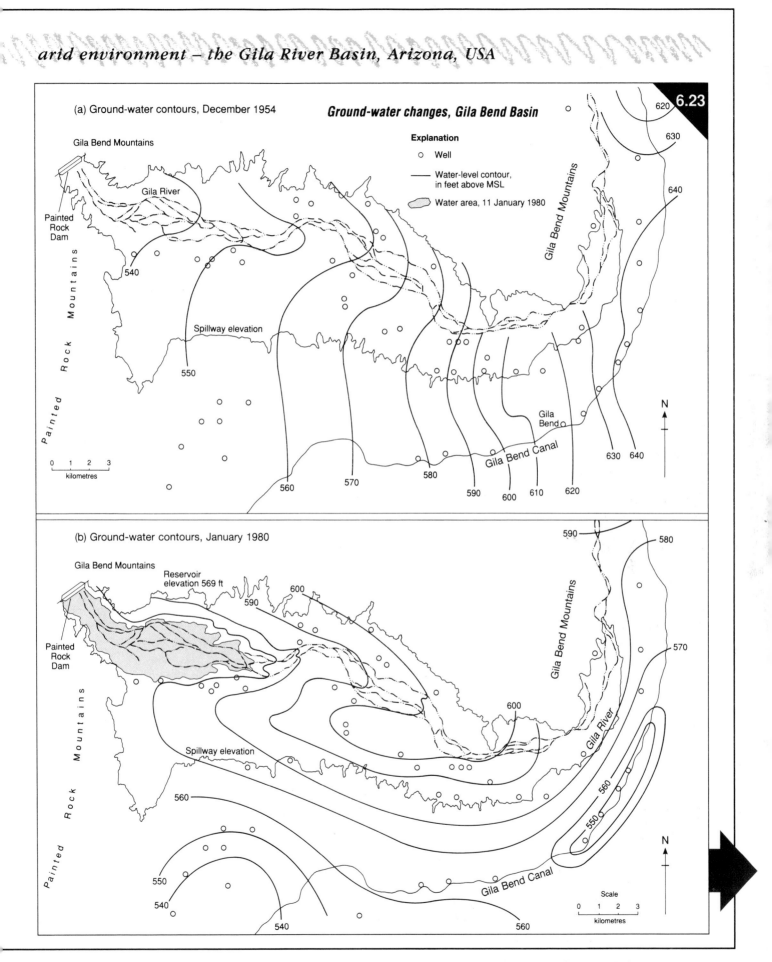

6.23

(a) Ground-water contours, December 1954

Ground-water changes, Gila Bend Basin

Gila Bend Mountains

Explanation

○ Well

── Water-level contour, in feet above MSL

▓ Water area, 11 January 1980

Gila River

Painted Rock Dam

Gila Bend Mountains

P a i n t e d   R o c k   M o u n t a i n s

Spillway elevation

550

540

N

Gila Bend

Gila Bend Canal

630 640

560   570   580   590   600   610   620

0 1 2 3
kilometres

(b) Ground-water contours, January 1980

Gila Bend Mountains

Reservoir elevation 569 ft

590

600

580

Painted Rock Dam

Gila Bend Mountains

P a i n t e d   R o c k   M o u n t a i n s

Spillway elevation

600

600

570

Gila River

560

560

550

N

550

540

540   560

Gila Bend Canal

Scale
0 1 2 3
kilometres

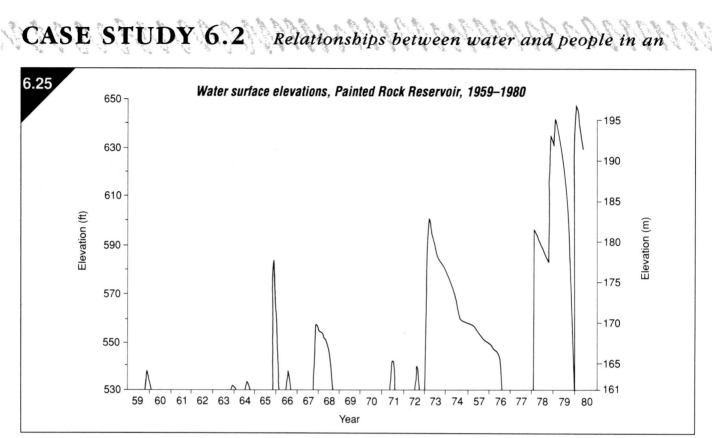

6.25

Water surface elevations, Painted Rock Reservoir, 1959–1980

significant impoundments since the dam was completed in 1959, it has never been full and has contained water for only 40 per cent of the time (resource 6.25). The input is controlled directly from the Gillespie Dam, the flow through which is itself determined by management policy in the Salt River Project upstream. The summer low season flows are largely Phoenix sewage effluent and irrigation return water.

Analysis of resource 6.26 enables us to follow three of the impoundments and their associated water budgets. As you work through each episode, pay particular attention to the timespans and phasing involved, and to the components of the water budget, which is built up from the following equation:

Bank storage (IV (d) and (e) on resource 6.26) In any stream, lake or reservoir there is normally a two-way movement of water between the water body and the surrounding subsurface materials. This component of groundwater is known as the bank store: the amount of storage change in an aquifer resulting from a change in stage or level in an adjacent surface-

water body such as a reservoir. As the Painted Rock reservoir fills up, i.e. its surface level rises, there tends to be a net flow or recharge into the surrounding aquiferous strata. As the water level falls during the declining stage, so water is released from the bank store into the reservoir. This is known as bank store return.

It has been found that the way a reservoir level is controlled can influence the size of this return. For instance, the 1973 flood was large but produced a low bank store return, whereas the 1979 floods yielded a high return. In 1973 the reservoir level was reduced relatively slowly, while in 1979 the release was rapid. As the bank store can be a valuable addition to reservoir capacity, especially in regions of such high summer evaporation this is an important understanding. If there is immediate need for additional water, then rapid lowering of the reservoir level will release more of the bank store. Conversely, if the aim is to conserve the bank store component of the groundwater store, then release rates should be low.

Activities

1 Define the term water budget deficit.

2 Draw a graph showing:

 a average monthly flows,

 b maximum monthly flows,

 c minimum monthly flows.

3 Draw a graph showing:

 a the percentage of annual ppt, by month,

 b the percentage of annual flow, by month.

4 List the four most significant features of the hydrology of the Upper Salt River Basin illustrated by the table and the graphs.

5 What characteristics typical of drainage basins in arid environments are exhibited by the Salt River data?

6.26

Flood event and water-budget analysis for Painted Rock reservoir

	January 1966	February 1973	Jan–April 1979
I Timing			
(a) Flow begun at Gillespie Dam	10–12–65	24–2–73	19–12–78
(b) Peak daily flow, Gillespie Dam (cfs)	48800	17000	90400
(c) Inflow to Painted Rock reservoir begun	27–12–65	4–3–73	20–12–79
(d) Painted Rock reservoir ceases	17–1–66	23–5–73	23–4–79
(e) Peak storage, Painted Rock reservoir (acre-ft)	215000	439500	1616468
(f) Date of peak storage, Painted Rock reservoir	13–1–66	20–5–73	17–4–79
(g) Flow ceases at Gillespie Dam	18–3–66	16–6–73	25–5–79
(h) Painted Rock reservoir drained	14–6–66	17–4–77	20–2–80
(i) Painted Rock reservoir outflow ceases	14–7–66	17–4–77	20–2–80
I Outflow (acre-ft)			
(a) Past Painted Rock dam	257349	560532	2179459
(b) Evaporation from Painted Rock reservoir	4863	155466	190450
(c) Ground surface evaporation	12939	63680	52874
Total	275161	779464	2422783
III Inflow (acre-ft)			
(a) From precipitation	1682	5123	19342
(b) From irrigation runoff	Negligible	Negligible	3200
(c) From Gila River	273479	773341	2395641
Total	275161	779464	2422783
IV Inputs and losses			
(a) Total flow over Gillespie Dam (acre-ft)	421968	910897	2682503
(b) Infiltration losses upstream from reservoir (acre-ft)	148489	137556	286862
(c) % flow that reaches Painted Rock reservoir	65	85	89
(d) Volume released from bank storage (acre-ft)	12000	26000	125000
(e) Average bank storage return/foot reservoir decline (acre/ft)	223	37	1106

Background

In the USSR, desert lands occupy about 250 million hectares, or about 10 per cent of the total country. Over 90 per cent of this desert area is found in the Kazakh, Uzbek and Turkmen republics (resource 6.27). Rivers and groundwater stores are fed from mountains to the south, and drain into two great inland seas, the Caspian Sea and the Aral Sea. The Aral Sea in particular is dependent upon rivers which cross the southern deserts, almost all of its water input being delivered by the Amu Darya and the Syr Darya. Increasing amounts of this water are being drawn off for irrigation schemes and rapidly expanding industrial cities. The resources set out below give very contrasting views of what is happening. The first extract is from a research paper read by Soviet scientists at a 1985 conference on arid lands, held in the USA. The other extracts were published in 1988.

An optimistic scenario

'The balanced development of industry and agriculture has made it possible to bring the economy of the formerly backward desert regions up to the level of developed areas and to build well-appointed cities and industrial centres, highways, and hydroelectric power stations, water reservoirs and canals that provide irrigation and supply water to the deserts.

Because of the natural conditions of the Soviet deserts, it has been deemed appropriate to use the major part of the territory as pasture, to develop irrigated agriculture on lands with an abundant water supply and to establish extractive industries in the desert and processing industries on oases.

The continued scientific and technological progress has made it possible to step up the rate of development in the desert areas. This process covers the following main areas: **1** pastoral livestock rising, **2** irrigated agriculture and the establishment of water installations, **3** forest plantation and **4** extractive industries.

Major water works have to be constructed in areas lacking groundwater or where this water has a high mineral content. A 205-kilometre water channel is nearing completion on a state farm in the Krasnovodsk region of Turkmenistan. The 174-kilometre Karakum canal will reach the heart of the Karakum desert. The total length of the water supply network will be 2852 kilometres; it will supply water to 300 000 hectares of pastures and irrigate up to 2500 hectares of desert lands where additional fodder will be grown. A water reservoir of 2 to 5 million cubic meters is to be constructed near the Bakhardok settlement. Watering places will become comfortable, green settlements of livestock raisers.

The system of water pipelines on the Mangyshlak peninsula and the hydraulic works drawing water from the Irtysh, Ishim, Tobol and other rivers to supply the central and northwestern regions of Kazakhstan lacking water and their settlements, railway stations and state and collective farms have become important installations.

The total irrigated territory is 8 to 10 million hectares. Its antiquity and stable development are due to the enormous advantages of the area's soils and climatic conditions. On the irrigated lands, it is possible to cultivate such crops as cotton, grapes and rice and to gather in two and, in some places, even more harvests a year of fodder crops and vegetables.

In recent years, the irrigation of arid lands in the Central Asian republics has undergone drastic changes; namely, the old irrigation system has

---

Key understandings

- That in an environmental system such as a drainage basin, a change in any one component will have a 'knock-on' effect through the rest of the system.

- That any environmental system has a finite resource capacity.

- That any management policy for the use of the resources of a system must take into account the inter-relationships between the components or parts of the system.

Activities

Read the resources carefully and then answer the following:

1 Summarise how the waters of the Amu Darya and Syr Darya rivers are being drawn off and used. How does this modify the functioning of the water throughput in the system?

2 What is happening to the Aral and Caspian Seas, their ecosystems and the people who depend on them?

3 Produce an impact assessment for the region, using the following matrix. (You may find it helpful to work with a partner.)

	Economic	Social	Environmental
Gains			
Losses			

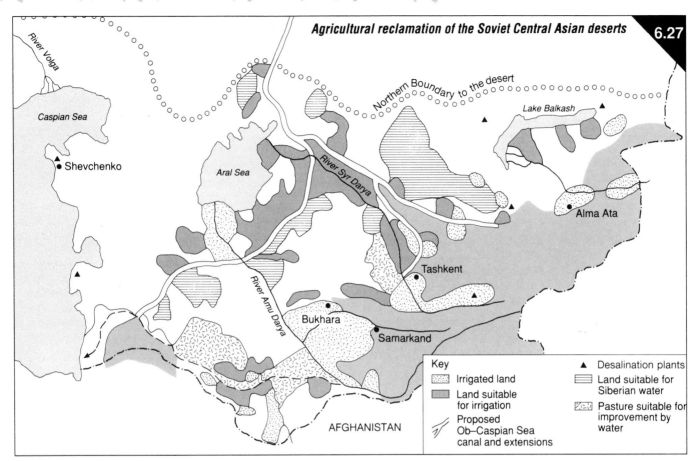

Agricultural reclamation of the Soviet Central Asian deserts 6.27

Key

Irrigated land

Land suitable for irrigation

Proposed Ob–Caspian Sea canal and extensions

▲ Desalination plants

Land suitable for Siberian water

Pasture suitable for improvement by water

been reconstructed, which has considerably increased the productivity of the irrigated lands. At the same time, projects for the integrated use of all major Central Asian rivers have been developed and to a considerable extent already implemented. It has thus become possible to actively control deserts through the irrigation of lands that were irrigated in antiquity and through the development of new virgin lands (resource 6.27).

As a result, large hydraulic works have been built in the desert zone of the Soviet Union together with water reservoirs and hydroelectric power stations, and major canals have been commissioned (the Fergana and Karakum gravity flow canals and the Karshin, Amu-Bukhar and Irtysh-Karaganda induced-flow canals). The canals redistribute some 40 cubic kilometers per year of water, making it possible to irrigate over 8.3 million hectares in the arid regions of Central Asia and Kazakhstan.

The 'Guidelines for the Economic and Social Development of the USSR for 1981–1985 and for the period up to 1990' provide for irrigation to be introduced over 1 065 000 to 1 108 000 hectares.

The irrigated lands of the Karshin steppe are divided into two zones: the upper one, where 350 000 hectares are irrigated, and the lower one, with 500 000 hectares. An irrigation scheme is now underway, and 200 000 hectares of the first stage of the project are to be developed.

The Lenin Canal in the Karakum desert is the major water facility in the Soviet Union's deserts. It withdraws water from the Amudarya river and transports it over 1400 kilometers to the ancient delta of the Atrek river, – 18 cubic kilometres will be withdrawn from Amudarya every year. The water reservoirs will have a capacity of 2500 million cubic metres, supplying water to 1.1

million hectares or 70 per cent of Turkmenistan's irrigated lands.

The fourth stage of the Karakum canal is now under construction, and another 61 000 hectares will be developed, additional water will be supplied to 94 000 hectares, new lands will be irrigated along the 1015-kilometre canal and the regulated volume of the reservoirs will be brought to 1473 million cubic meters.

The inflow of water through the fifth stage of the canal to the Precaspian lowlands will offer great prospects for transforming the deserts of the southwestern regions of Turkmenistan. The canal and the water reservoir of 650 million cubic metres will supply water to the pastures and 193 000 hectares of the Meshkhed-Missarian plateau.

Yet the water requirements of the Soviet Union's deserts, like in many other arid regions of the world, and the requirements of growing cities, industrial centers and livestock breeding by far surpass local water resources.

It is estimated that, out of the 26 million hectares suitable for irrigation, only 4 million hectares can be irrigated with water from the Aral Sea basin. Long-term regulation of the Syrdarya's flow and seasonal regulation of the Amudarya river will be established. Twenty nine new water reservoirs with a seasonal capacity of 53.8 cubic kilometers will be commissioned for irrigation and other uses, new canals will be constructed and existing ones will be widened and renovated. These water management projects will make it possible to enlarge the existing oases of irrigated agriculture and create new ones, such as Karshin. The construction of the Tuyamuyun hydraulic complex on the Amudarya

river will make it possible to irrigate 200 000 hectares of new lands and 500 000 hectares of old lands.

The development of new lands and the construction of large irrigation canals cause water and wind erosion under certain soil and climatic conditions. On such lands irrigation systems are being rearranged, protective forest plantations planted and gullies and banks of rivers and water reservoirs stabilized and afforested. In recent years, 14 800 kilometers of shelter belts have been planted along canals in Uzbekistan.

The effect of irrigated agriculture on human health is another important problem, since some infections can spread with irrigation water. The appearance of such infections is indicative of an incorrect functioning of irrigation and drinking water

supply systems. Complete elimination of previously massive and destructive diseases has been possible, owing to sanitation and hygiene measures that combat them in the irrigated areas, correct the operation of the irrigation systems, reduce losses of irrigation water and improve irrigation techniques.

Thus, our forecast for the future is optimistic. Planned social economy may guarantee the rational management of desert natural resources without damaging the environment of the desert.'

(Source: A G Babaev et al., 'Complex desert development and desertification control in the USSR', in *Arid Lands: Today and Tomorrow*, Belhaven Press, 1988, pp. 825–840)

A pessimistic scenario

6.28

Aral Sea 'will become lifeless lake of brine'

The Aral Sea, located among the deserts of the southern Soviet Union, is doomed unless radical steps are taken immediately. The sea – once the world's fourth largest lake – is rapidly disappearing. By early next century it will be only about 8 per cent of its size in 1960 and will be highly saline.

In 1960, the Aral Sea, a saline lake with no outlet to the sea, covered 68 000 square kilometres, but by last year it had dropped to 41 000 square kilometres. Its volume has fallen by more than half over the same period. Salinity has more than doubled to 27 grams of salt per litre of water.

The shrinkage has been caused by water being siphoned off for irrigation from two rivers that feed the lake – the Amudar'ya and Syrdar'ya. Last year virtually no water from the rivers reached the lake. About 100 cubic kilometres of water is being taken from the rivers to irrigate eight million hectares of land in the Aral Sea Basin.

The area has become an environmental disaster. Excessive salinity has killed off all 20 species of fish in the lake and destroyed a fishing industry that employed 60 000 people. Storms, heavily laden with dried salt, are dumping 43 million tonnes of salt annually on plants and pastures over 200 000 square kilometres of land surrounding the lake.

Plants are dying from exposure to sodium bicarbonate, sodium chloride, and

sodium sulphate. Residents near the lake are blaming an increase in cancer of the throat on the salt that they inhale.

The ecology of the large delta formed by the two rivers is threatened. Extremes of climate are now common because the moderating influence of the lake no longer exists. A shorter growing season caused by the climatic changes is damaging the growth of cotton.

The Soviet government has ignored 'angry' and 'eloquent' protests by scientists from the region. Three out of four plans to save some of the lake using a system of dikes are now obsolete because the lake is shrinking too rapidly.

Sometime next century the Aral Sea will become 'a lifeless residual brine lake'.

(Source: *New Scientist*, 18 February 1988)

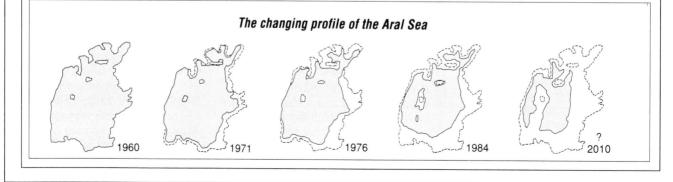

The changing profile of the Aral Sea

1960   1971   1976   1984   2010

6.29

Vanishing sea threatens 'ecological disaster'

The Soviet Union, faced with an ecological catastrophe in the dry steppes of Central Asia, has decided to reopen the highly controversial question of reversing the flow of the Siberian rivers.

After urgent representations on the scale of the ecological threat were made to Mr Gorbachev on his visit to Tashkent last week, it has been agreed to conduct a new feasibility study on the Siberian river project — only 18 months after a similar scheme was officially declared dead.

The country faces an appalling dilemma. The Siberian rivers project aroused furious opposition among Russian and international experts, who claimed that any diversion of the fresh water reaching the Arctic Ocean would have incalculable ecological consequences, and could even trigger a new ice age.

But that potential danger has to be balanced against that potentially graver catastrophe now under way around the Aral Sea.

Soviet scientists fear that the world's greatest man-made ecological disaster, with implications exceeding the Chernobyl nuclear accident, is now brewing in Central Asia, where the damage to the Aral Sea has been declared quite irreversible.

The Aral Sea has lost a barely credible 60 per cent of its water in the past 30 years. The sea level has fallen by almost 40 feet since large irrigation projects steadily diverted the flow from the two geat rivers of Central Asia, the Amu Darya and the Syr Darya.

In places, the Aral Sea has receded by 62.5 miles. In the 1960s, the lake's surface area was more than 25 800 square miles, about the size of Ireland. It is now down to barely 15 500 square miles, and a new salt desert has formed on the dry sea bed.

This desert itself is advancing, and its vast dust storms are swirling more than 50 million tons of salt-sand into the air each year, dropping up to half-a-ton of this crop-killing substance onto each hectare of cultivated land in the main Uzbekh farming region.

The rising salinity has now become a severe health hazard to the one million inhabitants of the Karakalpak region, immediately south of the Aral Sea. Hepatitis and other digestive illnesses are now endemic, with a consequent sharp rise in infant mortality.

Formerly pure artesian water is now becoming saline, as the salts filter through the sandy soil. The Amu Darya now contains 10 times more minerals than 12 years ago.

'The Aral Sea is a decisive catalyst for the climate of the whole of Asia. This is going to affect the weather, the rainfall and eventually the food supply of India too,' he said.

'By forcing the cold northerly and north-westerly winds from Siberia and the Arctic to gain height as they cross the Aral Sea, and its own micro-climatic zone, the Aral affects the snow formation on the Pamirs and Himalayas, and thus the climate of the Indian sub-continent. This catastrophe is global and it transcends national boundaries,' the professor went on.

Professor Yusupov, who confirmed that a new feasibility study on the Siberian rivers scheme was now under way, stressed that in the view of local scientists, the project would only take 6–7 per cent of the flow of the Siberian rivers, the Ob and Irtysh — too little to have any important ecological effects.

'Brought by a new canal to Uzbekistan, this water can work for the benefit of the whole Soviet Union. It can irrigate our crops before being sent to save the Aral Sea.

'Even so, we will never be able to restore the Aral Sea even to its current shrunken size. The best we can hope to do is to stabilise the sea at a far smaller level in the future, but hope that it will continue to fulfil its ecological role as the weather kitchen for Central Asia,' he added.

(Source: *The Guardian*, 18 April 1988)

6.30

The incredible shrinking sea

The Aral was mainly fed by the Amu Darya and Syr Darya rivers. Today the waters of these two great Central Asian rivers flow into the Aral Sea only on maps. In reality they have long since ceased feeding water into the sea.

The water is intercepted on the way, for various land-reclamation systems.

In the '60s the sea's surface exceeded 66 000 square kilometres. Today it has shrunk by more than a third. The water level has gone down by 13 m, and the coastline has receded 70–80 km. The volume of water in the Aral basin has been reduced by 640 cubic kilometres or 60 per cent.

Because of this, water salinity has more than doubled from a level of under nine grammes per litre.

The exposed sea bed has turned into desert. According to some estimates, up to 70 million tons of salt dust rise into the atmosphere from what once was the Aral Sea bed. A dust cloud, measuring as much as 400 km by 40 km, can even be seen from space.

The level of the Aral is going down nearly a metre a year. Scientists warn that if the trend persists, by the year 2000 only a tiny salt water lake will remain.

Three million people are directly affected by the situation, and excessive use of chemicals has compounded the whole problem.

The loss of the Sea is a tragedy: jobs for fishermen and sailors will be lost and the transport network will be devastated, not to mention the growing severity of the climate.

Of course, officials from the Ministry of Land Improvement and Water Conservation can say that in 1950 only 2.9 million hectares of land were irrigated here, and now it's 7.2 million which yield more than 15 billion roubles' worth of agricultural produce. On paper this compares favourably with the 3.8 million roubles of 30 years ago. After all, the country has gained 'cotton' independence.

True enough, the country gets 95 per cent of its cotton from here and about 40 per cent of its rice. But, paradoxically, 25 years ago one kilogramme of choice rice cost 70 kopecks at local markets; now it's two roubles. Moreover, the cotton today is of poor quality.

The cause of the Aral drying up is the enormous intake of water from the Amu Darya and Syr Darya by irrigation systems in Kirghizia, Uzbekistan, Tajikistan, Turkmenistan and Kazakhstan. All are unanimous in this respect. But opinions are divided as to who is to blame for this gigantic waste of water.

Some think that the Sea was sacrificed to the one-cop system — cotton — glossing over this by saying that the entire misfortune is the inevitable price for the country's economic need for cotton fibre, a strategic material.

At the same time serious doubts are being voiced: was this million-ton cotton overkill really worthwhile if the quality has been lost?

Moreover, the water from the Aral is far from being used in an optimal way, millions of gallons has leaked into the sands.

The larger part of water diverted for irrigation does not even reach its destination.

It is estimated that over the past ten years, 84 billion cubic metres of water have been used for irrigation in the Aral Sea basin. During the same period, a total of 100 billion cubic metres has seeped through canal walls and floor into the sands (particularly the Karakum Canal); remained in bogged up lands; been discharged into closed lakes, or simply evaporated.

The more lands incorporated into the irrigation projects of the 1970s, the greater the losses.

Hydraulic engineers claimed that because of the flat terrain and river water turbidity in Central Asia there was no need to encase the canal beds in concrete or to install flumes for small streams. A terrible loss of water belied these theories.

But the squandering of water does not end here. For example, in the Syr Darya's lower reaches, up to 5.5 cubic metres of water are used to irrigate just one square metre of rice fields. Just try and imagine a column of water five and a half metres high over each square metre of soil!

But the matter is further complicated by the fact that the effectiveness of irrigation falls steeply with the salination and pollution of the water.

In their lower reaches, the Amu Darya and Syr Darya carry solutions of soil salts, defoliants, insecticides, chemical fertilisers, industrial and sanitary sewage discharges.

The greater the amount of salts, the more water has to be used to get the same crop yield.

To maintain the present volume of water, the Aral must start receiving 30–35 cubic kilometres of water per year to make up for the evaporation loss.

Important as the economic and technical sides of the problem may be, its humanitarian aspect is ever more urgent. Putting off the solution of the acute social and ecological problems until the Aral is regained would be a deception and only aggravate the critical situation. Much-needed health services and water supply facilities, roads and child-care centres, must be built in two or three years at the most — well ahead of the schedule set by the government.

The lesson of the Aral gives one more opportunity to reflect on how carefree we walk the brink of an abyss and look into it with thoughtless impertinence.

The danger is quite real: should the Aral Sea go, people will leave the land which was deprived of its name by Man himself. The earth's face will be the bleaker and the sadder, with all of us the poorer for it and the more miserable.

(Source: *Soviet Weekly*, 20 May 1989)

CHAPTER 7

The world atmospheric system – the atmosphere at work

Introduction

The atmosphere is one of the great 'realms' of planet earth, along with the hydrosphere, lithosphere and biosphere, and behaves as an open sub-system within this global system. Matter and energy enter, are stored, transferred and exit from the atmosphere to and from the other components. We experience this behaviour as weather. The atmosphere consists of a mixture of gases, moisture in gaseous, liquid and solid form, and particulate matter (solid particles). In addition to its capacity as a store, its key characteristic is its dynamism. The three-dimensional movements within this global envelope keep the energy and matter in constant motion, redistributing them across the globe, e.g. water evaporated in one place, is transported, condenses and falls as rain elsewhere.

There are long-term regularities to atmospheric movements and hence discernible patterns in regional climates, e.g. trade wind belts, monsoons, Mediterranean climates. However, the sheer complexity of the 'atmospheric engine' causes bewildering fluctuations at more local scales and over brief time-spans. It is our limited understanding of the mechanisms involved in these fluctuations which makes forecasting so difficult, even with modern satellite and computer technology.

The three primary objectives of this and the two following chapters are, firstly to look critically at the usefulness of 'means' and 'averages' in the study of weather and climate; secondly, to improve your understanding of the processes at work in the atmosphere and their results; and thirdly, to illustrate the relationships between the behaviour of the atmosphere and human activities. This chapter describes the pattern of weather events across the globe during a single year, and thus emphasises variation over space. The events described also raise the issue of the impacts of human activity upon world weather patterns, as some scientists believe that the increase in 'extreme' events – hot, cold, wet, dry – in recent years, is a sign of climatic change. Variability over differing spatial and time scales is the central theme of Chapter 8 and is applied to tropical case studies. The scales vary from medium-term trends over the African Sahel region to pulses of rain within a single convection storm. Chapter 9 concentrates upon meteorological conditions in temperate latitudes, where convection processes are less dominant than in the tropics, and atmospheric behaviour is understandable largely in terms of 'battles' for supremacy between contrasting air masses.

7.1

Spectacular cloud formation – the atmosphere at work

CASE STUDY 7.1 *That was the year that was!*

Background

The climate of a place or region is worked out by averaging weather conditions over a lengthy period of time. By studying climatic data from all parts of the world, classifications of climatic types have been constructed, e.g. Köppen, Thornthwaite. These classifications provide useful guides to general conditions. There is a danger, however, that they can lead to the impression that this is what a region's climate is always like.

One valuable way of correcting this view is to examine the weather events and meteorological conditions across the world for a particular year. As the case studies of this and the following two chapters will reveal, the fundamental understanding about weather at any scale of time or space is its variability (resources 7.2 and 7.3). The main article is a review of 1987, and puts long-term averages into perspective, by showing what can and does happen.

Guideline: Read the 1987 review with an atlas and/or textbook beside you, so that you can make regular reference to (a) at least one map of 'World Climatic Types'; (b) seasonal climatic maps, e.g. precipitation, temperature, pressure/winds; (c) location maps.

Key understandings

- Long term climatic averages are useful guides, but should be regarded critically and their limitations constantly borne in mind.

- 'Actual' weather experienced at a given time and place may vary widely from that 'expected' from examination of averages.

- The greater the variation from average conditions, the greater the likelihood that a weather event will constitute an environmental hazard.

7.2

Britain enjoys warmest year since 1659 — official

Britain has enjoyed its warmest year since records began 330 years ago, according to figures to be published this week by the Meteorological Office.

The figures, which will re-open the controversy among scientists over whether the greenhouse effect has started already, show that this year's mild Christmas has continued a trend towards warmer weather in Britain started in July 1987.

A provisional assessment of the record of temperature for central England, the oldest and most reliable nationwide guide to weather, puts the mean temperature for the year at 10.7°C, narrowly beating the previous record set in 1949 of 10.61°C.

It also shows that 1989 saw the Met Office classify all four seasons of a year as very warm for the first time this century. Provisional figures suggest that 1989 was the sunniest year since at least 1909 and the driest since 1976.

The Met Office findings come at a time when some scientists have started to challenge the idea that the world's temperatures have been rising in the 1980s.

Some have also raised serious doubts about the original greenhouse effect theory, which argues that global temperatures will continue to rise because pollution traps the heat of the sun in the atmosphere.

It has been estimated that 1989 has been the fifth or sixth-hottest year in the 20th century around the world. The top seven have all been in the 1980s.

The warm weather in Britain has continued this month with average temperatures between 0.5°C and 1.5°C above normal in most parts and 5°C higher than normal on Christmas day. The London Weather Centre yesterday forecast more of the same over the bank holiday weekend for most of Britain with a chance of rain and a short spell of sleet over western regions tomorrow or Tuesday.

The spring-like weather has confused nature. Hedgehogs have stopped hibernating, flowers and trees are in full bloom. In Birmingham a pigeon has astonished the Royal Society for the Proection of Birds by hatching eggs in a flower pot.

In Wales the Nature Conservancy Council has been assessing the effects on the countryside. "Normally, the lakes high up in Snowdonia freeze at this time of year. But both last winter and this, they have remained frost-free," said Warren Martin, the council's spokesman.

(Source: Richard Palmer, *The Sunday Times,* 31 December 1989)

Key definition: Recurrent reference is made to 'El Niño'. This is a condition where the waters of the central and eastern tropical Pacific Ocean become unusually warm (a positive temperature anomaly). It occurs every few years, and affects the atmosphere and air masses above the ocean.

As the air masses move upwards and outwards from the eastern Pacific source region, they can influence meteorological conditions across many parts of the globe. Thus 'an El Niño year' is likely to see major upsets to 'normal' weather conditions. 1987 was a moderate El Niño year, with water temperatures in the eastern Pacific only 1–2°C above normal, unlike the severe 1982–3 year when positive water temperature anomalies reached 4°C, helping to explain the disastrous African Sahel droughts of 1983–4.

Britain in August 1989

Temperatures: August was slightly cooler than July although still above average for most of the country. This keeps 1989 on course to be close to the warmest year on record. The warmest anomalies were along eastern coasts and in central and southern England. Only maximum temperatures in the west of Scotland were average or slightly cooler than average.

Rainfall: Rainfall varied in Britain from 10 per cent to more than 240 per cent of average. The wettest locations were all in Scotland, although wet weather at the end of the month also resulted in higher than average rainfall totals for north-west England. Parts of the South-west and Midlands had less than 50 per cent average rainfall for the fourth successive month.

Sunshine: The unusually sunny weather of 1989 continued into August with only parts of Scotland and North-west England less sunny than average. Eastern England and the Midlands had the best sunshine in August with more than 150 per cent of average August sunshine. After several months of very good weather, Glasgow suffered in August, receiving an average of less than four hours sunshine a day.

Scatter graph: axes showing 0% to 200% Sunnier (vertical, up) / Cloudier (down) and Drier 0% to Wetter 250% (horizontal). Labelled points: Scarborough, Nottingham, Guernsey, Douglas, Eskdalemuir, Stornaway. ⊕ Average conditions in Britain, Aug 1989.

The month in brief

Max temp 1.3°C above average
Rainfall 88% of average.
Sunshine 121% of average
Warmest: Ross-on-Wye 22.9 °C
Sunniest: Folkestone 275 hours
Wettest: Eskdalemuir (S Scotland) 231 mm rain
Coldest: Lerwick 14.5°C
Cloudiest: Stornaway 110 hours' sun
Driest: Guernsey 6 mm rain
(All average figures are based on the 1951-80 average.)
(Source: Michael Hulme, *The Guardian*, 1 September 1989)

Global highlights of 1987

Record cold in Europe

Severe winter weather during the first three weeks of January caused hundreds of deaths in Europe. A massive dome of cold air became entrenched over northern Scandinavia and northern USSR in mid-December of 1986. It migrated westward and southward so that by January 12 much of the continent was under its influence. On that day, central England had its coldest day since 1945, with London recording – 9°C. In Leningrad, USSR, temperatures dipped to – 45°C, reportedly the coldest in 250 years.

Coastal and river ice brought a halt to shipping in northern Europe. The cold was also accompanied by a major snowstorm that snarled rail and road transport in western Europe on January 11 to 13. Snow fell as far south as the French Riviera. On January 14, East Berlin recorded an all-time record low of –11°C, while Paris measured a snowfall of 14 centimeters – the fourth heaviest on record.

During the first two weeks of the month, the cold was blamed for 77 deaths in the USSR, including 48 from heating accidents and 29 from avalanches. In Poland, home fires claimed 27 lives. By the time the

cold began easing around January 19, the total reported deaths from snow and cold across Europe and the USSR neared 350.

The interior of North America was experiencing record mildness. Parts of Alberta, Canada, enjoyed the warmest January ever, with temperatures averaging up to 10°C above normal. The January warmth turned out to be part of a remarkably persistent weather anomaly. From December 1986 through June 1987, monthly average temperatures across a large area of Canada remained above normal. From December through April, readings averaged 6°C above normal in an area extending

7.4

In Leningrad (St. Petersburg), temperatures dipped to –45°C. In this photograph, you can see ice on the River Neva

from eastern Alberta to western Ontario. The relative warmth across the continent is a feature often associated with warm ocean waters in the eastern tropical Pacific Ocean, i.e. the El Niño condition.

Early in the year, heavy rains along the coast of Peru and Ecuador resulted from the El Niño, which extended from the central equatorial Pacific to the coast of South America. From January 4 to February 14, rainfall along the coast of Ecuador ranged from 200 to 800 per cent of normal, with totals of up to 600 millimeters. In April, coastal areas were again inundated with 200 to 600 millimeters of rain. Reports indicated that the El Niño disrupted the fish catch in both Ecuador and Peru.

Another typical impact of an El Niño is decreased rainfall in southern Africa, and 1987 was no exception. Hot, dry weather in southern Mozambique, especially in January and February, hurt subsistence corn crops and worsened food shortages. Similar weather conditions affected South Africa, Botswana, Zimbabwe, and Zambia from January through April.

For Botswana, this was the sixth consecutive year that dryness reduced yields. Cereal production of about 25 000 metric tons was one-half 'normal' production. In Zambia,

national corn production was 30 per cent below the previous year's, with harvest losses ranging from 50 to 100 per cent in the drought-stricken south. South Africa's corn production of about 7.4 million tons was more than 20 per cent below normal.

Dryness and fires in China

With rainfall totals in both March and April less than 50 per cent of the long-term mean, forests in the western portion of Heilongjiang Province in northeastern China became dangerously dry. A fire first reported on May 6 developed into China's worst forest fire in 40 years. Not until rain began falling on May 24 was the fire brought under control. Between the 6th and 24th, high winds and dry weather combined to spread the fire, which eventually razed 1 million hectares of land, 70 per cent of which was forest. The fire partially or totally destroyed three towns and several villages and forced the evacuation of 60 000 people. Some 200 people died in the flames.

Winter in spring

Unseasonable snow and cold hit the eastern Mediterranean countries in March and April. Italy shivered through its coldest March weather in at least 19 years. On March 16, several centimeters of snow covered

the streets of Florence. The freezing temperatures devastated Italian citrus crops, which were further damaged by the ensuing hot summer weather. The orange crop was reduced 29 per cent from 1986 levels. In Greece, severe cold in March and floods and low temperatures in April reduced the almond and citrus crops some 46 per cent. The impact of the spring freezes will be felt for years, as 5.6 million fruit trees were damaged.

Greece's heat wave

In marked contrast to the cold and wet weather in the spring, a heat wave of tragic proportions gripped south eastern Europe in late July. The most intense heat lasted from July 21 through July 27, when temperatures in Athens, Greece, rose to between 35°C and 42°C every day. With little air conditioning available, the heat led to numerous deaths in Greece – at least 700, according to media reports.

For northern and western Europe, the summer of 1987 was depressingly cloudy, cool, and wet. Many areas in Scandinavia, Britain, France, Germany, and Poland measured twice their normal rainfall from June through early August. What was too wet for people was even too wet for plants: the damp weather delayed growth and damaged crops throughout the area. Sweden's potato crop production was down 16 per cent from 1986 levels; in Finland, losses came to 42 per cent, with grain production down 34 per cent.

In the Alps, a July rainstorm triggered flooding and mud slides, killing scores of vacationers. From July 15 to 19, thunderstorms dropped 272 millimeters of rain over southern Switzerland, northern Italy, and southeastern France.

In the Lake Como district of Italy, a mud slide caused an apartment block to crash into a hotel, killing a dozen people. Across northern Italy, the death toll reached at least 40. In France, mud slides killed some 30 people at a campsite in the south east.

Tragedy in South America

Mud slides caused by heavy rains exacted a large toll on other continents. In northern Venezuela on September 6, intense rainfall triggered a mud slide on a mountain road about 55 km west of Caracas. Reports indicated that at least 200 people died when their cars were engulfed by mud. In addition, floodwaters devastated seven small towns in the area, increasing the toll to 500 dead or missing, 1000 injured, and 20 000 left homeless.

On September 27, a mud slide roared down a mountain in northern Colombia, killing at least 183 people. A week of heavy rains triggered the slide, which dumped tons of mud and rock upon some 60 houses at the base of Sugar Loaf Mountain, part of a mountain chain that surrounds Medellin.

On the other side of the Pacific basin, landslides contributed to the large death toll in South Korea from heavy rains during July. At least 250 people died, including 123 from the effects of Typhoon Thelma on July 15. On October 24 and 25, Typhoon Lynn smashed into Taiwan, causing floods and landslides that claimed 26 lives.

Summer drought in southern Asia

A warming of the eastern Pacific Ocean is often accompanied by drought in southern and southeastern Asia, and this year was no exception. The Indian southwest monsoon arrived late and brought erratic rains to many areas. June-through-September rainfall totaled as little as 50 per cent of normal in northwestern India and northern Pakistan.

The effect on water supplies and crops was dramatic. India's rice production was forecast to drop 22 per cent from 1986 levels, with peanut production down 26 per cent. Dry weather also affected

harvests in Kampuchea, Laos, Thailand, the Philippines, and Indonesia. Rice crops were forecasted to be the least productive in seven years in Thailand, where Bangkok's July rainfall of 32 millimeters was 18 per cent of normal.

In sharp contrast, there was excessive rainfall from July to September in eastern Nepal, northeastern India, and Bangladesh. As is often the case when heavy rains fall over the Gangetic River basin, the flood damage downstream in Bangladesh was catastrophic. One-third of the country's land was flooded, affecting over 23 million people and damaging more than 1 700 000 houses. The news media reported 1100 deaths in Bangladesh, and more than 25 000 cattle drowned.

Another in the long list of weather tragedies during the summer of 1987 was drought in Ethiopia. Rainfall less than one-half normal in northern Ethiopia during June and July resulted in reduced subsistence crop production in areas not yet fully recovered from the famine of 1984–85.

To the west, the hot and dry summer in the Sahel – especially in Niger and parts of Sudan and Chad – reduced cereal yields following two years of relatively good rainfall. The drier climate which began affecting this region in the late 1960s seems to continue.

In southern Africa, on the other hand, a late September rainstorm caused enormous damage. September is at the tail end of the winter dry season in the Republic of South Africa, so heavy rains are rare this time of the year. On September 27 through 29, continuous heavy rains pelted the southeast coast, bringing 337 millimeters of rain to Cape St. Lucia and 298 millimeters to the city of Durban. The resulting flooding in Natal province left 184 dead and thousands homeless.

The Edmonton tornado

On Friday, July 31, an eastward-moving cold front colliding with warm, unstable air initiated severe thunderstorms in Alberta, Canada. The storms spawned a tornado that devastated eastern parts of Edmonton. The tornado toppled transmission towers, blew a giant oil storage tank a distance of nearly 300 metres, and tossed cars around like toys. Twenty-seven people lost their lives, 300 were injured, and estimated property losses exceeded $200 million.

England's great October storm

The British Isles often feel the brunt of storms that intensify over the North Atlantic and move rapidly eastward. This storm, however, was exceptional. On the night of October 14, a wave formed on the polar front several hundred kilometers west-north-west of Spain.

To British meteorologists, the developing low-pressure system seemed similar to the other lows that had recently been swept up by strong westerly winds aloft and brought rain and moderate winds to the British Isles. This low, however, intensified explosively as it tracked towards southern England on Thursday, the 15th. Late Thursday night hurricane-force winds struck England without warning. In London winds gusted up to 151 kmph – the strongest ever recorded in the capital. Gusts reached 177 kmph on the island of Guernsey off England's southeastern coast.

Transportation was paralyzed across the southern third of England as fallen trees blocked roads. The wind also knocked down buildings and hundreds of kilometers of power lines. Millions of people in London and surrounding counties were without power for several hours. Though electricity was restored in time for most Londoners' breakfasts on Friday morning, some areas in England were still without power two weeks later.

The same storm also affected Portugal, Spain and France. The death toll in western Europe reached 22, including 13 in England.

Typhoon Niña

As usual, numerous typhoons struck the Philippines this year. Unfortunately, the residents of southeastern Luzon had become accustomed to the storms and did not take the warnings for Typhoon Niña too seriously as the cyclone approached the central Philippines from the east on November 26. After the storm's winds of 206 kilometers per hour suddenly sent huge waves crashing into the coastal village of Matnog in Sorsogon Province overnight, the residents had no time to evacuate. Two hundred people from the village were killed.

At the height of the storm, more than 114 000 people in four provinces were forced to flee to higher ground. The death toll reached 360. In Manila, about 400 kilometers northwest of Sorsogon, power failed in large parts of the city, but no serious storm damage was reported.

(Source: Douglas Le Comte, 'The Weather of 1987: Global Highlights'. *Weatherwise,* 41(1), February 1988, pp.10–13.)

7.5

Hot news from the Pacific

The evidence is there for everyone to see: daffodils already in flower, cherry blossom peeping through in the parks, hedgehogs still snuffling in gardens when they should be hibernating. And that is just in Britain.

Elsewhere in the world the normal seasonal weather patterns have been turned on their heads also.

- In California the temperature has slumped to a record low of –3.3°F and an unprecedented 6in of snow fell around Hollywood. Radio stations in Los Angeles played Winter Wonderland, and gave children instructions about how to make snowmen.
- In Alaska a record low temperature of –80°F has led to normally hardy husky dogs being kept indoors out of the cold.
- In Australia the summer has been ruined by the wettest weather for 13 years.
- In China several rivers have dried up after the worst drought in 30 years.
- In France the mildest winter for 60 years has brought forest fires in southern regions.
- In Moscow normally frozen rivers and lakes have been thawing and there is still water skiing in the Baltic.

One phrase is now thrown around with abandon: the greenhouse effect. This is the widely accepted view that a build-up of certain gases in the atmosphere, principally carbon dioxide and chlorofluorocarbons, are forming a giant cover, trapping the earth's heat in much the same way as a giant garden greenhouse. The build-up of gases has come with the world's growing industrialisation: the burning of fossil fuels in power stations, the destruction of Brazilian rainforests, the use of motor cars, and the use of aerosols and refrigerating units.

Scientists agree that the greenhouse effect exists. Where they disagree is on the danger it poses to the world, and its likely impact on our weather. Those who see it as a large threat maintain that temperatures will rise by up to 5°C in the next 50 years, with disastrous consequences as the polar ice caps melt. Others hold that our temperate winter and the topsy-turvy patterns elsewhere have no connection at all with the greenhouse effect, or that if they do it will be at least 10 years before any connection can be proved.

What all sides seem able to agree on is that the immediate cause of the mild winter in Britain is an anticyclone (an area of high pressure) which has settled over Europe, and that this has its roots in what is happening in the southeast Pacific.

This section of the Pacific covers a quarter of the globe. When it is warmer than average, the effect is to increase atmospheric temperature, a phenomenon given the Spanish name El Niño (baby boy). At the moment, cold water from the ocean depths has been welling to the surface, and the knock-on effect is that the atmosphere in the area has been cooled, an effect called La Niña (baby girl). Hence the snow in California.

The Pacific's sea temperature also affects atmospheric pressure and the weather over the Atlantic. This, in turn, has a bearing on the weather in Britain by affecting the position of the Atlantic jet stream, a ribbon of high-speed air moving at between 100 and 200 knots at a height of 10km to 15km. This jet stream's position is dependent on the temperature difference between the equator and the north pole (resources 7.6 and 7.7).

The shift in this jet stream has caused an area of low pressure to pass mainly over the northernmost area of Britain. This partly explains why in western Scotland stormy weather has restricted 50 small fishing boats in Mallaig to port for almost the whole winter.

(Source: Amit Roy, *The Sunday Times,* 12 February 1989)

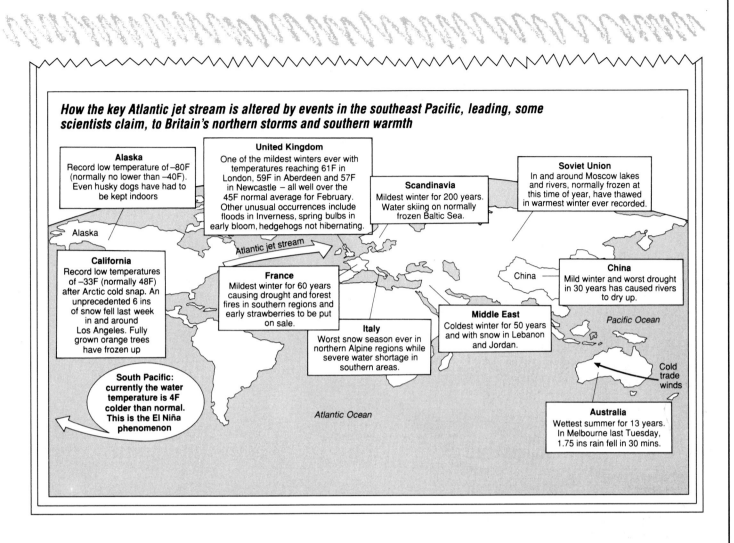

How the key Atlantic jet stream is altered by events in the southeast Pacific, leading, some scientists claim, to Britain's northern storms and southern warmth

Alaska
Record low temperature of –80F (normally no lower than –40F). Even husky dogs have had to be kept indoors

United Kingdom
One of the mildest winters ever with temperatures reaching 61F in London, 59F in Aberdeen and 57F in Newcastle – all well over the 45F normal average for February. Other unusual occurrences include floods in Inverness, spring bulbs in early bloom, hedgehogs not hibernating.

Scandinavia
Mildest winter for 200 years. Water skiing on normally frozen Baltic Sea.

Soviet Union
In and around Moscow lakes and rivers, normally frozen at this time of year, have thawed in warmest winter ever recorded.

California
Record low temperatures of –33F (normally 48F) after Arctic cold snap. An unprecedented 6 ins of snow fell last week in and around Los Angeles. Fully grown orange trees have frozen up

France
Mildest winter for 60 years causing drought and forest fires in southern regions and early strawberries to be put on sale.

Italy
Worst snow season ever in northern Alpine regions while severe water shortage in southern areas.

Middle East
Coldest winter for 50 years and with snow in Lebanon and Jordan.

China
Mild winter and worst drought in 30 years has caused rivers to dry up.

South Pacific:
currently the water temperature is 4F colder than normal. This is the El Niña phenomenon

Australia
Wettest summer for 13 years. In Melbourne last Tuesday, 1.75 ins rain fell in 30 mins.

Atlantic jet stream

Cold trade winds

Pacific Ocean

Atlantic Ocean

Alaska

China

Activities

1 Using two world outline maps locate and label on one the weather events summarised in the review. On the other, label the impacts of these events upon the environment and include their effects upon humans.

2 Describe and explain the atmospheric processes and conditions which caused any **two** of the events from different regions. In addition to the review text, refer to atlases and reference texts. One aspect to focus on is what weather conditions would be expected in that region at that time of year

and how different was this particular event. (Note: If you are part of a group, why not decide among yourselves, which events to explore, so that you can exchange information?)

3 Scientists are suggesting that 'extreme' weather events are becoming more common across the globe. Certainly, the months of the 1988–89 northern hemisphere winter produced some highly unusual conditions (resources 7.5 and 7.6).

a Make lists of places with unusual mildness; coldness; wetness; dryness. Are there any patterns?

b Summarise the possible reasons given why these may be signals of a longer-term shift in global weather and climatic patterns.

4 **Suggestion for an on-going project:** Throughout your study year, build up a wall chart of weather events reported from around the world, noting dates, locations and what happened. You could hold monthly discussions to review these events, and in this way assemble useful case studies. An alternative format would be to build up a data-base on a 'micro'. This is especially valuable if you have access to satellite imagery reception.

7.6

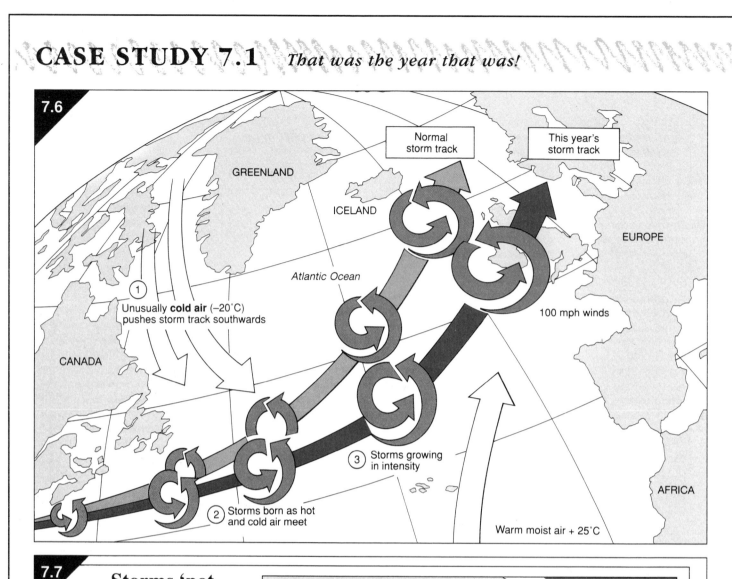

Normal storm track

This year's storm track

GREENLAND

ICELAND

EUROPE

Atlantic Ocean

① Unusually **cold air** (−20˚C) pushes storm track southwards

100 mph winds

CANADA

③ Storms growing in intensity

AFRICA

② Storms born as hot and cold air meet

Warm moist air + 25˚C

7.7

Storms 'not unprecedented'

The occurrence of two severe storms across large areas of Britain within a month, is unusual but not unprecedented.

On average around five or six depressions with very low central pressure will affect the North Atlantic each winter.

'What is unusual is the combination of a southerly track of these depressions and development of maximum intensity as they cross the country.'

The windiest weather for 30 years was recorded in the two weeks after the storm of January 25, and February as a whole will undoubtedly turn out to be exceptional.

(Source: Nigel Williams, *The Guardian*, 27 February 1990)

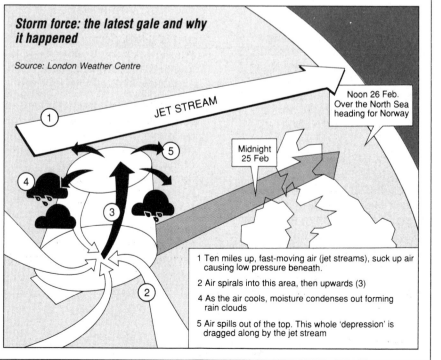

Storm force: the latest gale and why it happened

Source: London Weather Centre

JET STREAM

Noon 26 Feb. Over the North Sea heading for Norway

Midnight 25 Feb

1 Ten miles up, fast-moving air (jet streams), suck up air causing low pressure beneath.

2 Air spirals into this area, then upwards (3)

4 As the air cools, moisture condenses out forming rain clouds

5 Air spills out of the top. This whole 'depression' is dragged along by the jet stream

CHAPTER 8

Tropical climate and weather

Introduction

Unlike temperature, which is always present, precipitation is episodic. These episodes occur at varying timescales from long-term climatic fluctuations to pulsations within individual storms. We may also use different spatial scales, from macro-patterns across continents, e.g. as in atlas rainfall maps, to micro-distributions within individual convection storms. Studies of tropical rainforest or savanna environments make it clear that long-term averages give us only the most general clue as to what is 'adequate' in terms of water needs. Today, much more interest is focused upon medium and short-term fluctuations, and on the concepts of **intensity, variability** and **reliability** over **time** and **space**.

The principal message of these case studies is that moisture availability in hot environments varies in a complex pattern over time and space at all scales. Moisture inputs to environmental systems tend to occur in intense surges which are likely to be localised spatially and short-lived in time. Slight variations in location, timing and intensity especially of the small number of weather systems which produce the majority of the rain, may make a crucial difference between flood and drought in a region (resource 8.1). Precipitation can be seen to be highly sensitive to the strength and location of the mechanisms which energise moisture release. All lifeforms and geomorphic processes reflect this sensitivity. Human skills in water management are based on reconciling spatial and temporal maldistribution, and defending against extremes of flood and drought.

8.1

Flooding in Calcutta, India, during the monsoon

Key understandings

◆ 'Precipitation and water balance are by far the most important and sensitive ingredients of climate in the tropics. The whole range of human activities depends upon an adequate supply of water. Yet this is exactly what is not realised over a very large fraction of the tropical continents and islands.'

◆ 'It almost never rains in a cumulus regime, in contrast to the climates with stratus precipitation in higher latitudes!'

◆ 'The raininess of a particular season depends on whether or not a few events with very large precipitation will occur.'

(Source: H Riehl, *Climate and weather in the Tropics,* Academic Press, 1979 (pp 81, 108, 119))

CASE STUDY 8.1 *Energy and moisture in the tropics*

Background

This first case study is really an introductory exercise to help your understanding of how tropical meteorology works. The list of key characteristics is a summary which you can build on by reference to notes and text books if necessary. The activities based on resources 8.2–8.6 then provide you with an opportunity to check your understanding.

Activities

1 In what ways do the materials in resources 8.2 to 8.6 illustrate the key characteristics of tropical rainfall and its implications for human activities?

2 Read again the list of key characteristics of tropical meteorology. How do these characteristics help to explain the events of resource 8.1?

3 For the weather stations of resource 8.4, what are the approximate dates of the overhead sun? Is there a relationship between rainfall and the overhead sun?

Key characteristics of tropical meteorology

◆ Many books published until quite recently, have oversimplified tropical climates. As the data base improves, from weather stations and satellite imagery (resource 8.2), the true complexity and variety of tropical climates is becoming apparent.

◆ An easterly circulation dominates. These lower and middle tropospheric Easterlies, popularly known as the NE and SE Trades, are often overlain by westerly airstreams in the upper troposphere, in places sufficiently concentrated and vigorous to be called a 'jet stream'.

◆ The twin Hadley cell structure dominates, with converging and ascending air near the equator, and descending, diverging air over the sub-tropical deserts (resource 8.3).

◆ The inner zone of convergent air, known as the equatorial trough, or inter-tropical convergence zone (ITCZ), provides the source of the majority of the precipitation. Because of the contrasting distribution of land and sea in the Northern and Southern hemispheres, the average position of the equatorial trough is 5°N.

◆ The Hadley cells, the ITCZ and the Trade belts swing North and South, following the zone of maximum radiation, i.e. the overhead sun, through the year. This swing controls the seasonality of precipitation and temperature, with maxima occurring 1–2 months after the passage of the overhead sun.

◆ The seasonal rhythm of precipitation in a particular region is determined by the passage of the ITCZ. An inner equatorial zone has twin maxima, following the equinoxes, while an outer envelope is more likely to record a single rainfall maximum (resource 8.4). The length of the rainless season increases as one approaches the sub-tropical high pressure systems.

◆ If altitude is taken into account, precipitation tends to decrease away from the equator. Notice, however, that there may be a zone of slightly lower totals around the equator itself.

◆ Convection processes and hence cumuliform clouds dominate, leading to intense pulses of rain rather than steady, protracted falls.

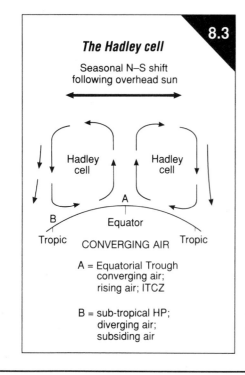

The Hadley cell 8.3

Seasonal N–S shift following overhead sun

Hadley cell   Hadley cell

A

B   Equator

Tropic   CONVERGING AIR   Tropic

A = Equatorial Trough converging air; rising air; ITCZ

B = sub-tropical HP; diverging air; subsiding air

8.2

Cloud belts over West Africa

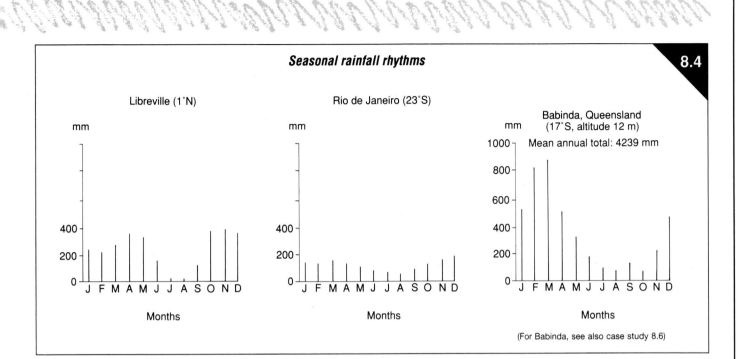

Seasonal rainfall rhythms

8.4

Libreville (1°N)

Rio de Janeiro (23°S)

Babinda, Queensland
(17°S, altitude 12 m)
Mean annual total: 4239 mm

Months

Months

Months

(For Babinda, see also case study 8.6)

8.5

TV report, 13.2.84

'The State of Maputu in Mozambique has been hit by a tropical cyclone which caused two days of intense rainfall. This has culminated in the major rivers flooding and what an observer calls 'a wall of water up to 40 ft high' sweeping across the flat landscape, flooding approximately one third of the state. This follows five years of the most severe drought much of Southern Africa, including Mozambique, has experienced in the past 50 years. Thus, in less than a week, the famine remains as imminent but its cause has become flood, not drought.'

8.6

When the monsoon fails

The drought of 1982–83, one of the worst in recent memory, is now over in India. Bountiful monsoon rains have recharged reservoirs. The countryside is green again. The severity of drought is gauged mainly by two factors – the geographical extent of deficient rainfall areas and the degree of deficiency itself. This in turn is related to a particular area's monsoon history. For example, two previous good monsoons and a subsequent poor monsoon might not be as bad as three consecutive average monsoons. By these indices this last drought was fairly serious. Monsoon rainfall deficiency was about 50 per cent. Except for the basins of perennial rivers and their irrigation project command areas, nearly the whole of India was affected, including some hill resorts.

A particularly disturbing feature highlighted by this drought is the over-use and depletion of potable water resources, an imbalance which cannot be rectified simply by an average or good monsoon. Metropolitan cities went without. Train-loads of water had to be dispatched to slake the thirst of Madras city. Other cities too had to manage with a few minutes' supply for public taps.

A place called Cherrapunji holds the world record for the highest annual rainfall. Yet, even there, a complete turn-around can occur as it did in 1899 when only 170 mm of rain fell. Freak conditions also occur for the worse.

At the start of 1983's monsoon in June, 1270 mm of rain fell in 48 hours, double the average annual quota, and flooded vast areas of the Saurashtra region of Gujarat. Lives were lost and extensive damage was done to property, crops and cattle.

(Source: *Geographical Magazine*, February 1984, Volume LV1 (2))

CASE STUDY 8.2 *Hurricane Gilbert, September 1988*

Background

Among the most spectacular manifestations of the combination of atmospheric energy and moisture in the tropics are the violent storms known as cyclones or hurricanes. They are generated over both the Atlantic and Pacific Oceans, usually within 15° of the Equator, then moving in curving tracks, outwards across the Tropics. They are seasonal, being most common in the autumn, when ocean temperatures are at their maximum i.e after the summer passage of the overhead sun.

They vary in track, intensity and frequency. Hurricane prone regions may go unthreatened for years, then find themselves hit in successive seasons. As this case study shows, Hurricane Gilbert in September 1988 was perhaps the most powerful storm to cross the Caribbean. In September 1989, however, Hurricane Hugo was almost as ferocious although its track was different (resource 8.7).

Conditions favouring hurricane formation

- Sea surface temperatures in excess of 30°C. Convectively unstable air (no strong inversions which would prevent the growth of deep clouds).
- High relative humidity in the middle troposphere.
- Little change of the horizontal wind with increasing height (low vertical wind shear).
- An existing cyclonic rotation (counterclockwise in the Northern Hemisphere) of the winds in the lower troposphere.

Hurricane Gilbert

The September 1988 Hurricane Gilbert was described by meteorologists at the US National Hurricane Center in Miami as the most intense western-hemisphere tropical cyclone on record. Large areas of Jamaica were devastated and the country's Prime Minister, Edward Seaga, pronounced it the worst natural disaster ever to strike his country. Greatest loss of life, however, occurred in Mexico where Gilbert hit twice, first of all traversing the Yucatan Peninsula and two days later making landfall some 150 km south of the border with the USA, finally dissipating near the city of Monterrey.

During its most intense phase at the western end of the Caribbean Sea,

---

Key understandings

- ◆ Tropical disturbance – a convectively active region with wind speeds of 20 knots or less and no more than one closed pressure contour at the surface.

- ◆ Tropical depression – maximum wind speed between 20 and 34 knots and two or more closed pressure contours at the surface.

- ◆ Tropical storm – maximum wind speed between 34 and 64 knots.

- ◆ Hurricane – maximum wind speed greater than 64 knots.

Carolina flees Hugo's approach

Hurricane Hugo ploughed into the coast of South Carolina last night, with its 125 mph winds blowing across a 200 mile front, spawning tornados, causing widespread floods and smashing beachfront properties.

Hugo was continuing to gain in strength and speed as it approached the American mainland, tearing down on the barrier islands at 125 mph, moving at 20 mph and gaining in ferocious intensity. According to meteorologists, hurricane-force winds extended 100 miles on either side of the eye and tropical-force winds a further 250 miles. A slight northerly change of course was expected to take Hugo just north of Charleston, with Myrtle Beach and Georgetown, further up the coast, in the greatest jeopardy.

The coincidence of a high tide, due at 2 am today local time, threatened ever more severe flooding. Yesterday afternoon, Charleston harbour's water levels were already two feet above the normal high tide. Eight inches of rainfall were predicted along the coast in the 24 hours starting at 6 pm local time.

After hitting land, Hugo was expected to loop north and east, passing to the north of Augusta, Georgia, and heading for Lexington, north Carolina. Pennsylvania was also in its sights. The rest of the storm, expected to lose force over land, could reach the Washington DC-Maryland area by Sunday.

(Source: Simon Tisdall, *The Guardian*, 22 September 1989)

Hurricane Hugo

8.7

Gilbert was estimated to have a central pressure of 885 mbar, and maximum sustained winds in its circulation over 150 kt(knots), with highest gusts in excess of 175 kt. The central pressure outrivalled the 899 mbar of 1980s hurricane Allen and the 892 mbar of the Florida Keys hurricane of 1935. (Typhoon Tip in the western North Pacific reached a central pressure of 870 mbar in October 1979.)

Gilbert, at that stage an un-named tropical depression with maximum sustained winds around 30 kt, was first spotted on Thursday 8 September some 300 km east of Barbados. It brushed past Barbados and St Lucia the following day with limited wind-damage and some flooding, and was upgraded to 'tropical storm' status (mean winds 34 kt or more) and 'christened' at 1000 GMT on Saturday 10th when 300 km west-north-west of St Lucia. Hurricane Gilbert's track is shown in resource 8.8.

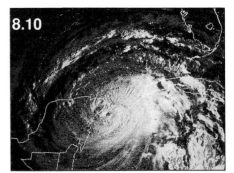
8.10

Close-up of Hurricane Gilbert in the Gulf of Mexico

8.9

Hurricane Gilbert approaching the Caribbean from Mexico

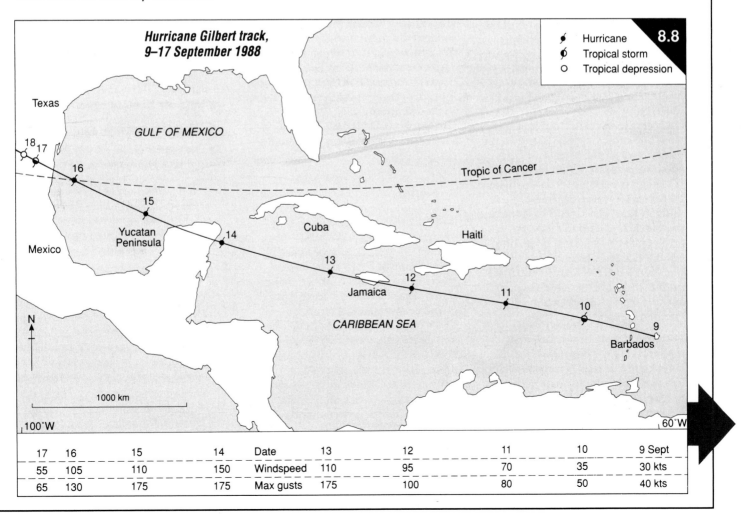

Hurricane Gilbert track, 9–17 September 1988

8.8

	Hurricane
	Tropical storm
O	Tropical depression

Texas

GULF OF MEXICO

Tropic of Cancer

18 17

16

15

Yucatan Peninsula

Mexico

14

Cuba

Haiti

13

12

Jamaica

11

10

CARIBBEAN SEA

9

Barbados

N

1000 km

100°W

60°W

17	16	15	14	Date	13	12	11	10	9 Sept
55	105	110	150	Windspeed	110	95	70	35	30 kts
65	130	175	175	Max gusts	175	100	80	50	40 kts

Gathering strength over the warm waters of the eastern Caribbean, Gilbert achieved 'hurricane' status (mean winds 64 kt or more) at 0230 GMT on the 11th, with gale force winds brushing the south coasts of Puerto Rico and the Dominican Republic. The eye of the storm travelled the length of Jamaica between 1500 GMT on Monday 12th and 0100 GMT on Tuesday 13th (Jamaica local time is five hours slow of Greenwich) so that the island was swept by the full force of the storm, first from the north and then from the south. Central pressure at this stage was estimated at 960 mbar, with maximum sustained winds of 100 kn and highest gusts 120 kt.

The US meteorologists grade hurricanes using the five-point-Saffir/Simpson Damage Potential Scale. Few hurricanes acquire Category Five status, with sustained winds over 135 kn and barometric pressure in the eye below 920 mbar. The disaster potential of such a creature is described as 'catastrophic'. Hurricane Gilbert was a Category Five storm for about 31 hours, from 1600 GMT on the 13th until 2300 GMT on the 14th, as it covered the 600 km from just south-west of Grand Cayman Island to the north coast of the Yucatan Peninsula. Maximum depth of 885 mbar was achieved at 2200 GMT on the 13th at 19.5°N 83.5'W, approximately midway between Grand Cayman and the Mexican island of Cozumel. Strongest winds of 150 kt, gusting 175 kt, occurred slightly later, between 0100 GMT and 1300 GMT on the 14th, laying waste Cozumel and the low-lying east coast of Yucatan.

With the supply of warmth and moisture cut off during its passage across the Yucatan Peninsula, Gilbert lost power by the time its eye reached the Gulf of Mexico. The weakening now ceased, but no significant renewed intensification occurred as was feared. Nor was there any significant change in course as was predicted, so the advised evacuation of the Texan cities of Galveston, Corpus Christi and Brownsville in the event proved unnecessary. However, Brownsville on the Mexican border was only 150 km north of Gilbert's eye at landfall and was thus uncomfortably close, suffering winds gusting over 50 kt, a substantial tidal surge, and 137 mm of rain. In addition, the dying hurricane spawned numerous tornadoes as far afield as the large Texan city of San Antonio.

Landfall occurred at 2200 GMT on Friday 16th on a sparsely inhabited stretch of Mexican coastline midway between Tampico and the US border; mean winds were still 105 kt and central pressure 954 mbar. Gilbert now weakened rapidly, losing 'hurricane' status about 10 hours later, and it was finally down-graded to a 'tropical depression' at 1600 GMT on the 17th, near the city of Saltillo. The centre of the storm passed about 30 km south of Monterrey, with sustained winds of 45 kn, but it was the 210 mm of rain which caused the Santa Catarina River to break its banks, claiming 200 lives in that city. With over three million people living in the mountainous Monterrey–Saltillo area, the potential for greater loss of life was mercifully not fulfilled.

Further to the Monterrey and Brownsville rainfall figures quoted above, 107 mm fell at both Beeville and McAllen in south Texas, and 68 mm fell at Corpus Christi. After Gilbert dissipated, a large residual area of middle-level warmth and moisture in the atmosphere drifted north across Texas bringing further thunderstorms and tornadoes. 118 mm of rain fell at Abilene, 74 mm at Wichita Falls, and 57 mm at Fort Worth. Subsequently, these remnants were absorbed by a temperature-latitude depression which nearly a week after Gilbert's death brought heavy rain and high winds to the British Isles.

(Source: P Eden, 'Hurricane Gilbert', *Weather*, 43(12), December 1988, pp.446-448.)

Activities

1 Approximately how quickly did 'Gilbert' move in a WNW direction?

2 Why was Jamaica swept by winds 'first from the north and then from the south'?

3 Why do forecasters expect hurricanes such as 'Gilbert' to lose power when they cross land?

4 Why did forecasters predict that 'Gilbert' would swing northwards towards Texas? (Use a textbook or atlas to find out the 'normal' tracks of Caribbean/Gulf of Mexico hurricanes.)

5 What characteristics made 'Gilbert' one of the greatest tropical cyclones on record?

6 Using resources 8.8 – 8.10, draw a sketch of the hurricane, marking on it:

   a the 'eye',

   b the direction of the spiralling air movements,

   c the path of movement,

   d the dimensions (in kilometres),

   e the length of life as a hurricane (information given in text).

7 After 'Gilbert' dissipated, how was the remaining energy used in intensifying other weather systems far away from the hurricane track?

8 If you are working in a group, then organise yourselves to complete both of these tasks. If you are working alone, then either task will suffice.

   a Produce a wall-chart built around a large version of the map (resource 8.8), showing the diary of hurricane Gilbert, i.e. label the map with the life history events given in the article.

   b Produce a set of weather reports for radio newscasts for each day from 9th to 17th September.

CASE STUDY 8.3 *Seasonal rainfall rhythms and water budgets – Sri Lanka*

Background

The essential purpose of water management schemes is to control and modify natural water budget fluctuations to suit human needs and policies, i.e. to change an erratic water source to a stable supply.

This Sri Lanka case study (resource 8.11) illustrates these principles, by exhibiting rapid variations of water availability over time and space, and by suggesting implications for stream-flow, weathering and for management policies.

Variations across Sri Lanka

Sri Lanka (6°– 10°N) is dominated by strong seasonality in precipitation inputs. The **wet zone** of resource 8.11 consists of drainage basins with a water surplus regime throughout the year. This mountainous southwest receives most rain from the summer (SW) monsoon, giving totals in excess of 3000 mm/year. The rest of the island, the **dry zone**, consists of drainage basins where seasonal water deficits are widespread. Much of the rainfall of this zone occurs during the northerly winter monsoon.

On resource 8.11 Dimbula illustrates the wet zone, while other stations show how the length and severity of the water deficit periods vary across the dry zone. Note: water deficiency, or negative water balance, exists at a station whenever PE is greater than P. Notice too, how deficiencies are made up at different stages of the dry season. In the first part of the dry season, the deficiency is reduced by drawing on moisture stored at and below the surface i.e. the 'soil moisture utilisation' element. However, where the dry season is long, this reserve becomes exhausted and the drought is intensified, e.g. wilt and dormancy become the responses to plant stress. It follows that when the rains do arrive, one of their early tasks is to restock the store, i.e. the 'soil moisture recharge' element, before the period of genuine water surplus can be said to have arrived.

Activities

1   For each of the five regions of the dry zone, use the graphs to describe their moisture budget rhythms through the year.

2   The government has asked you, as a hydrologist, to prepare a brief report on the water needs of Sri Lanka, and the implications for water storage and irrigation. Your report should (a) illustrate the basic understanding that water deficits tend to increase outwards from the southwestern and central regions; (b) indicate which regions are in greatest need of water storage and irrigated agriculture. (Use atlases and reference texts to help you with background, e.g. population distribution; existing agriculture.)

Key understandings

◆ Seasonality of precipitation means that for any area, such as a drainage basin, the volume of water stored at the surface, in the regolith, within plants and animals, varies through the year. We can think of this in terms of a **moisture budget**: the balance at a given time may be defined as the relationship between water supply (input) from precipitation, and water need as measured by **potential evapotranspiration** (output). Additional supply may be available from the soil moisture store, and when this is taken into account, the net balance can be estimated.

◆ **Water surplus** – when demand (need) can be supplied from rainfall and soil moisture store without diminishing that store.

◆ **Water deficit** – when demand (output) is greater than the supply available (input) from the combined sources, i.e. the store is diminished.

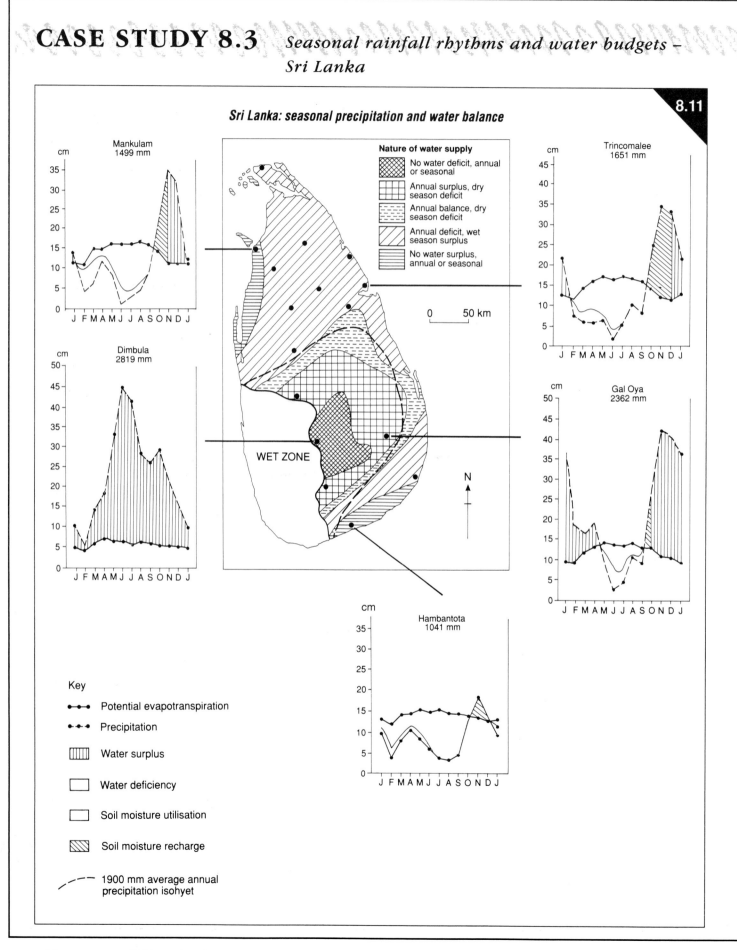

8.11

Sri Lanka: seasonal precipitation and water balance

Mankulam
1499 mm

Dimbula
2819 mm

Nature of water supply

No water deficit, annual or seasonal

Annual surplus, dry season deficit

Annual balance, dry season deficit

Annual deficit, wet season surplus

No water surplus, annual or seasonal

0   50 km

WET ZONE

N

Trincomalee
1651 mm

Gal Oya
2362 mm

Hambantota
1041 mm

Key

●━●━● Potential evapotranspiration

●┅●┅● Precipitation

Water surplus

Water deficiency

Soil moisture utilisation

Soil moisture recharge

1900 mm average annual precipitation isohyet

Background

The seasonality exhibited by Sri Lanka (see pages 165 – 166) is equally strongly developed throughout the Indian subcontinent. Two well-known features of the Indian summer or southwest monsoon are first, that the dates of the onset and cessation of the rains are predictable and second, that the 'break' of the monsoon moves steadily northwards (resources 8.12(a) and (b)). Ecosystem and human activity rhythms are closely adapted to this pattern. (Resource 8.13) The data in this case study questions this apparently straightforward process. Before studying the materials, check your understanding of the way the Indian monsoon system works.

Questioning the Indian monsoon

Using resource 8.12 test the following hypotheses:

- That the summer monsoon moves steadily northwards and retreats in the reverse direction.
- That the rainy season gets progressively shorter from south to north. (It may help to draw resource 8.12(b) on tracing paper, overlay it on resource 8.12(a), then shade in zones with varying lengths of wet season.)

Key understandings

The Indian summer monsoon:

◆ Arrives at varying dates

◆ Advances in a series of pulses or surges

◆ Produces widely different rainfall from year to year

◆ Is tending to arrive later each year

◆ Is increasingly unreliable as total rainfall decreases.

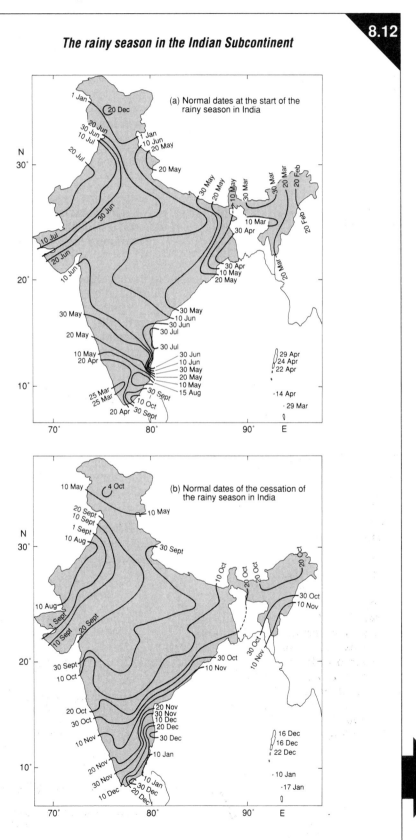

8.12

The rainy season in the Indian Subcontinent

(a) Normal dates at the start of the rainy season in India

(b) Normal dates of the cessation of the rainy season in India

Your study of resource 8.12 will have shown a complex pattern. Detailed analysis allows the generalisation of resource 8.14 to be made: the Indian monsoon progresses generally northwards but in three main pulses. What is equally significant, however, is the trend shown by the graphs of resource 8.15. The summer monsoon seems to be arriving later each year. This trend has serious environmental implications, for any region with a prolonged dry season adapts its rhythms to the arrival of the rains, e.g. plant germination, animal reproduction, tilling and planting by farmers. The advance of the monsoon is believed to be related to the size of the Eurasian winter snow cover, and especially to the Himalayan snowpack. There is evidence that over the past three decades, despite global fears of warming from the 'greenhouse effect', the northern hemisphere has been getting a little cooler. This has meant heavier snowfalls, lying longer, thereby delaying the northward swing of the monsoon. Furthermore, the variability of the rainfall when it does arrive, increases as length of rainy season decreases.

From this critical review of the monsoon, it is possible to identify a set of rainfall regions, each with its own agricultural potentials. These are summarised in resource 8.14.

(Sources: adapted from: (i) N. Singh, 'On the duration of the rainy season over different parts of India', *Theoretical and Applied Climatology*, 37,1986, pp.51-62.); (ii) I. Subbaramayya et al, 'Variations in the onset of the summer monsoon over India', *Meteorological Magazine*, 116,1987, pp.309-316.); (iii) V.M. Meher-Homji, 'On the Monsoons of Tamilnadu', *Indian Geographical Journal*, L(1), June 1975, pp.25-30.)

From the diary of a traveller

The monsoon hijacked every conversation. People kept seeing signs. One man told me that he had observed partridge feather clouds, another sparrows bathing in the dust. both were considered propitious.

I hadn't known sun like this before. It penetrated the crown of the head and imploded in the brain so that you got dazzle inside you as well as out. Even the smallest movement activated the sweat glands. They soaked clothes and flooded shoes; walking became a mushy business, like treading grapes. The temperature was 42 degrees but felt higher.

The stress was taking its annual toll. On 29 may a scolding husband drove his 32-year-old wife to suicide at the village of Vilappiplsala; according to the *Indian Express*, 'she hanged herself at the end of a sari from a tree-top'. At the groundnut oil town of Amreli, a clash between cart-pullers and shopkeepers left two dead and nine injured. In Attingal a man named Nirmal Kumar was stabbed to death by bus neighbours. Four died during Punjab riots and, in Bihar, a massacre claimed forty-one victims.

'All is normal,' a man remarked to me in a coffee house. 'But those who survive the days must then survive the nights. They are the worst. Sleep becomes so difficult we dream with our eves open'.

(Source: Alexander Frater, *Chasing the Monsoon*, Viking, 1991)

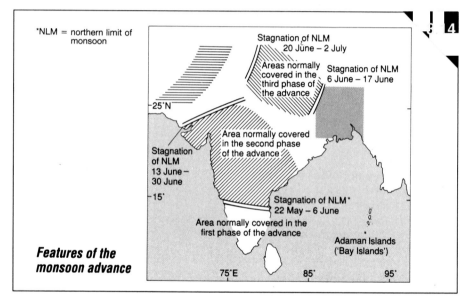

*NLM = northern limit of monsoon

Stagnation of NLM 20 June – 2 July

Areas normally covered in the third phase of the advance

Stagnation of NLM 6 June – 17 June

Area normally covered in the second phase of the advance

Stagnation of NLM 13 June – 30 June

Stagnation of NLM* 22 May – 6 June

Area normally covered in the first phase of the advance

Adaman Islands ('Bay Islands')

Features of the monsoon advance

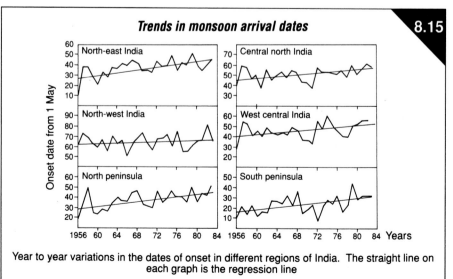

Trends in monsoon arrival dates

8.15

Year to year variations in the dates of onset in different regions of India. The straight line on each graph is the regression line

8.16

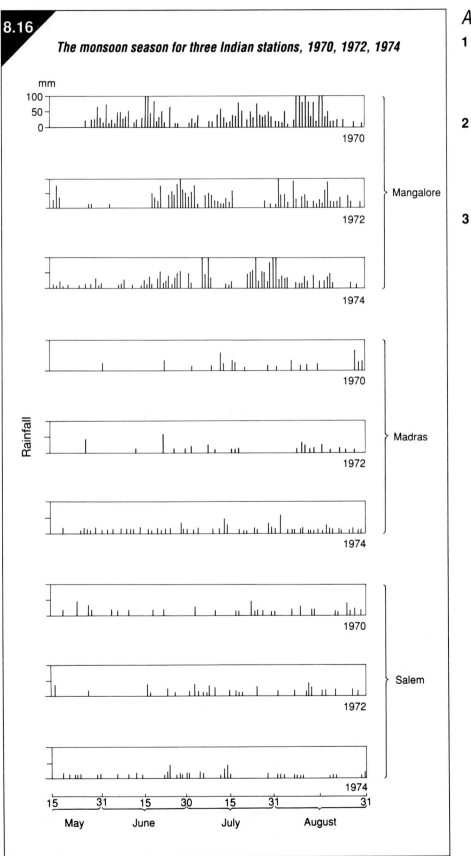

The monsoon season for three Indian stations, 1970, 1972, 1974

Activities

1 Use resource 8.15 to analyse (a) the variability of the monsoon arrival dates and (b) how much later the monsoon rains are now arriving.

2 Using resources 8.12, 8.15 and 8.16 identify with a partner which parts of the subcontinent endure the greatest environmental hazards. Give your reasons for this.

3 Use the graphs of resource 8.16 to answer the following:

a What does the concept of 'reliability' mean in relation to the Indian summer monsoon

b If you were a farmer relying on the arrival of the rains to plant and grow your crops, in which year would you have done (i) best, (ii) worst, and why?

c How is the answer to (b) affected by where you live?

CASE STUDY 8.5 *Diurnal rhythms of precipitation –*

Background

Two common perceptions of tropical rainfall are firstly, that most precipitation occurs in heavy afternoon downpours, and secondly, that during the 'wet' season at least, these rainstorms occur every day with monotonous regularity. Data from Guatemala and Fiji test the former perception, while case studies from Venezuela and Bangkok examine the latter.

Key understandings

◆ There are diurnal rhythms and regularities in tropical rainfall, but environmental conditions cause significant local variations and make generalisations dangerous.

◆ In humid tropical environments, the majority of rainfall tends to occur in a small number of intense downpours.

Part I: Guatemala city

Location: 14°N; altitude 1501 m; at the end of a N–S depression between volcanic ranges rising to 3000 m.

The wet season begins in May (resource 8.17(a)), following the movement northwards of the ITCZ to a position just off the south coast of Central America. By late October, when the ITCZ moves away equatorwards, 95 per cent of the annual rainfall has been received, most arriving from the Pacific side. Caribbean air provides significant precipitation in this area only when easterly disturbances within the North East Trades cross Central America.

Resource 8.17(b) supports the claim for afternoon rainfall maxima. Throughout the wet season, peak amounts occur between 1400 and 1800 hours, with very little falling between dawn and midday. There are, however, significant falls throughout the evening, (i.e. well after sunset) and the removal of

incoming solar radiation to energise convective instability. The afternoon peak coincides with the period of maximum surface and lower atmosphere heating typical of tropical landmass conditions. The prolongation through the evening seems to be related to Guatemala city's location in the lee of a mountain mass.

(From: D B Frost, 'Diurnal precipitation patterns at Guatemala City, 1930–1969', *Singapore Journal of Tropical Geography*, 3(1), 1982, pp.1–15.)

Activity

Draw a labelled diagram to explain the diurnal pattern of rainfall in Guatemala.

Part II: Nandi Airport, Fiji

Location: 18°S; altitude 16 m; on the western, leeward side of the largest island of the Fijian group, Vitu Levu, 1880 mm mean annual rainfall.

Fiji has two well-defined seasons: a dry season (May–October) and a wet season (November–April). In the dry season the subtropical anticyclones move slowly eastwards immediately to the south of the islands, bringing a persistent South East airflow of dry, stable air. Approximately 25 per cent of the annual rainfall falls during this 'dry' season. It occurs in irregular episodes from bands of clouds associated with upper tropospheric troughs which weaken the anticyclonic circulation. In the wet season the subtropical high pressure systems move further south exposing Fiji to the disturbed weather conditions and convective instability along the South Pacific component of the Monsoon Trough (ITCZ).

Resource 8.18(a) confirms the general hypothesis of an afternoon rainfall peak, with over 50 per cent

of the total occurring between 1200–1800 hours, and 10 per cent during the single hour, 1500–1600. The 3 per cent or so which falls in other individual hours represents the 'baseline' contributions from larger-scale weathering-producing systems. Their passage across Fiji is unlikely to be tied to particular hours of the day, e.g. the high level troughs in the South East Trades, and the deeper disturbances along the ITCZ.

On Fiji, the afternoon maxima are enhanced by the air/land/sea interactions which create the well-known land and sea breeze rhythm (resource 8.18(d)). This mechanism is a specialised version of the solar radiation cycle and is common in island and coastal environments. The extent and strength of the process is limited by the shallow depth of the circulation cell.

(Source: S K Sharma, 'Diurnal variation of rainfall at Nandi Airport, Fiji', *Weather*, 38(8), 1983, pp.231–239.)

Activities

1 Using resource 8.18(b), compare the contribution of the afternoon precipitation in the wet and dry seasons.

2 Using resource 8.18(c), explain why atmospheric pressure falls during the afternoon peak precipitation period. (Base your answer on the convection cell model.)

8.17

Guatemala City: seasonal and diurnal rainfall regimes

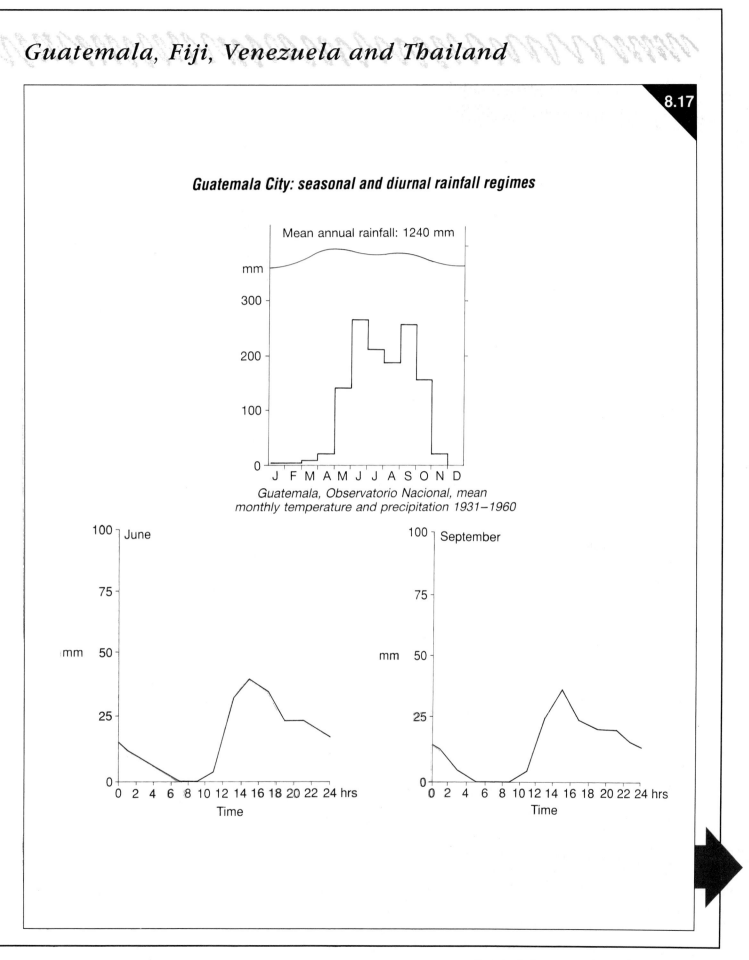

Mean annual rainfall: 1240 mm

*Guatemala, Observatorio Nacional, mean
monthly temperature and precipitation 1931–1960*

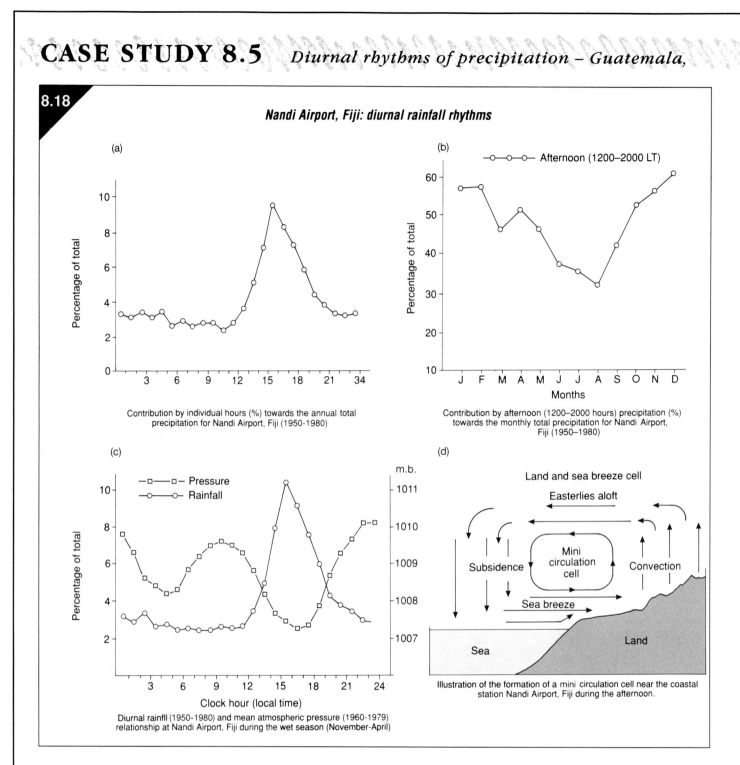

8.18

Nandi Airport, Fiji: diurnal rainfall rhythms

(a)

Contribution by individual hours (%) towards the annual total
precipitation for Nandi Airport, Fiji (1950-1980)

(b)

—o—o— Afternoon (1200–2000 LT)

Contribution by afternoon (1200–2000 hours) precipitation (%)
towards the monthly total precipitation for Nandi Airport,
Fiji (1950–1980)

(c)

—□—□— Pressure
—o—o— Rainfall

Diurnal rainfll (1950-1980) and mean atmospheric pressure (1960-1979)
relationship at Nandi Airport, Fiji during the wet season (November-April)

(d)

Land and sea breeze cell

Easterlies aloft

Subsidence

Mini circulation cell

Convection

Sea breeze

Sea

Land

Illustration of the formation of a mini circulation cell near the coastal
station Nandi Airport, Fiji during the afternoon.

Part III: Rainfall concentration. The examples of Venezuela and Thailand

Venezuela has a mean rainy season length of 100 days. Main rainstorm episodes last from one to nine days, with an average of two days, and produce 75 per cent of the total precipitation. The remainder comes from irregular, lighter falls. Resource 8.19(a) shows that in 1969, there were 14 rain episodes, but two of these delivered 50 per cent of the total. If we focus on one month, in one particular area, the episodic pulses can be even more dramatic. Resources 8.19(b) and (c) summarise the pattern for the unusually wet month of June 1969 in the Lago de Valencia district of N.C. Venezuela. The mean June rainfall is 115 mm, with June 1969 producing 200 mm, yet 75 per cent of this was amassed by only four episodes. On most other days there was only a brief shower.

(Source: H Riehl, *'Climate and weather in the Tropics'*, Academic Press, 1979.)

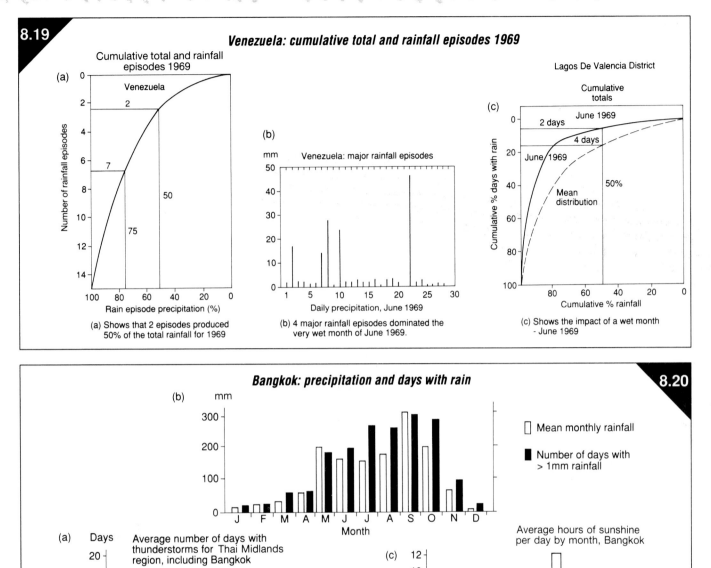

8.19

Venezuela: cumulative total and rainfall episodes 1969

(a) Cumulative total and rainfall episodes 1969

Venezuela

(a) Shows that 2 episodes produced 50% of the total rainfall for 1969

(b) Venezuela: major rainfall episodes

(b) 4 major rainfall episodes dominated the very wet month of June 1969.

(c) Lagos De Valencia District

Cumulative totals

June 1969

Mean distribution

(c) Shows the impact of a wet month - June 1969

Bangkok: precipitation and days with rain **8.20**

(b)

☐ Mean monthly rainfall

■ Number of days with > 1mm rainfall

(a) Average number of days with thunderstorms for Thai Midlands region, including Bangkok

(c) Average hours of sunshine per day by month, Bangkok

Activities

1 Use the information for Venezuela and Bangkok (resources 8.19 and 8.20) to test the following hypotheses:

- Even at humid tropical stations, significant rainfall does not occur every day.
- The majority of the precipitation is supplied by a small number of major episodes.

2 Use resource 8.20(a) to answer the following:

a Estimate the mean annual rainfall of Bangkok.

b How long is the 'wet' season, i.e. months with more than 100 mm precipitation?

c Which is the wettest month?

d On how many days in each month during the wet season does significant rain fall? What is the highest figure?

3 How does the information on resources 8.20(a) and (b) suggest that most of the rainfall is in intense convection storms?

Background

Most tropical precipitation results from vigorous convection processes at work within warm, unstable air masses. The combination of heat, abundant moisture and available energy can produce an almost incredible intensity of rainfall, especially when the convection currents are boosted by orographic uplift. Storms vary in scale from individual convection cells covering perhaps 25 sq km, through to synoptic-scale disturbances of clusters of cells along the ITCZ and spreading over hundreds of square kilometres to the violent spirals of tropical cyclones such as Hurricane Gilbert, illustrated on pages 162 – 164. Whatever scale the storm, the precipitation is based upon the complex structure of individual convection cells which are seen as cumulonimbus clouds, and contain tubes of vigorous updrafts and downdrafts of air (resource 8.21).

The Babinda weather station (17°S) from which the data in this case study are taken, lies at 20 m above msl., in an experimental reserve of tropical rainforest, backed by a mountain range over 1200 m (resource 8.22), approximately 50 km south of Cairns. There is a single wet season, January–March, when the monsoonal trough (ITCZ)

Key understandings

◆ Tropical storms vary greatly in their size and intensity.

◆ Convection storms are made up of a complex set of cells which results in rainfall occurring as a succession of brief, intense pulses.

◆ The importance of a small number of severe storms to annual rainfall totals in the tropics.

◆ Local conditions influence the intensity and the environmental impact of storms.

8.21

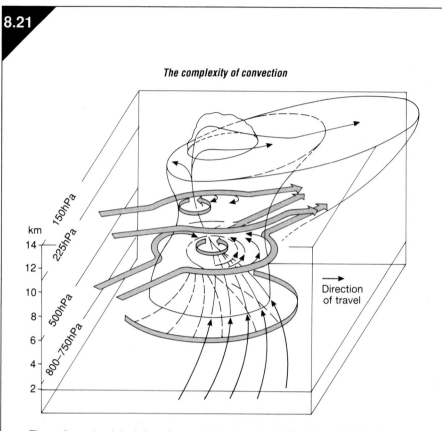

The complexity of convection

Three-dimensional depiction of a cumulonimbus cloud. The thin, solid inflowing and ascending streamlines represent the trajectory of moist air originating in low levels. The heavy dashed streamlines show the entry and descent of potentially cold and dry middle-level air feeding the downrushing and diverging downdraught. The surface boundary between the inflow and downdraught is shown as a barbed band. The internal circular arrows show the net updraught rotation.

8.22

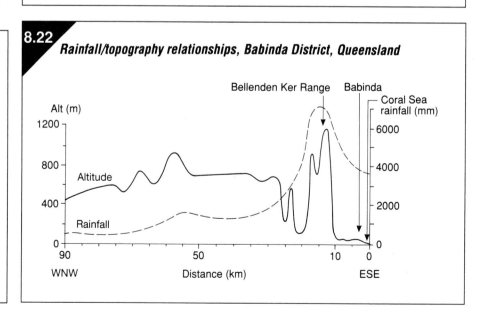

Rainfall/topography relationships, Babinda District, Queensland

reaches its most southerly limit (page 160). Tropical lows develop along this ITCZ and sometimes intensify to tropical cyclones over the Coral Sea and Gulf of Carpentaria. These well organised weather systems move on to the Queensland coast, bringing intense rains. Daily falls of more than 250 mm are common, with Babinda township having endured deluges of more than 500 mm in a 24 hour period. The intensity is clearly boosted by the mountains, as resource 8.23 shows.

The two graphs, for 19 and 20 December 1976 (resources 8.24 and 8.25 overleaf) show vividly what can happen when a cyclone arrives. The rainfall of 19 December was 'normal' for disturbances moving along the ITCZ. Each vertical line on the graph represents the rain arriving in a six minute period, and it is clear that almost all of the 24 hour total of 94.3 mm was delivered in three separate storms. Each storm consisted of a series of pulses or surges with a maximum intensity of 6 mm/6 minute period.

Resource 8.25 for 20 December, represents an 'extreme' event. Although the centre or 'eye' of the cyclone lay almost 500 km to the west, the massive convergence of warm, moist, unstable air along its eastern flank brought a violent spiralling northerly airstream along the Queensland coast. At Babinda, boosted by orographic uplift, the tropical maritime air delivered 464 mm of rain, more than 10 per cent of the year's total. Over 350 mm arrived in the six hours from 0230 to 0830 hours.

(Source: M Bonnell, and D A Gilmour, 'Variations in short-term rainfall intensity in relation to synoptic climatological aspects of humid tropical NE Queensland coast', *Singapore Journal of Tropical Geography*, 1(2), December 1980, pp.16–30.)

8.23

Babinda during the rainy season

Flooding in a deforested area, Babinda District

Activities

1   What proportion of Babinda's mean annual rainfall arrives in the January–March wet season? (Use resource 8.4 on page 161).

2   From resource 8.22, describe and explain the relationship between rainfall and topography.

3   Why should the ITCZ be at its most southerly location in January?

4   In Queensland, the 'cyclone season' is December–January yet in the Caribbean and Gulf of Mexico it peaks in September (see Hurricane Gilbert on pages 162 – 164). Why?

5   On 20 December 1976:

   a How many rainstorms were there?

   b What was the maximum intensity of rain for a six minute spell?

   c How many six minute spells showed more than 10 mm of rainfall?

6   Explain briefly how the rainfall records support the following ideas:

   • That tropical rainfall occurs mainly in intense storms.
   • That within the storms much of the rain arrives in a series of heavy pulses or bursts.
   • That these pulses can be explained by the internal structure and dynamics of cumulonimbus clouds.

7   Why should the tropical maritime airstream which caused the deluge of 20 December be:

   a 'unstable',

   b 'converging', and

   c from a 'northerly' direction?

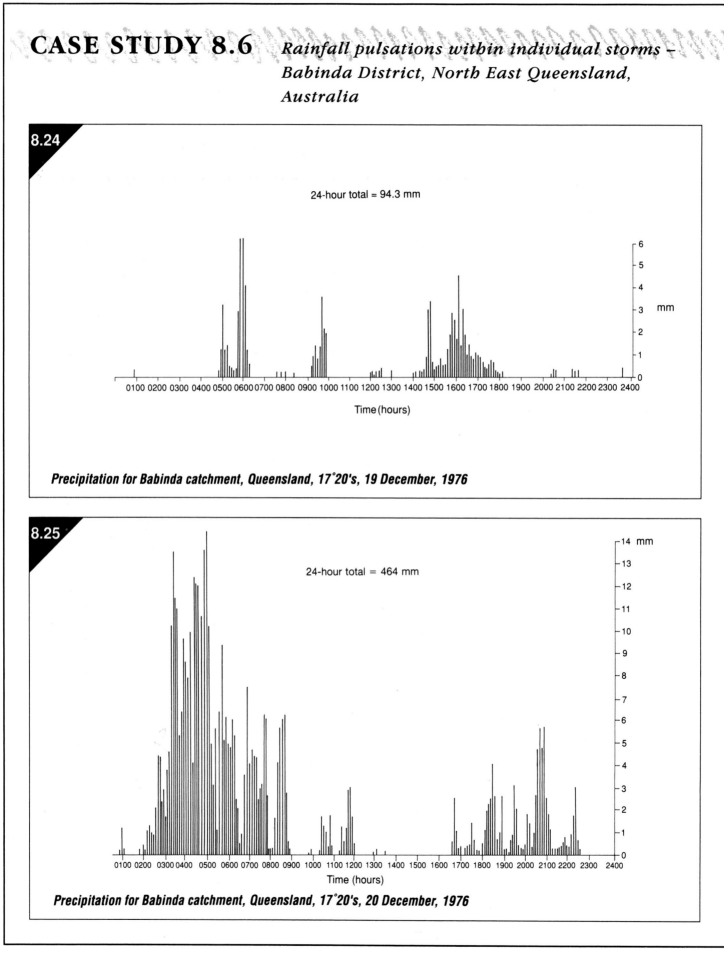

8.24

24-hour total = 94.3 mm

mm

Time (hours)

Precipitation for Babinda catchment, Queensland, 17°20's, 19 December, 1976

8.25

14 mm

24-hour total = 464 mm

Time (hours)

Precipitation for Babinda catchment, Queensland, 17°20's, 20 December, 1976

CHAPTER 9

The British Isles: 'We don't have climate, we just have weather'

Introduction

The comment above is a popular view of British conditions, because we are frequently frustrated, annoyed or discomforted by the changeability of our weather. Furthermore, even though the British Isles are fairly small, the variety of weather conditions found on any particular day can be surprising. For illustrations of these characteristics, we need look no further than our TV screens or newspapers. Resources 9.1 and 9.2 record a typical day in March, while the title of the article (in resource 9.4 on page 179) sends a direct message.

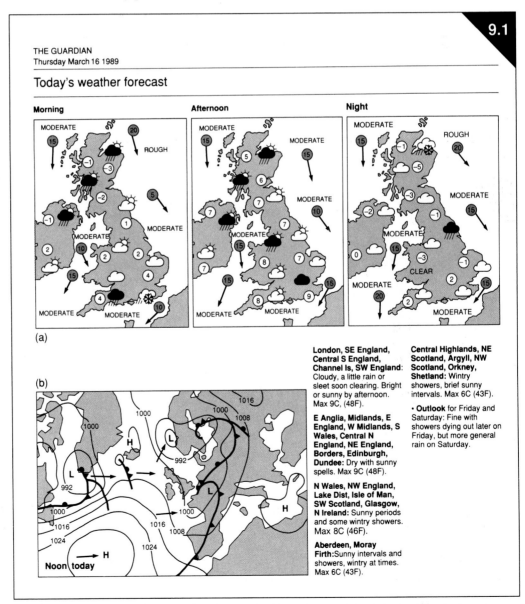

9.1

THE GUARDIAN
Thursday March 16 1989

Today's weather forecast

(a)

(b)

London, SE England, Central S England, Channel Is, SW England: Cloudy, a little rain or sleet soon clearing. Bright or sunny by afternoon. Max 9C, (48F).

E Anglia, Midlands, E England, W Midlands, S Wales, Central N England, NE England, Borders, Edinburgh, Dundee: Dry with sunny spells. Max 9C (48F).

N Wales, NW England, Lake Dist, Isle of Man, SW Scotland, Glasgow, N Ireland: Sunny periods and some wintry showers. Max 8C (46F).

Aberdeen, Moray Firth: Sunny intervals and showers, wintry at times. Max 6C (43F).

Central Highlands, NE Scotland, Argyll, NW Scotland, Orkney, Shetland: Wintry showers, brief sunny intervals. Max 6C (43F).

• **Outlook** for Friday and Saturday: Fine with showers dying out later on Friday, but more general rain on Saturday.

Yesterday's summary

Around Britain

Report for the 24 hours ended 6 pm yesterday:

	Sun-shine hrs	Rain in	Temp °C L	H	Weather (day)
ENGLAND					
Aspatria	6.9	.01	−2	7	Snow pm
Birmingham	−	.13	0	5	Sleet am
Bristol	−	.25	3	5	Rain
Buxton	−	.01	2	6	Sleet
Leeds	0.4	−	0	7	Bright
London	−	.92	6	7	Sleet pm
Manchester	0.4	−	−2	7	Bright pm
Newcastle	6.2	.06	0	7	Shwrs pm
Norwich	−	.34	4	7	Rain
Nottingham	−	.03	0	6	Rain pm
Plymouth	−	.27	6	7	Rain
Ross-on-wye	−	.26	3	6	Sleet
EAST COAST					
Scarborough	1.4	−	1	7	Bright
Bridlington	1.3	−	−1	7	Cloudy
Skegness	−	.18	2	6	Rain
Hunstanton	−	.19	1	7	Rain
Cromer	−	.19	2	6	Rain
Lowestoft	−	.28	3	7	Rain
Clacton	−	.35	6	8	Rain
Southend	−	.47	5	7	Rain
Margate	−	.41	7	8	Rain
Herne Bay	−	.56	5	7	Rain
SOUTH COAST					
Folkestone	−	.67	6	10	Rain
Hastings	0.1	.65	7	10	Rain
Eastbourne	0.3	.70	7	11	Rain
Brighton	0.1	.41	6	10	Rain
Worthing	0.2	.30	6	11	Showers
Littlehampton	−	.52	6	10	Showers
Bognor Regis	−	.35	7	10	Rain
Southsea	−	.33	6	8	Rain pm
Sandown	−	.42	7	9	Rain
Shanklin	−	.77	6	9	Rain
Ventnor	−	.70	6	10	Rain
Bournemouth	−	.72	5	7	Rain
Poole	−	.77	6	9	Sleet pm
Swanage	−	.57	6	7	Rain
Weymouth	−	.71	5	6	Rain
Exmouth	−	.57	5	6	Rain
Teignmouth	−	.67	6	6	Rain
Torquay	−	.59	6	6	Rain
Falmouth	0.1	.67	6	6	Showers
WEST COAST					
Newquay	−	.36	5	7	Showers
Saunton S	−	.53	7	5	Rain
Ilfracombe	−	.51	4	7	Rain
Minehead	−	.33	3	5	Rain
Weston-s-Mare	−	.18	3	7	Rain
Southport	0.8	.02	1	8	Hail pm
Blackpool	5.8	.02	2	8	Hail pm
Morecambe	6.0	−	2	8	Sunny
Douglas	8.3	−	1	7	Hail pm
WALES					
Anglesey	6.7	.01	3	8	Sunny
Cardiff	−	.20	2	5	Sleet am
Colwyn Bay	2.7	−	2	6	Bright
Tenby	2.0	.06	3	9	Cloudy
SCOTLAND					
Aberdeen	5.9	.17	1	6	Snow am
Aviemore	2.1	−	−2	3	Snow
Edinburgh	2.8	.02	−3	7	Hail
Eskdalemuir	5.1	.01	−4	6	Snow pm
Glasgow	7.9	.01	−4	7	Shwrs pm
Kinloss	2.8	.02	−1	6	Hail
Lerwick	6.6	.11	−1	2	Snow
Leuchars	7.7	−	−3	8	Shwrs am
Prestwick	5.8	−	−2	7	Shwrs pm
Stornoway	4.4	.19	0	4	Bright
NORTHERN IRELAND					
Belfast	8.4	.03	7	5	Hail pm

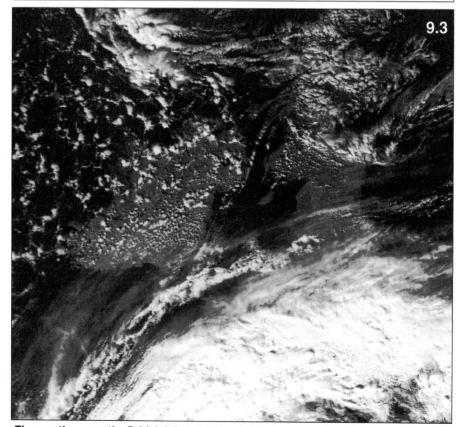

9.3

The weather over the British Isles, 16 March 1989, as seen by satellite

Weather mapping exercise

1   Select one weather station from each region on the table (resource 9.2).

2   On a large outline map of the British Isles, draw a circle (with a diameter of not more than 1 cm) at the location of each of your selected stations.

3   Add the information from the table to each station circle. (There are standard notations and conventions for plotting on synoptic weather maps. Check a reference manual such as The Meteorological Observer's Handbook, or a standard text on meteorology.) If you are unable to find the standard system, then make up your own.

4   Use the maps on resource 9.1 to:

   a add approximate wind direction, strength and pressure to your stations;

   b draw the isobars across your map. Notice that the newspaper map has an 8 mb. isobar interval. More detailed weather maps use a 4 mb. interval, so draw in as accurately as possible, the 996 and 1004 mb. isobars on your map.

5   Write a brief description of the weather situation shown by your map and the satellite photo (resource 9.3) and attempt to explain these conditions.

6   Use resource 9.1(b) to explain the 'Outlook for Friday and Saturday'. (The arrows on resource 9.1(b) indicate the direction of movement of the main pressure systems.)

7   **Project suggestion:** you could carry out similar exercises on a weekly basis for, say a month, and build up an account of the weather. You should include a description and an interpretation of the weather in terms of pressure systems, air masses, atmospheric processes, variations from 'norms', impacts on human activities etc. If you have access to satellite imagery reception/storage, and to data-basing via a micro-system, then clearly, you can build these into

CASE STUDY 9.1 *Exploring variability*

Background

The newspaper article (resource 9.4) is brief and apparently straightforward. Yet if you read it carefully, you will realise that it raises a number of important questions about British weather, and requires you to check your understanding of the way the atmosphere works to give the weather and climate we experience. Use reference texts and other background sources to help you answer the questions below, all arising from this one article. (You may find labelled diagrams the most effective way to answer some of the questions.)

Key understandings

◆ Rapid variability over time and space are a typical feature of British weather conditions.

◆ Monthly and longer-term averages must be treated with a great deal of caution.

Activities

1 Why is the angle of the sun in the sky increasing, and why should this affect British weather?

2 Why should the North Sea water temperature be 3°C lower than those of the Atlantic South of Ireland, and why is water 'close inshore' usually cooler at this time of year?

3 Why do soil temperatures remain low except near the surface, and what effects does this have on our lives?

4 What is meant by 'polar maritime airstreams', and why do they commonly arrive from the northwest?

5 What type of airstream can bring the British Isles an early 'heatwave'?

6 List the key characteristics of March weather.

7 Explain why March is a month of 'many weathers'.

9.4

Many weathers of March

During the month of March the sun gains a good deal of height in the sky. By the Spring Equinox on or around March 21 (which can vary slightly due to Leap Years) the sun is overhead on the Equator and really quite powerful, even in Britain.

The seas around the British Isles are still cold with the Southwest Approaches at 9°C (48°F) and the North Sea at a miserable 6°C (43°F), thus barely above the winter minima. The soil temperatures, like the seas, are still low in March, particularly at a depth of a metre or so, where they are just about at their winter minimum, though in the uppermost layers a couple of sunny days can be sufficient to start seeds germinating. Water from the mains, coming from fairly deep in the ground, provides a very cold supply.

The abiding impression of March is therefore one of cold air but warm sunshine. This leads to a high frequency of cumulus clouds, which often form after a clear, sunny start to the day. By noon, lots of these 'cotton-wool' clouds may be marching across the sky. When conditions are right they may grow into cumulonimbus and give a shower.

These convective conditions are especially a feature of polar maritime airstreams from the northwest. By contrast, at the end of the month, if a southerly or southeasterly develops then something approaching a heatwave can occur as warm air from Spain and France reaches us. This happened in 1965. Winter can return very rapidly after a warm spell ('one swallow does not make a summer'), and the frequency of snow falling is still very high, especially in Scotland or the mountains of Ireland, Cumbria, or Snowdonia.

Snow lying, however, is usually more short-lived than in February, due to the more rapid melting by the sun.

Persistent fog is fairly uncommon inland on low ground. Gales are still very much on the cards – indeed this is often a windy month since the vigorous depressions of winter are still common and the sun's warmth usually prevents cold, stagnant daytime conditions. March tends to be a dry month and the combination of sunshine, wind, and low humidities will often dry out the ground surprisingly quickly.

The best known weather saying about March is 'In like a lion, out like a lamb.' Certainly, the weather tends to improve during the month, so this description is more likely to come true than not: but it can still spring a surprise, with a cold windy, northerly type of weather, even at the month's end. March is said to be a month of 'many weathers' which correctly emphasises its changeability.

(Source: Dick File, London Weather Centre, *The Guardian*, 17 March 1989)

Explaining this variability

The famous variability of British weather can be explained by an understanding of air masses, what happens when they move as airstreams and what happens when they meet and mix as frontal systems. (Check your understanding of the nature and functioning of a frontal system.) An air mass may be defined as:

'An almost homogeneous mass of air of great lateral extent, with marked horizontal temperature and humidity uniformity acquired from prolonged contact in its ... source region.'

'A large body of air whose physical properties, especially temperature, moisture content and **lapse rate** are more or less uniform horizontally for hundreds of kilometres.'

Applying this idea of air masses and airstreams to the British Isles, our weather variability becomes comprehensible: The British Isles is a battleground between different air masses, as summarised in resource 9.5. Our weather depends upon which air mass or airstream is dominant at a given time. Our more disturbed weather conditions tend to result from the churning mixture of two or three air masses in what are variously called frontal systems, mid-latitude, depressions, troughs of low pressure or low pressure systems, e.g. the 'hurricane' of 16–17 October 1987 (see also the 16–17 March 1989 data, on pages 177 – 178).

Using air masses for explanation

• **Character** As the atmosphere acquires many of its characteristics from the surface over which it lies, these characteristics are determined by (a) the nature of the source region and (b) how long the air spends over this source region. Hence the names: Polar or Tropical; Maritime or Continental, giving Pc; Pm; Tm; Tc types. An 'A' type (Arctic) may be added, for air from the polar icecap.

• **Movement** Once an air mass moves from its source region, its

characteristics are progressively modified, according to (a) the nature of the surfaces over which it passes, and (b) the route the airstream takes and the time it spends over the various surfaces. For instance, in the very cold spell of January 1987, the polar continental (Pc) air was drawn quickly and directly from its Russian source region and so was little modified when it crossed Britain as a cold easterly airstream..In contrast, in exceptionally mild winters such as that of 1988–89, Pc air rarely arrives, and when it does, it has usually passed in a lengthy arc across south-central Europe and so has been much modified i.e. warmed.

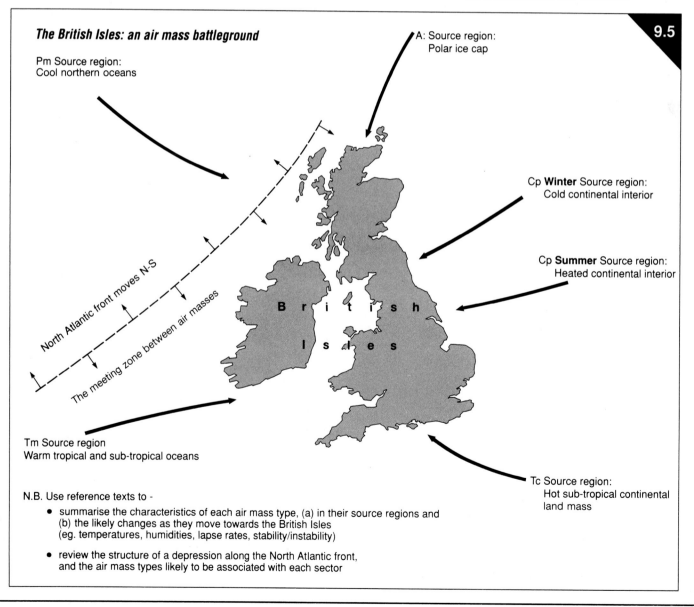

The British Isles: an air mass battleground

9.5

Pm Source region:
Cool northern oceans

A: Source region:
Polar ice cap

Cp **Winter** Source region:
Cold continental interior

Cp **Summer** Source region:
Heated continental interior

North Atlantic front moves N-S

The meeting zone between air masses

B r i t i s h

I s l e s

Tm Source region
Warm tropical and sub-tropical oceans

Tc Source region:
Hot sub-tropical continental
land mass

N.B. Use reference texts to -

• summarise the characteristics of each air mass type, (a) in their source regions and
  (b) the likely changes as they move towards the British Isles
  (eg. temperatures, humidities, lapse rates, stability/instability)

• review the structure of a depression along the North Atlantic front,
  and the air mass types likely to be associated with each sector

CASE STUDY 9.2 *Assessing the air mass battle – an example of a measure*

Background and key understandings

As we examine past weather records, can we identify how the air mass battle (see pages 179 – 180) was going in different years, and are there medium term trends? There are a variety of measures or indicators we could use, e.g. temperatures, humidities, precipitation types, cloud and sunshine amounts, wind direction and strength, atmospheric pressure. One straightforward and commonly used method to study winter conditions at least, is the use of 'frost days', i.e. the number of days in a year when the minimum temperature drops below 0°C at some time during the 24 hour period. For instance, we might draw

the conclusion that in winters which record unusually high numbers of frost days, Pc airstreams or directly drawn-in Pm airstreams tend to dominate.

Clearly, factors such as latitude, altitude, relief, aspect, proximity to the sea, vegetation cover, soil type, and urban influence all play their part, and produce local and regional variations in frost days. However, any variability in the records of individual stations from year to year may be explainable in terms of which air masses were predominant. This line of thinking will be given increased validity if a number of weather stations show similar fluctuations. The case study below

uses nine quite distinct stations: an altitude range from 15 to 242 m; from maritime (Tynemouth) to semi-rural, inland (Watnall), suburban (Manchester Ringway) and upland (Eskdalemuir).

Air masses and air temperatures

Data on frosts were extracted from the Monthly Weather Report and as these data have only been published since January 1956 it was impractical to extend the analysis over a longer time span. The period of analysis includes the severe winters of 1963 and 1979 and the run of mild

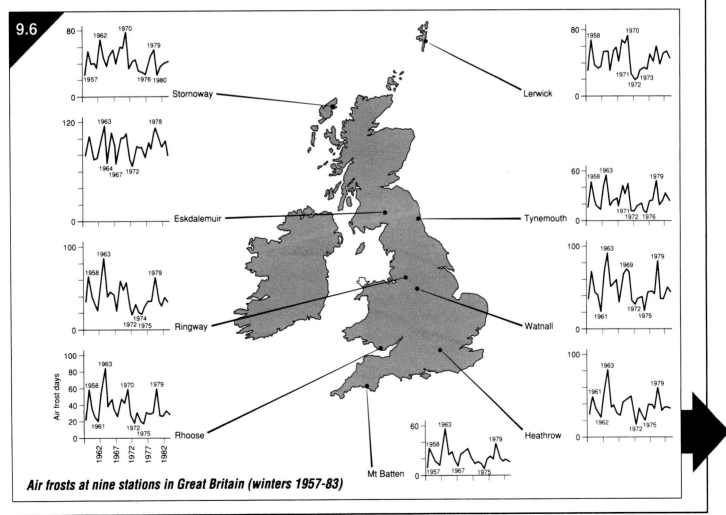

Air frosts at nine stations in Great Britain (winters 1957-83)

Statistical summary of frost data

Station and region	Altitude (m)	27 year mean No. of days	SD (±)	Maximum No. of days	Year	Minimum No. of days	Year
Eskdalemuir (Scotland W)	242	90.9	14	116	1963 1979	67	1972
Watnall (Midland Counties)	117	50.4	17	92	1963	25	1961 1975
Lerwick (Scotland N)	82	45.2	15	73	1970	19	1972
Stornoway (Scotland N)	15	44.4	14	79	1970	25	1957 1980
Manchester Airport (Ringway) (England NW)	75	40.9	15	87	1963	20	1972
Heathrow (England SE & Central S)	25	38.1	14	84	1963	5	1972
Rhoose (Wales S)	65	36.7	16	85	1963	17	1972 1975
Tynemouth (England E & NE)	30	26.5	13	58	1963	9	1976
Plymouth (Mt Batten) (England SW)	27	21.4	10	55	1963	7	1975

Descriptive statistics

The 27 year mean ranges from 21.4 frosts at Mount Batten, in the mild winter climate of the south-west, to 90.9 frosts at Eskdalemuir, situated in a clearing in Eskdalemuir Forest in the foothills of the Southern Uplands of Scotland, the only station at an altitude above 120 m (resources 9.6 and 9.7). However, even the moderate mean of Mount Batten seems high compared with the 1957–81 winter mean of 1.6 frosts for St Mary's, Isles of Scilly.

The well-exposed coastal situation of Tynemouth ensures a relatively small number of frosts but at both Stornoway and Lerwick, in spite of the maritime influence, the number of frosts is much greater. At these latter stations it is likely that the higher figure is due to the fact that air-mass temperatures are lower on average in these northern latitudes, leading more easily to frosts by slight radiation cooling. In spite of higher average air-mass temperatures, the number of frosts at Ringway and Heathrow is only slightly lower than at Lerwick, the result of a greater frequency of clear skies and light winds, conditions favourable to radiation cooling. Watnall, the

station farthest away from any maritime influence, is second only to Eskdalemuir in the number of frosts recorded. Combined with an altitude of 117 m, the more 'continental' situation and semi-rural setting to the north-west of Nottingham produces a large number of radiation frosts, resulting in a total in excess even of that of Lerwick. The doubling of altitude, and consequent lowering of average temperature levels, from Watnall to Eskdalemuir gives rise to an 80 per cent increase in frosts.

The number of frosts for each station for each year has been plotted in resource 9.7. The three years experiencing the greatest and the three years experiencing the least number of frosts have been indicated for each station. The remarkably frost-free period of the early 1970s stands out clearly at most stations. The exceptionally severe winter of 1963 produced the greatest number of frosts at seven of the nine stations, with values more than three standard deviations away from the mean in some cases (resource 9.8). However, at Stornoway and Lerwick 1970 was the most severe year, 1963 producing only four frosts more than average at

Stornoway. The almost constant winds from an easterly point from late December 1962 until early March 1963, bringing bitterly cold polar continental air, arrived with little modification over the southern part of Great Britain but were increasingly modified in the north by the longer passage over the relatively warm waters of the North Sea. February 1986 again demonstrated that north and west Scotland experience less severe conditions in easterly weather types during winter. Stornoway recorded only five more frosts than usual (1956–83 February mean) whereas Heathrow registered +16. The frost anomaly pattern for the nine stations in February 1986 was very similar to that for February 1963 (resource 9.8) although, as the cold easterly winds were confined to the month of February, the overall winter anomaly was much smaller than in 1963. The exceptional nature of 1963 can be illustrated by the fact that at Heathrow the second most severe year (1979) produced only 59 frosts, compared with the 84 of 1963.

Station	Winter 1963 Total Frosts	Winter 1963 SD(+)*	February 1963 SD(+)	February 1986 SD(+)
Heathrow	84	3.3	2.5	2.5
Mt Batten	55	3.3	1.8	2.2
Rhoose	85	3.1	2.2	2.2
Ringway	87	3.0	2.7	2.1
Watnall	92	2.4	2.5	1.9
Tynemouth	58	2.4	2.5	1.6
Eskdalemuir	116	1.8	2.3	1.7
Lerwick	56	0.7	1.0	1.2
Stornoway	48	0.3	0.6	1.0

Frosts in the 1963 winter and February 1986 frost anomalies — **9.8**

* SD(+) indicates number of standard deviations above the mean.

Some useful sources of data, definitions and conventions

G Manley, (1970) The climate of the British Isles. In C C Wallen (Ed) Climates of northern and western Europe, (World Survey of Climatology, 5), Elsevier

Meteorological Office (1956–83) Mon. Weather Rep. HMSO

Meteorological Office (1972) Meteorol. Glossary. (5th ed.) HMSO

Meteorological Office (1980) Mon. Weather Survey and Prospects. HMSO

H C Shellard, (1968) 'The winter of 1962–63 in the United Kingdom, a climatological survey', *Meteorology Magazine*, 97, pp. 129–141

In 1970 persistent north-westerly winds in November, February, March and April brought cold maritime polar air over the country, resulting in total winter frosts being above average at all nine stations ($\geq$ +1 SD) but with maximum positive anomalies of +1.9 SD at Lerwick and +2.6 SD at Stornoway.

1972 was the year which produced the lowest total number of frosts at the nine stations combined. A largely frost-free October and April and mild southerly or south-westerly winds from December to March gave below average totals everywhere, with Heathrow receiving only 39 per cent of its usual number. Of the three Scottish stations, 1972 was the year with least frost at Lerwick and Eskdalemuir (both –1.7 SD) but at Stornoway 15 winters had lower totals and in 1972 it received only two frosts less than normal. In March Stornoway, with 12 frosts, was the only station to record an above average figure (+5). Lerwick, also with a March mean of seven, recorded only a single frost. The reasons for this substantial difference between the two stations and between Stornoway and the eight other stations may be found in a detailed examination of the daily synoptic situations. Six of the frosts at Stornoway occurred between March 8–16 when fairly strong anticyclonic easterly winds prevailed over most of the British Isles but with cold conditions of slack pressure over north-west Scotland. The lighter winds of the cols were more favourable for frost occurrence. Lerwick frequently experienced the south-westerly winds to the north of the ridge of high pressure extending from Eastern Europe. The other main period of frosts at Stornoway was between March 27–30, when the north-westerly or westerly winds associated with a vigorous depression brought cold (maritime) polar air to the whole of the British Isles. At Stornoway the winds were much lighter than over England and Wales and on the 29th and 30th cold conditions again prevailed, the temperature dropping to –3°C. Lerwick recorded its single frost on the 27th, under the influence of the calm conditions near the centre of the low pressure system.

(Source: D G Tout, 'The variability of days of air frost in Great Britain, 1957–83', *Weather*, 42(9), September 1987, pp.268–272.)

Activities

1 Use the data to establish whether there is a relationship between:

   a Altitude and number of frost days.

   b Latitude and number of frost days.
   (Spearman's rank correlation technique will help.)

2 Do the nine graphs of resource 9.6 share common tendencies and characteristics? If so, draw a single, generalised graph which sums up the overall pattern. Label this graph, stating the key features.

3 Use the data to test the hypothesis that winter temperatures in the British Isles vary widely in their intensity.

4 To what extent does this case study support the idea that weather conditions in a region can be explained in terms of predominant air masses and airstreams?

Background

Detailed data for individual stations is valuable because it allows us to explore beyond the generally available mean temperature and rainfall figures, e.g. variability, extremes, relationships between meteorological elements etc. It also allows us to question stereotyped images. For instance, before you study the data for Prabost, Isle of Skye (resource 9.9), locate Skye on an atlas and write down what you expect the weather and climate to be. Then scrutinise the data and see how close your estimate was! What are the main surprises?

Activities

You can go on to ask all sorts of questions from this data, especially if you create a data base on a micro with an enquiry facility. For instance:

a When would it be best to take a holiday on Skye?

b How far do air mass types help to account for the climate?

c Do the figures help to explain why agriculture over much of Skye is classified as 'marginal'?

9.9 The climate of Prabost, Isle of Skye, averages and extremes for 25 years (1960–84)

	Air temperature (°C)								Rainfall (mm)							Sunshine (hr) †						Surface Wind*					
	Mean Daily Max	Mean Daily Min	Mean of Mnth Extrms Max	Mean of Mnth Extrms Min	Extreme Max °C	Year	Extreme Min °C	Year	Avge amt	Wettest mm	Year	Driest mm	Year	Highest Daily Fall	Year	Avge amt	% Poss-ible	Sunniest hr	Year	Least sunniest hr	Year	W +SW	S +SE	E +NE	N +NW	Mean Std mph	Gale
Dec	6.6	2.1	10.8	-3.2	13.7	1972	-8.4	1961	200	364	1961	60	1978	65	1980	31	19	66	1961	11	75,80	10	12	5	4	15	7
Jan	5.8	1.2	10.2	-4.3	13.0	1971	-8.2	1972	170	372	1972	37	1963	58	1962	37	20	83	1963	8	1983	13	13	5	4	16	7
Feb	6.2	1.2	9.9	-4.2	12.7	60,75	-8.6	1960	110	211	1960	9	1962	51	1974	75	32	120	1975	38	1965	7	13	5	3	14	5
Mar	7.9	2.1	11.9	-2.5	16.1	1974	-6.5	1969	139	375	1979	28	1967	73	1968	102	30	139	1974	49	1983	9	11	6	5	15	5
Apr	10.3	3.4	15.5	-1.6	22.6	1984	-4.0	1968	85	178	1973	4	1974	46	1965	150	38	258	1974	99	1982	9	8	6	7	13	5
May	13.4	5.8	20.0	0.7	26.1	1978	-2.5	1980	86	196	1979	15	1980	39	1964	181	38	300	1975	113	1970	8	9	7	7	12	2
Jun	15.6	8.4	22.3	4.0	27.2	1975	0.9	1975	108	192	1962	19	1982	49	1973	166	34	250	1970	104	1984	12	8	4	6	12	1
Jly	15.9	9.8	22.9	5.6	27.0	1976	3.4	1974	107	179	1961	45	1977	45	1961	128	26	197	62,63	56	1979	13	7	3	8	11	1
Aug	16.4	9.8	21.7	5.7	28.4	1975	3.3	1964	112	192	1982	45	1982	41	1964	132	30	272	1976	66	1978	11	9	7	7	10	1
Sep	14.1	8.5	18.5	3.7	22.6	1971	0.4	1975	186	364	1975	51	1972	60	1975	91	25	144	1960	50	1966	11	10	4	5	12	4
Oct	11.8	6.6	16.2	1.6	18.9	1969	-1.4	1973	209	386	1973	40	1960	75	1984	70	24	113	1973	41	1970	11	11	4	5	15	4
Nov	8.0	3.2	12.3	-1.9	14.0	1978	-4.5	1973	223	424	1973	82	1968	58	1979	43	21	78	67,82	27	67,82	10	10	5	5	14	6
YEAR	10.6	5.1	24.3	-5.7	28.4	1975	-8.6	1960	1737	2261	1960	1369	1968	75	1984	1205	30	1447	1968	1060	1981	120	121	58	66	14	45

d = Number of Days
Wind directions at 09h GMT
†1966–84, 19 years

	Soil Temp+		Frost		Humidity 09h		Trans-piration		Precipitation			Snow		Hail	Thunder	Sunny Dull		Vis. 09h		Cloud. 09h		Air mass type. 09h ‡					
	30cm C	100cm C	Air	Grnd	Mean %	<70%	Mean mm	Max mm	<0.2 mm	>5 mm	>25 mm	Fall	Lie	d	d	>50%	<1hr	>50 km	<1 km	The Storr	Cuill-in	Pm	nPm		F	Tm	A
Dec	4.9	6.5	8	18	88	1	12	37	4	13	1	8	6			5	22	12	0	19	24	7	6	6	4	3	5
Jan	3.2	4.1	9	20	88	1	11	30	5	12	1	7	7	1		5	21	12	0	19	25	6	8	6	3	3	5
Feb	3.1	4.2	10	19	85	3	17	55	10	8	<1	6	5	1		8	12	10	<1	15	19	4	7	4	2	6	5
Mar	4.3	4.3	6	18	83	3	27	61	9	9	1	6	5	1		9	11	11	<1	16	21	7	7	5	3	4	5
Apr	5.6	5.0	3	14	79	7	36	61	11	6	<1	4	3	1	<1	11	11	11	<1	18	23	4	9	4	5	5	5
May	8.7	6.7	1	7	77	10	55	70	13	6	<1	2	1	<1	<1	12	6	14	<1	13	16	4	11	3	2	5	4
Jun	12.4	9.7	0	2	81	5	68	100	10	7	<1	<1	1	<1	<1	10	8	13	<1	17	21	5	12	4	5	2	2
Jly	14.2	11.5	0	1	86	2	51	85	10	7	<1	0	0	<1	<1	7	11	13	<1	22	24	5	11	6	7	1	1
Aug	14.1	12.4	0	1	86	3	45	66	10	8	<1	0	0	<1	<1	9	11	13	<1	19	20	5	11	5	5	4	1
Sep	11.5	11.5	0	2	88	1	31	50	5	12	1	0	0	1	<1	7	12	12	<1	20	25	9	10	6	5	1	1
Oct	9.0	9.8	<1	7	88	1	19	46	5	13	1	1	<1	3	<1	6	14	11	<1	17	23	9	8	6	4	1	3
Nov	7.0	8.2	4	15	88	1	15	48	5	15	2	3	3	8	<1	5	17	14	<1	17	24	9	6	3	2	2	4
YEAR	8.2	7.8	42	124	85	39	388	452	98	115	8	46	30	30	7	94	151	149	1	210	266	72	106	63	46	37	41

'cms' show depth below surface

d = Number of Days

The Storr & Cuillin are hills.

‡1966–84, 19 years

WINTER: Dec Jan Feb — SPRING: Mar Apr May — SUMMER: Jun Jly Aug — AUTUMN: Sep Oct Nov

CASE STUDY 9.4 *Local weather – a field experiment in micrometeorology*

Background

This case study is valuable in two ways: firstly, it identifies how environmental conditions such as surface type, gradient and slope orientation, affect local temperatures, humidities and wind characteristics; secondly, it outlines how to collect relevant data in the field and how to analyse it. Thus, the experiment provides a useful example of how to organise and carry out a piece of group fieldwork, how to process and interpret the results and how to present them succinctly.

Micrometeorology of a moorland lake

'As part of my first year undergraduate field trip I conducted a micrometeorology experiment with about fifteen students around the Avon Reservoir in south Dartmoor (Nat. Ref. SX 677653). The aim of the experiment was to investigate the effect of the high moorland lake (335 m) on meteorological conditions in the vicinity, from the lake edge up to the summits of the nearby hills to the east and north. We also sampled the temperatures of the streams running into, and out of, the reservoir, and also the water temperature along the eastern and northern edges of the lake. This was to help with interpretation of the meteorological observations, and also to study the deep (25 m) lake's effect on the properties of the water passing through it.

By chance the prevailing conditions on the day of the experiment, Tuesday 21 April 1987, were very favourable for achieving clear results. The excellent weather of the Easter period, 1987, had begun to establish itself. The prevailing wind in south Devon was from the south or south-east with a speed of about 4ms-1, thus blowing almost at right angles to the concrete dam at the

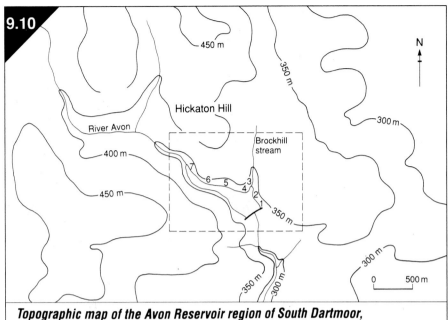

Topographic map of the Avon Reservoir region of South Dartmoor, with the study of resource 9.11 enlarged in dashed box. The lakeside positions of the students' transects are numbered.

downstream end of the reservoir (see resource 9.10) and allowing the air to undergo the maximum modification possible. There was also no cloud to reduce the radiation from the sun so that the effect of slope aspect was maximal.

After sampling the temperature of the River Avon downstream from the dam, the students were spread out in pairs around the eastern and northern edges of the lake. Moving away from the water's edge they took measurements of the wind speed (using air meters), and dry- and wet-bulb temperatures (using whirling hygrometers) roughly every 50 m for 500 m, ending near the summit of either Gripper's Hill or Hickaton Hill. To try to reduce observational error, they took five measurements of the wet- and dry-bulb temperatures at each location, and ran the air meter for 200 seconds. The experiment was conducted in the middle of the day over one and a half hours, from 1130 BST to 1300 BST.

The fields of wind speed and temperature around the lake are shown in resource 9.11. In the wind

field the influence of the topography around the lake is clearly visible and consistent with previous studies. Note that the pattern is not due to the abrupt change in roughness that occurs when air passes from the lake to the shore.

Resource 9.11 shows an area of maximum wind speed to the east of the lake (along the observation transect of group 1). Gripper's Hill acts somewhat like a ridge to the prevailing flow and this maximum speed is along the highest section of the Hill. Studies suggest that flow passing perpendicularly over a ridge will result in speeds near the crest of about 1.5 times the magnitude of the average local flow (the actual value depends on the roughness and height/width ratio of the ridge). Our peak wind value is in agreement with the suggested increase of other research but the wind decrease downstream is faster than they found, probably because the actual topography was not an idealised A-shaped ridge and also because the wind is channelled along the Avon valley.

This channelling is clear in resource 9.11, as the wind speed along the lake edge to the north-west is consistently higher than up the slope to its right. The wind speed is only about that of the geostrophic wind, rather than stronger, as the high concrete wall at the base of the reservoir places the valley base in a sheltered position. Note that the area north-east of the lake is effectively sheltered by a combination of being in the lee of Gripper's Hill and the funnelling effect of the Avon valley. The topographic steering of the wind can be best seen where air passing across the lake reaches the northern shore near pair 4's lakeside measurement spot (see resource 9.10 for position). Detailed study of the topography in this region reveals the existence of a knoll or isolated small hill. Results of numerical studies show that the maximum speed of flow over such an isolated hill occurs near the top on the upwind slope, as indeed the deformation of the 3ms-1 isopleth suggests. The flow is also partly steered around the left of the knoll, as is consistent with the direction of the prevailing wind. There is an area of calm upslope, behind this knoll, which is probably associated with the remains of Bronze Age hut circles. On the northern edge of the study area, at the top of Hickaton Hill, the wind has regained, or exceeded, its geostrophic value.

The temperature field, shown in resource 9.11 (b), illustrates the effect of the lake most clearly. The surface temperature of the lake along its southern and eastern flanks was about 9.5°C, while along its northern edge the water was slightly warmer, at 11°C. This temperature gradient was probably due to the wind piling the water up along the northern edge of the lake and so causing some cooler, deeper water to upwell in the southern part of the reservoir. The air temperature in areas exposed to the sun was between 13° and 14°C, as is seen to the east of the dam. The lake has a strong local effect on this temperature as the areas where the

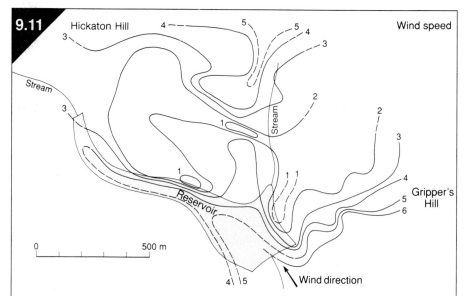

(a) Wind speed field over the Avon Reservoir littoral. (Isopleths in ms. The direction of the wind is marked, its strength was 4ms.)

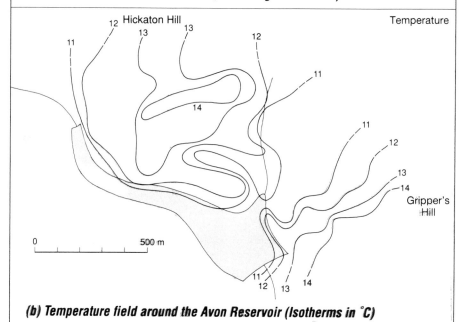

(b) Temperature field around the Avon Reservoir (Isotherms in °C)

wind was directed by the topography after passing over the lake (i.e. along the Avon valley, around the bottom of Hickaton Hill, and up the Brockhill valley) only attain temperatures of 11°C – 12°C. This local cooling effect (at the observation height of 1–2 m) is restricted to 50–200 m from the shoreline.

The region on the slopes of Hickaton Hill, partly protected by topography,

and some 300 m from the lake, recorded the highest temperatures. The south-facing slope and the darkening of the local vegetation in the vicinity of the many Bronze Age hut circles contributed to this. The evidence suggests that the zone between Gripper's Hill and Brockhill Stream was cool, not because of influence of the lake, as the wind was not directed that way, but perhaps due to a combination of slope aspect, lighter-coloured vegetation in the area not absorbing as much radiation and damper soil leading to evaporation-related temperature loss. The existence of this cool region is merely speculation, however, as no measurements were taken in the interior of the area. Note that while areas of calm that are well-exposed to the sun (such as the south face of Hickaton Hill) have high temperatures, areas such as the west face of Gripper's Hill that are oriented away from the sun are 2–3°C cooler. Such west-facing slopes would receive some 15–20 per cent less solar radiation than south-facing slopes around the equinoxes in this latitude.

The relative humidity field combines the effects of the lake and temperature. Regions of cooler temperature away from the influence of the lake tend to have higher humidities (e.g. the west side of Gripper's Hill) because of the decreased quantity of water vapour supportable in the atmosphere at lower temperatures. The relative humidity was between 55 per cent and 60 per cent at 13.5°C, so the effect of the wind picking up moisture off the lake is seen on the northern side of the reservoir. Humidities in excess of 75 per cent were recorded in this region. The higher humidities upstream along the Brockhill valley are likely due to the marshy conditions in that region.

The other set of measurements taken consisted of water temperatures along the streams leading into and out of the reservoir. In the streams above the lake, and those flowing into the Avon downstream, the temperature of the water was between 12°C and 13°C. However, the Avon river below the dam was only at 8°C because the water being released from the reservoir was from the cooler mid-depths. Mixing of this cold water with warmer tributary streams raised the temperature locally by up to 2°C. This colder lake water came from a region where the relatively warm, buoyant surface waters mixed with the deeper waters

of the lake. These deeper waters would have been formed in the previous winter, and have a temperature of about 4°C.

Conclusions

This experiment was a simple but successful demonstration of the combined effects of moorland topography and a lake on the micrometeorology of a valley. The channelling of the wind by the slopes of Hickaton Hill, and the changes in temperature and humidity that this lake-affected air caused in such regions were seen and compared well with theory and related experiments. Contrasts between sunlit and less-exposed hillsides were also encountered. In addition the buffering effect of the lake on the water flowing through it was seen in stream temperatures.

The Dean Moor area, of which this valley forms a part, is interesting from a climate change perspective as well, for there are numerous remains of stone hut circles or enclosures from the Bronze Age. These tend to cluster on south-facing slopes, as on Hickaton Hill where they had a small effect on the microclimate. From examining these remains the students estimated a valley population of scores if not several hundred people, with substantial circles up to 400 m in altitude. Given the sparsity of present day settlement above 200 m and the mean atmospheric lapse rate, this suggests a climatic deterioration of up to 2°C over the last 3000 years.

(Source: adapted from: G R Bigg, 'Micrometeorology of a moorland lake', *Weather*, 43(6), June 1988, pp.222–227.)

Activities

Study the materials carefully before completing the following questions:

1 What are the aims of the experiment?

2 What data is collected, i.e. what variables are used?

3 How is the data collected?

4 Summarise the key findings

5 How are these findings interpreted and explained?

Background

In the chapter on tropical weather (Chapter 8), one of the important understandings developed was the intensity and localisation of rainfall resulting from convection processes. In temperate environments such as the British Isles, similar properties are found, although with less ferocious intensity. Convection storms give us our heaviest rainfall and constitute a significant flood hazard, especially in urbanised catchments where impermeable surfaces predominate, i.e. overland flow delivers incoming water rapidly to river channels. This case study from the Thames valley, displays all these features.

Key understanding

◆ Convection storms are frequently intense, but highly localised.

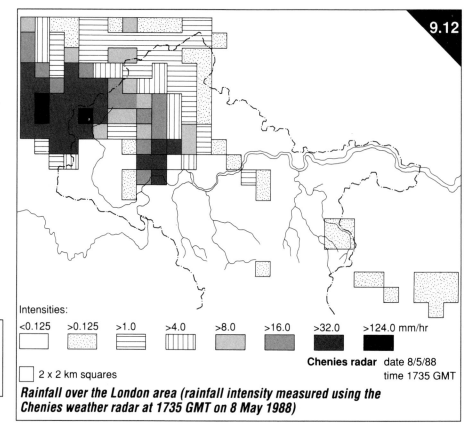

Intensities:

| <0.125 | >0.125 | >1.0 | >4.0 | >8.0 | >16.0 | >32.0 | >124.0 mm/hr |

Chenies radar   date 8/5/88
time 1735 GMT

2 x 2 km squares

Rainfall over the London area (rainfall intensity measured using the Chenies weather radar at 1735 GMT on 8 May 1988)

Thunderstorms over north-west London – 8 May 1988

During the early hours of Sunday, 8 May 1988 a shallow low pressure area moved northwards from the Paris Basin into the Straits of Dover and brought hot humid air, originating from North Africa, across Europe into the south-east of England. This humid airflow came into contact with colder air which was lying across Britain at the time, triggering intense thunderstorms in London and the Thames Valley. The synoptic situation changed little during the day with the depression finally moving away eastwards during the early hours of Monday, 9 May.

The most significant rainfalls were recorded in north-west London in the boroughs of Hillingdon and Harrow. Two thunderstorms affected the area: the first between 0500 GMT and 0730 GMT and the second between 1700 GMT and 1815 GMT. The telemetered raingauge at Ruislip recorded 53.0 mm during the first storm with a maximum intensity of

11.8 mm in 15 minutes (47.2 mm/hr). During the second storm a total of 34.2 mm was recorded with a maximum intensity of 16.2 mm in 15 minutes (64.8 mm/hr). Details of amounts recorded at other raingauges in the area are given in resource 9.13.

The estimated point return period of the first thunderstorm at Uxbridge (63.5 mm in 2.5 hrs) is 100 years. The maximum recorded rainfall total for the second storm was at Ruislip with 34.2 mm falling in 75 minutes, giving an estimated point return period of 25 years.

The combined effect of these thunderstorms gave rise to widespread flooding of property in the Colne, Brent and Crane river catchments. Road and rail travel was widely disrupted for several days. 'Red' flood warnings were issued to the Metropolitan Police by Thames Water for both events.

Resource 9.12 shows a typical 2 km weather radar display covering the

region, which proved an invaluable tool for flood duty officers during the storm. Resource 9.14 illustrates the storm profiles recorded at Ruislip and the catchment response in the Yeading Brook West Branch which drains part of the London Borough of Hillingdon.

(Source: C M Haggett, Flood Warning Co-ordinator, Thames Water Authority, Waltham Cross, in *Weather*, 43(7), July 1988.)

two London thunderstorms

Rainfall amounts at other locations

	Storm 1	Storm 2	Total
Uxbridge	63.5	25.0	88.5
Northwood	48.5	23.0	71.5
Hampstead	31.0	26.0	57.0
Harrow Weald	42.4	12.2	54.6
Ealing	15.8	27.0	42.8
Holland Park	14.2	12.4	26.6

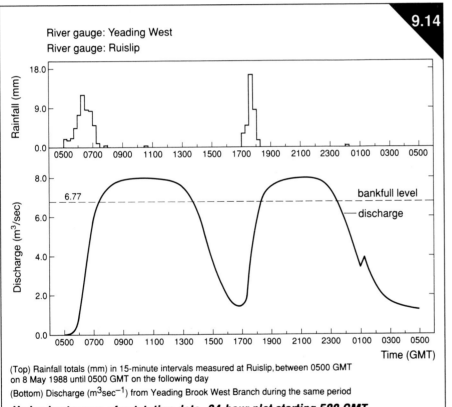

River gauge: Yeading West
River gauge: Ruislip

9.14

(Top) Rainfall totals (mm) in 15-minute intervals measured at Ruislip, between 0500 GMT on 8 May 1988 until 0500 GMT on the following day

(Bottom) Discharge (m³sec⁻¹) from Yeading Brook West Branch during the same period

Hydro-hyetogram of outstation data, 24-hour plot starting 500 GMT on 8 May 1988

Activities

1 Use the case study to illustrate the following concepts associated with convection precipitation:

   intensity, localisation, pulsation, suddenness, steep hydrograph and resultant flooding.

2 What characteristics of the storm hydrograph (resource 9.14) suggest that the storm was intense and that the catchment is extensively urbanised? (See also Chapter 5.)

3 With a partner, make a list of the main elements of a storm, and then compare this London event with the Babinda deluge described in case study 8.6.

CHAPTER 10

The complex world of the soil

Introduction

Soil is a mixture of mineral particles, finely divided organic matter, water, air and living organisms such as bacteria and earthworms (resource 10.1).

The essential role of soil is to provide plants (primary producers) with water, inorganic nutrients, e.g. nitrogen, potassium, a supply of oxygen for root respiration, and an anchorage to support them. It is the critical interface between the atmosphere, lithosphere, hydrosphere and biosphere. As the soil has an especially close symbiotic (two-way) relationship with plants and other organisms, it is included in the biosphere section of this book. As the case studies will show, however, soil study involves recurrent reference to all of the macro-systems of planet earth, e.g. weathering processes of the lithosphere; water storage and movement in the hydrosphere. Furthermore, there are few soils left in the world which have not been influenced directly or indirectly by human activities, and it can be argued that carelessness with or misuse of the soil resource is emerging as one of the major global issues.

As soils are the outcome of diverse environmental processes operating over varying timescales, there is an enormous range of soil types. In consequence, assembling them into general categories is problematic: too many categories and the classification may be confusing; too few categories and there is a danger of overgeneralisation. The criteria used vary according to what the classification is to be used for, e.g. engineers, agriculturalists, hydrologists each have their own interests in soil properties. One of the most useful for general use by geographers is based on the climate–vegetation–soil relationship. However, as the case studies illustrate, when you use different references, check the criteria and nomenclature of the classification being used. This applies too, to the vertical structure of soil, i.e. the horizons of the soil profile, where different lettering systems may be used.

The first four case studies from the UK, Germany, Tanzania and Nigeria focus upon the profile structure, how sensitive it is to variations in environmental conditions, how sensitively humans may respond, and how profile changes can cause problems. The final case study takes up the theme of soil erosion by examining both the demands made upon the soil which trigger positive feedback, and the possible strategies for re-establishing negative feedback and equilibrium and by questioning some popular assumptions.

▶ *You should check your understanding of the following:*

- Key **processes**

  oxidation, reduction, hydrolysis, chelation, leaching, illuviation, eluviation, freezing and thawing, induration, gleying.

- Key **properties** and their role in soil functioning

  mineral and organic composition, soil depth and horizon character, soil structure and aggregates, pore space – size, shape, number, alkalinity-acidity (pH), infiltration and water-holding capacities.

- Soil **types** used in case studies

  podzol, rendzina, brown earth, latosol, laterite soil, gley.

10.1

Rotting granite, Mount Oberon (Victoria, Australia). This weathered material is not yet a true soil

CASE STUDY 10.1 *Finding a natural soil profile in Britain – the Abernethy forest, Scotland*

Background

The climax vegetation of at least 90 per cent of the land surface of Britain is woodland and therefore, the natural soils should be forest-related. Today less than 9 per cent of the country is wooded – the lowest proportion of any Western European nation – and soils in deforested areas have become modified, particularly by agricultural practices. Even so-called 'ancient woodlands' have often been managed and used over the centuries. Thus, soil profiles which represent the responses to largely natural processes are rare. It is believed that some which come nearest to this 'ideal' state are found under remnants of the native Scots Pine woodlands of the Scottish Highlands.

One such area is the northern section of the Abernethy Forest, across the northern flanks of the Cairngorm massif sloping down to the River Spey and surrounding Loch Garten. Even here, there has been clearance by burning and grazing, so that only patches of natural forest and hence soils remain (resource 10.2). This upland region saw the final disappearance of ice caps from the upper Cairngorms less than 10 000 years ago and as case studies in Chapter 5 show, such areas are often veneered with extensive spreads of glacial and fluvio-glacial deposits. The parent materials of the soils of the Abernethy Forest are meltwater sands and gravels derived from acid schist and granite rocks which make up most of the surrounding mountains. It is irregular, hummocky terrain, with steep-sided kame mounds and kettle holes, sometimes infilled to marsh, and in other places still containing lakes, e.g. Loch Garten. The vegetation cover varies from closed canopy Scots Pine with a narrow range of sub-canopy species, to more open conditions with juniper, blaeberry and heather. In some of the open areas, birch has spread. Summers are cool and damp, while winters, although not severe by Highland standards, can bring prolonged snow cover.

Environmental characteristics

I Parent materials Fluvioglacial sands and gravels and glacial tills (ground moraine), both dominated by schist and granite debris.

II Climate 'A fairly warm and moist climate (greater than 1500 mm mean annual rainfall) with accumulated temperatures (above 5.6°C) of 1100–1375 day °C and a moisture deficit of 25–50 mm ... Moderate exposure, with wind speeds 2.6-4.4 m/s and rather severe winters with accumulated frost of 110–230 day °C.'

III Vegetation There are two characteristic plant communities, dependent upon the light conditions. First, under closed canopy pine forest, the species range is poor and the floor is dominated by mosses, with frequent rotting tree stumps supporting luxuriant blaeberry growth. The second type is more open woodland where the greater light penetration encourages juniper shrub along with heather and blaeberry, plus a carpet of mosses. A third community is open birch woodland with a species-rich understorey which has colonised areas cleared of native pines. Boggy hollows of kettle holes and channels support sphagnum moss mires.

Remnant of natural forest, Abernethy, Rothiemurchus, Scotland

Key understandings

◆ There is a direct relationship between climate, vegetation, parent materials and soil charac-teristics.

◆ Over time, soil processes are likely to produce an horizon structure in the profile.

◆ Each horizon has distinctive characteristics of composition, texture, colour, permeability, water-holding capacity.

◆ Water is a key vehicle in the operation of these selective soil processes.

The soil profiles

Under these environmental conditions 'podzolisation is the foremost pedogenic (soil forming) process and must have been active since at least 7000 B P (Before the Present) when the pollen records suggest that Scots Pine replaced juniper scrub and a later period of birch or birch/hazel dominance'. The principal outcomes are the mature podzol profiles of profiles A and B on resource 10.3, the humus iron podzol being the most widespread under the Abernethy pine forests. In the cool temperate, moist environment, the pine needle and moss litter decomposes slowly to produce a surface mat of raw humus (upper L horizon) or mor. In the process, **polyphenols** are released which cause iron and aluminium oxides and clays to disperse. The persistent water inputs to the soil lead to vigorous leaching of the humus, oxides and clays, giving the pale grey eluvial horizon (E). Deposition of these materials lower down the profile creates the darker, enriched illuvial zones (Bh and Bs).

The impacts upon the soil of forest clearance are illustrated in profile C (resource 10.3). The heather-moor communities yield reduced litter supplies. As a result of this decreased input of **DOM** (dead organic matter), the L, F and H organic horizons are impoverished and rarely exceed 15 cm. Over longer timescales this will reduce the enrichment of the lower, illuvial zones. The effects of poor drainage and waterlogging leading to **anaerobic** conditions are highlighted by profile D (resource 10.3). Water collects and lies in hollows and channels, with little throughput. This reduces the oxygen content, inhibits bacterial activity and slows down decomposition of DOM. A bed of partially decomposed organic matter, i.e. peat, then builds up. The subdivision shown denotes differences in compaction and density between shallow and deep peat. In the **kettle hollows** of

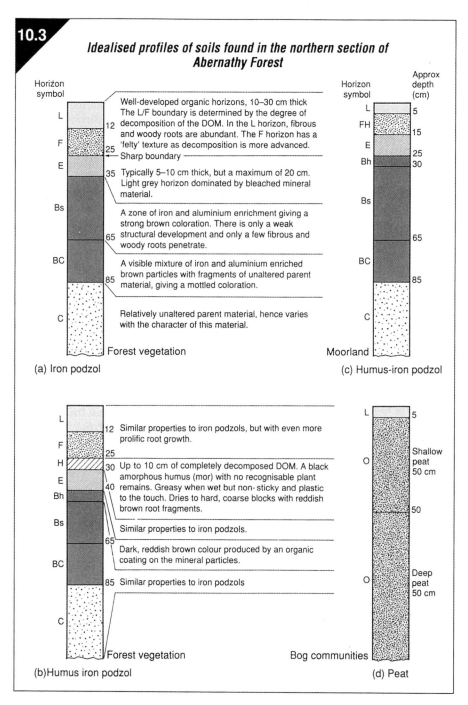

10.3 **Idealised profiles of soils found in the northern section of Abernathy Forest**

(a) Iron podzol

Horizon symbol	depth (cm)	
L	12	Well-developed organic horizons, 10–30 cm thick. The L/F boundary is determined by the degree of decomposition of the DOM. In the L horizon, fibrous and woody roots are abundant. The F horizon has a 'felty' texture as decomposition is more advanced.
F	25	
		— Sharp boundary —
E	35	Typically 5–10 cm thick, but a maximum of 20 cm. Light grey horizon dominated by bleached mineral material.
Bs	65	A zone of iron and aluminium enrichment giving a strong brown coloration. There is only a weak structural development and only a few fibrous and woody roots penetrate.
BC	85	A visible mixture of iron and aluminium enriched brown particles with fragments of unaltered parent material, giving a mottled coloration.
C		Relatively unaltered parent material, hence varies with the character of this material.

Forest vegetation

(c) Humus-iron podzol

Horizon symbol	Approx depth (cm)
L	5
FH	15
E	25
Bh	30
Bs	65
BC	85
C	

Moorland

(b) Humus iron podzol

Horizon symbol	depth	
L	12	Similar properties to iron podzols, but with even more prolific root growth.
F	25	
H	30	Up to 10 cm of completely decomposed DOM. A black amorphous humus (mor) with no recognisable plant remains. Greasy when wet but non-sticky and plastic to the touch. Dries to hard, coarse blocks with reddish brown root fragments.
E	40	
Bh		
Bs	65	Similar properties to iron podzols.
		Dark, reddish brown colour produced by an organic coating on the mineral particles.
BC	85	Similar properties to iron podzols.
C		

Forest vegetation

(d) Peat

	depth
L	5
O	Shallow peat 50 cm
	50
O	Deep peat 50 cm

Bog communities

Abernethy the peat may attain a thickness of 6.5 m.

(Source: J H Gauld, 'Native Pinewood Soils in the Northern Section of Abernethy Forest', *Scottish Geographical Magazine* (98), April 1982, pp.48–56.)

Activities

1 What are the most identifiable features of a podsol soil?

2 What are the most important differences between the four soil profiles of resource 10.3? How do you explain these differences?

CASE STUDY 10.2 *Soils, location and time – the Isar Valley, South Germany*

Background

Two important factors which influence soil development are the location on a slope and the time over which pedogenic processes have been operating. As the case studies in Chapter 2 show, a slope can be regarded as a cascade with material moving selectively downslope over time. Thus, we can expect soil profiles to vary in depth and composition from the top to the foot of a slope. For example, selective downward transport of finer material may result in soils near the foot of a slope being deeper and containing higher proportions of fine particles than soils further upslope. This hypothesis assumes that the slope is of uniform age and the soil-forming processes have been at work on all sections of the slope for the same length of time. In many cases, however, this may not be true, for a slope may contain segments of differing ages. Soils on such compound slopes are likely to vary in maturity, this being indicated by depth of the soil profile and clarity of the horizon structure.

This case study, from the Isar Valley to the south of Munich in southern Germany, explores both of these ideas. As with the Abernethy Forest examples in the previous case study, the parent materials for most of the soils are glacial and fluvio-glacial deposits. In contrast to the Scottish materials, this debris is mostly calcareous, its source being the Bavarian Alps to the south which were the ice source region. As this icesheet finally withdrew it left the flanks stretching north towards Munich heavily veneered with debris. These deposits include drumlin fields, and soil profiles taken across individual drumlins reveal how sensitively soil character responds to slope evolution processes. In the post-glacial period the River Isar, flowing NNE through Munich, has both degraded and aggraded its valley. The degradation (downcutting) has removed huge volumes of glacial and fluvio-glacial debris including **pro-glacial** lake bed deposits, while the aggradation (deposition) has reorganised much of this material into a set of broad terraces. Thus, the valley cross-profile is a series of steps of different ages, and resulting in differentiated soil profiles.

Note: The profile lettering notation used in this case study is different from that of the previous case study, illustrating the range of classification systems in use and hence the need for care in their use.

Key understandings

◆ Soil types and profiles are likely to vary according to location on a slope.

◆ Separate segments of a slope may be of differing ages.

◆ Time is an important factor in soil development.

Location and soil profiles

The impact of location upon soil character is shown clearly in resource 10.4, where even on relatively small topographic features such as drumlins, quite distinct soil types have evolved. Under natural conditions, this would be reflected in vegetation response, which would by the operation of negative feedback, sustain the distinctiveness. Today, with the land under pastoral grassland farming, there is likely to be a tendency for the differences to diminish.

The cross-section of resource 10.5 lays out the suite (set) of calcareous gravel and alluvium terraces deposited by the River Isar, the highest and most distant from today's river being the oldest. Profiles 4 – 7 (overleaf) reflect this age sequence and illustrate a close relationship between soil type, parent material and timescale.

Activities

1 What are the key differences between a 'young' and a 'mature' soil suggested by analysis of profiles 1–7?

2 Suggest a model of the stages of soil formation on these calcareous sediments. What local factors might modify this model?

3 Two significant changes in the upper horizons over time appear to be the decline of calcareous material and the increase in the clay complex. Use reference texts to outline the processes involved in this change.

4 Group discussion: The end product of pedogenesis (soil formation) in the Abernethy Forest (case study 10.1) is a podsol soil, whereas in the Isar Valley it seems to be a brown earth. Yet both localities border recently glaciated uplands in temperate latitudes, and in both cases the parent materials are glacial and fluvio-glacial debris. Use your understandings of pedogenic processes and reference tests to explain the different outcomes.

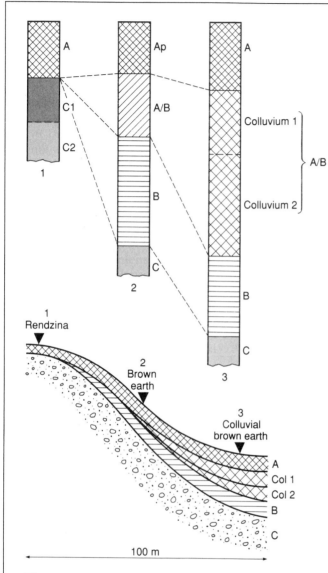

Profile 1: Drumlin crest: rendzina

Horizon	Depth (cm)	Properties
A	0–15	Very dark greyish brown stony humose clay loam with angular blocky structure
C1	15–30	Weakly weathered stony calcareous sandy loam
C2	> 30	Calcareous moraine parent material

Profile 2: Drumlin flank: brown earth

Ap	0–15	Very dark greyish brown stony humose clay with subangular blocky structure
A/B	15–35	Greyish brown stony clay loam with subangular blocky structure
B	35–70	Yellowish brown stony clay loam with subangular blocky structure
C	>70	Calcareous moraine parent material

Profile 3: Drumlin hollow: dark brown earth

A	0–20	Dark greyish brown humose sandy clay loam, stony with subangular blocky structure
A/B	20–70	Brownish grey humose colluvial sandy clay loam with subangular blocky structure
B	70–100	Greyish brown stony sandy clay loam with subangular blocky structure
C	>100	Calcareous moraine parent material

▼ Position of profiles

Soil sequence on drumlins

Profile 1: Across the drumlin crests, erosion has removed part of the decalcified soils, and freely drained rendzinas have developed from the calcareous ground moraine. The profile is relatively shallow and immature.

Profile 2: The active decalcification (removal of calcium) is evident on the drumlin flank, where mature, freely draining brown earths have formed, with well-developed A horizons (Ap, A/B). Free calcium carbonate amounts are low, but calcium is still the main cation among the exchangeable ions, indicating that while leaching is active it is not depleting the calcium absorbed on the clay particle surfaces. Thus, the pH remains high, i.e. the soil is alkaline.

Profile 3: Erosion from the crests and transport down the flanks via the gradual sediment cascade have thickened the upper horizons of the soils in the hollows between the drumlins. Excess water draining from the flanks accelerates leaching, and cation levels associated with the clay complex are lower than in profile 2. So, hydrogen ion levels are higher and pH values lower, i.e. the soil is more acid, in spite of the calcareous colluvial material delivered by downslope creep. Note that organic matter persists to greater depths than in the other profiles.

10.5

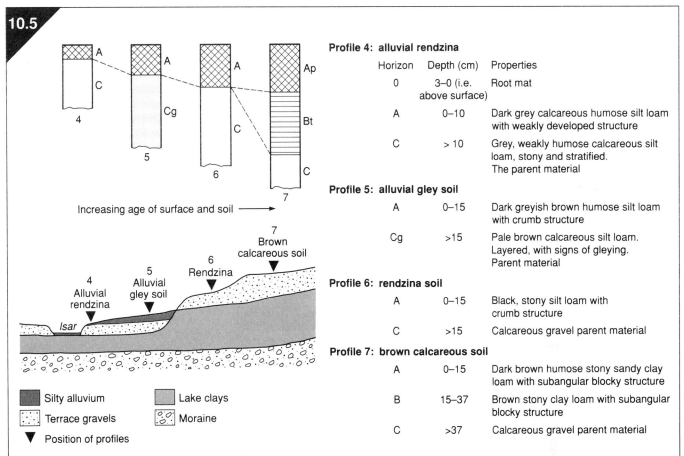

Increasing age of surface and soil ⟶

7
Brown
calcareous soil
6
Rendzina
5
Alluvial
gley soil
4
Alluvial
rendzina
Isar

- Silty alluvium
- Lake clays
- Terrace gravels
- Moraine
- ▼ Position of profiles

Profile 4: alluvial rendzina

Horizon	Depth (cm)	Properties
0	3–0 (i.e. above surface)	Root mat
A	0–10	Dark grey calcareous humose silt loam with weakly developed structure
C	> 10	Grey, weakly humose calcareous silt loam, stony and stratified. The parent material

Profile 5: alluvial gley soil

A	0–15	Dark greyish brown humose silt loam with crumb structure
Cg	>15	Pale brown calcareous silt loam. Layered, with signs of gleying. Parent material

Profile 6: rendzina soil

A	0–15	Black, stony silt loam with crumb structure
C	>15	Calcareous gravel parent material

Profile 7: brown calcareous soil

A	0–15	Dark brown humose stony sandy clay loam with subangular blocky structure
B	15–37	Brown stony clay loam with subangular blocky structure
C	>37	Calcareous gravel parent material

Soil sequence on alluvial deposits of the River Isar

Profile 4: River alluvium of the present floodplain. This most recent level is still inundated and disturbed by the Isar floods and consists of grey calcareous alluvium. It is stratified as a result of the flood sedimentation, but soil forming processes have not yet organised an horizon structure. Some organic matter is accumulating, but the soil is very calcareous and has a low clay content. This is an alluvial rendzina.

Profile 5: Upper floodplain alluvium. No longer subject to flooding, and possesses a deep A horizon from increments by past successive floods. The sub-soil is still layered but is being modified by gleying, indicating the high level of the water table. This is a young soil best designated an alluvial gley soil.

Profile 6: An early post-glacial (Holocene) gravel terrace. The coarse calcareous gravels of the parent materials were laid down by fast-flowing waters in a cooler, wetter climatic episode soon after the disappearance of the icesheets. Over approximately 7000 years, from this parent material, a rendzina soil has formed. The A horizon has only half the $CaCO_3$ but much higher clay content than the alluvial floodplain soils (profiles 4 and 5). The organic matter content is high and the soil possesses a clear crumb structure. These properties reflect the work of soil formation processes over long periods.

Profile 7: A late-glacial (Würm, the last glacial advance) gravel terrace. This is the earliest terrace laid down by meltwaters late in the Pleistocene period, perhaps 10 000 BP during the last stages of the Würm glacial episode. As a result, the soil profile shows the greatest maturity of the set. Despite modification of the surface horizons by cultivation in many areas, the character of the B horizon shows that these soils are beyond the rendzina stage and may be designated brown calcareous soils. This maturity and the long timespan over which the soil forming processes have operated are indicated by the significant accumulation of the clay content in the B horizon. This differentiates the profile by accentuating the colour and texture contrasts between the eluvial and illuvial horizons. For example, where natural vegetation remains leaching has removed the carbonates from the A and B horizons and a modern humus forms.

(Adapted from: E M Bridges, 'Glacial Landscapes and Soils in Southern Germany', Swansea Geographer, 11, 1973, pp.1–7.)

Background

The high plateaus of Central and East Africa are underlain by a geologically ancient platform, across which millions of years of weathering and erosion have produced a huge peneplain. In such environments, despite long-term climatic fluctuations, we might expect to find mature soil profiles. This is especially so in the humid and sub-humid tropics, where temperatures and at least seasonally abundant moisture, sustain high rates of mechanical and chemical weathering. As a result, weathering depths may exceed 10 m and iron oxides in the upper soil zones give these regions their predominantly red coloration.

Because of the scale, superficial monotony and age of these high, savanna-clad plains, it is easy to assume that the soils are homogeneous. Indeed, the majority do fall within the broad group known as **latosols**. They may also be referred to as **tropical red earths, ferralitic soils** or **lateritic soils**. (N.B. the term 'laterite' is often used inaccurately. It has a very specific meaning, as case study 10.4, clarifies.) Yet this case study shows clearly that the mature soils of the central African peneplains are varied. They are sensitively adjusted to local environmental conditions, especially to changes of gradient and position on a slope, for these plains are rarely 'flat'.

The analysis focuses upon a single slope in northern Tanzania in the territory of the Wasukuma tribal group of farmer/pastoralists, who have fully understood the properties and capabilities of the local soils. Although almost on the Equator, rains are seasonal, occurring between November and April, with a break some time during January–February, and totalling approximately 700 mm. The natural vegetation is savanna with scattered trees, known as miombo-brachystegia, or miombo bush.

Key understandings

◆ Across ancient and apparently homogeneous landscapes, soil types will be delicately adjusted to local environmental conditions.

◆ In similar geologic and climatic conditions, edaphic (soil character) variations are likely to be controlled significantly by gradient, orientation and position on the slope.

◆ Response to local soil variations by traditional societies is often sensitive and sophisticated.

Soil profiles and land use in northern Tanzania

Resource 10.6 depicts the slope analysed in the cross-section of resource 10.7. There are three landform elements common to the region: ridge crests of granitic boulders resembling large-scale tors; lengthy pediment slopes of gentle gradients (less than 3°); shallow, broad valley floors only seasonally carrying water. The crystalline granitic bedrocks have abundant felspars which are susceptible to chemical weathering. The photograph was taken in late August, well into the dry season, but the landuse contrasts can still be seen. The rocky ridge is used for fuelwood and construction wood; the long slope is cropped, using shifting cultivation with cattle and goat grazing after the harvest, and the moister valley floor has traditionally provided dry season grazing and thatching grasses.

The debris supply to the soil store from the parent material is delivered in two ways: first by the downward progress of sub-surface weathering, and second by sub-aerial denudation of the exposed ridge crest. The soil catena (sequence of profiles down the slope) illustrates clearly how the slope behaves as a cascade of the selective downslope transformation and translocation of material. The debris and organic matter change form by mechanical disintegration (comminution) and chemical breakdown (decomposition). The eluviation process then progressively moves the finer and more soluble materials downslope, where they are redeposited and so create illuviated horizons. The final stop in the cascade is the colluvial zone at the slope foot, where the finest and most soluble materials collect. This 'mbuga' zone is equivalent to the 'dambos' found across much of Central Africa.

Activities

1 Explain why sandy soils predominate on the upper slope, while clay proportions are higher in the lower slope profiles.

2 Use this catena to define and illustrate the following terms: eluvial; illuvial; colluvial.

3 Explain the character and use of the 'mbuga' soils of the valley floor.

4 What is meant by an 'ironstone pan', how is it formed and what effects does it have on soil drainage?

5 Explain the land use system developed by the Wasukuma in terms of the soil properties and water characteristics.

Slope profile – Ukiriguru, Tanzania

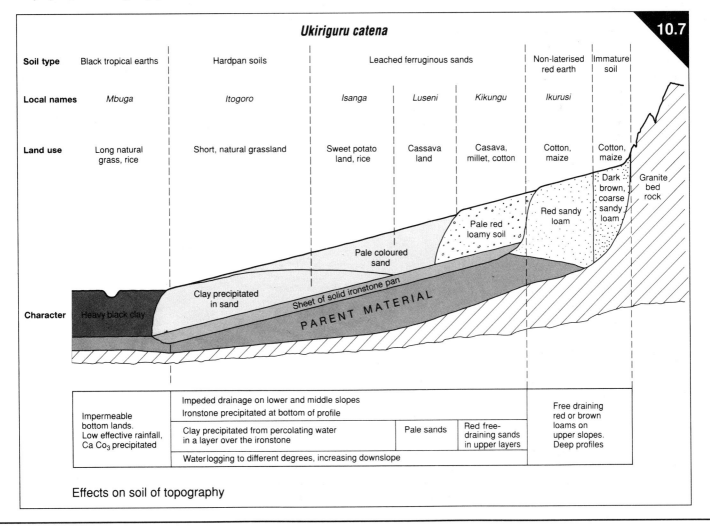

Ukiriguru catena

10.7

Soil type	Black tropical earths	Hardpan soils	Leached ferruginous sands			Non-laterised red earth	Immature soil
Local names	*Mbuga*	*Itogoro*	*Isanga*	*Luseni*	*Kikungu*	*Ikurusi*	
Land use	Long natural grass, rice	Short, natural grassland	Sweet potato land, rice	Cassava land	Casava, millet, cotton	Cotton, maize	Cotton, maize
Character	Heavy black clay	Clay precipitated in sand · Sheet of solid ironstone pan · PARENT MATERIAL	Pale coloured sand	Pale red loamy soil	Red sandy loam	Dark brown, coarse sandy loam	Granite bed rock

Impermeable bottom lands. Low effective rainfall, Ca Co₃ precipitated	Impeded drainage on lower and middle slopes			Free draining red or brown loams on upper slopes. Deep profiles
	Ironstone precipitated at bottom of profile			
	Clay precipitated from percolating water in a layer over the ironstone	Pale sands	Red free-draining sands in upper layers	
	Waterlogging to different degrees, increasing downslope			

Effects on soil of topography

CASE STUDY 10.4 *Laterite – a tough crust to crack –*

Background

Perhaps the best-known product of the deep weathering processes is laterite. Some accounts give the impression that 'laterite' is a general term which can be used for all regoliths developed in the humid tropics. This is not the case, although by definition a laterite is clearly a product of the processes active in such environments.

Laterite is a highly weathered material rich in secondary oxides especially of iron and ranging from yellow to red in colour. Primary silicates and bases are poorly represented, but there may be considerable quantities of quartz and kaolinite. It is either hard or capable of hardening irreversibly on exposure to repeated wetting and drying, as illustrated by its widespread use as a building material.

Apart from the ability to achieve considerable thickness, distinguishing features are:

(i) the presence of a thick, iron-rich zone (ferric, oxidised iron) in the upper horizons of the profile, (resource 10.8);

(ii) removal of most of the silica and almost all of the bases;

(iii) the tendency for the iron-rich zone to harden irreversibly on drying and exposure to the air;

(iv) the evolution of a zonal profile which includes mottled and pallid horizons below the iron-rich zone.

Resource 10.9 (a) illustrates the ideal profile but it must be stressed that not all lateritic soils possess the full set – only the iron-rich zone is essential. Strictly, 'laterite' is the term for the iron-rich zone, and 'lateritic soil' the term for a profile containing the zone. This zone, once hardened, forms a cuirasse, and becomes known variously as **indurated laterite**, **duricrust** or **plinthite**.

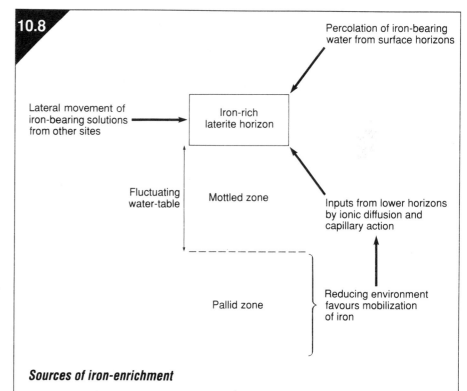

10.8

Sources of iron-enrichment

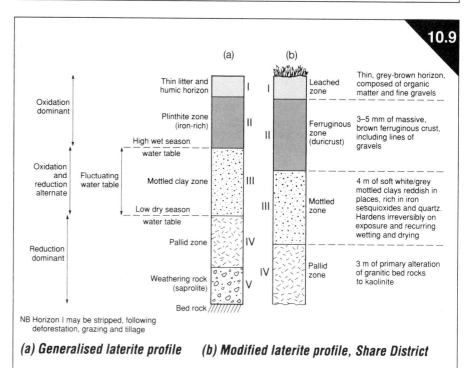

10.9

(a) Generalised laterite profile   *(b) Modified laterite profile, Share District*

NB Horizon I may be stripped, following deforestation, grazing and tillage

Laterite: A zone of hardened material, varying in texture, often with concretions, but more or less massive, consisting essentially of iron oxide with or without clastic quartz and containing small amounts of aluminium and manganese. Most frequently red in colour.

the Share District, Ilorin, Nigeria

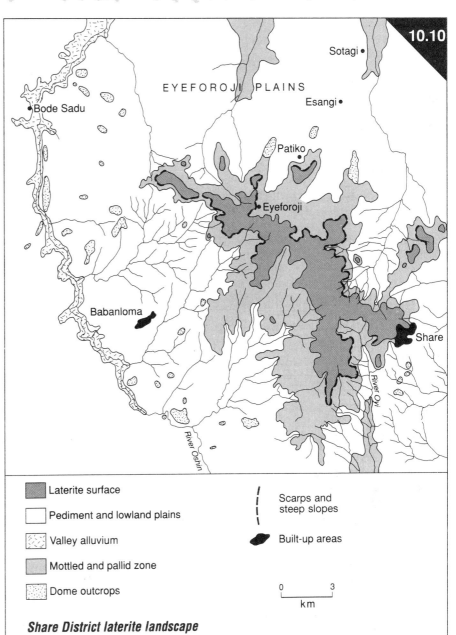

Key understandings

◆ Laterite soils are a form of latosol containing a thick iron-rich horizon in the upper profile, and the outcome of prolonged weathering.

◆ Laterite is an iron-rich zone which hardens irreversibly to a crust when exposed at the surface.

◆ The laterite zone only develops fully in regoliths with marked seasonal fluctuations in water-table.

Key / legend:

- Laterite surface
- Pediment and lowland plains
- Valley alluvium
- Mottled and pallid zone
- Dome outcrops
- Scarps and steep slopes
- Built-up areas

0 3
km

Map labels: Sotagi, EYEFOROJI PLAINS, Esangi, Bode Sadu, Patiko, Eyeforoji, Babanloma, Share, River Oyi, River Oshin

Share District laterite landscape

10.10

Laterites are developed extensively in the tropics, especially over flat, tabular and gently rolling terrain and they vary widely in detail. Yet two fundamental types have been recognised: **primary laterites**, which have evolved in situ and **secondary laterites** which are composed of lateritic materials created elsewhere, fragmented, transported and redeposited in the new location.

The two essential conditions of the weathering environment appear to be:

(i) free-draining conditions to permit active decomposition and leaching of the more mobile minerals, e.g. desilicification;

(ii) a significant seasonality in rainfall which causes fluctuations in the water-table.

Effective laterisation requires a minimum annual rainfall of 1000 mm on basic rocks and 1200 mm on acidic rocks, and while there appears to be no upper limit, there must be some seasonality.

True laterites tend to have thin litter (Ai) and humic (A2) horizons, and in many regions are thought to have developed fully only after deforestation by climatic change or human activity, e.g. laterites are widespread under savanna vegetation accepted as an **anthropogenic** climax. Exposure to erosive agencies such as water, temperature change and wind may result in the stripping of the A horizons. Once exposed, the laterite becomes indurated, creating duricrusts which cause so many of the problems for both regeneration of climax vegetation and for farming activities.

The laterites of Ilorin, Nigeria

The Share District is located in the Guinea savanna belt, where grass is interspersed with scattered fire-resistant tree species. The mean annual rainfall of 1000–1300 mm falls from April to October, causing significant water budget deficits for at least three months, and producing the fluctuating water-table essential for the full development of laterites. The crystalline and sedimentary

The complex world of the soil   199

CASE STUDY 10.4 *Laterite – a tough crust to crack – the Share District, Ilorin, Nigeria*

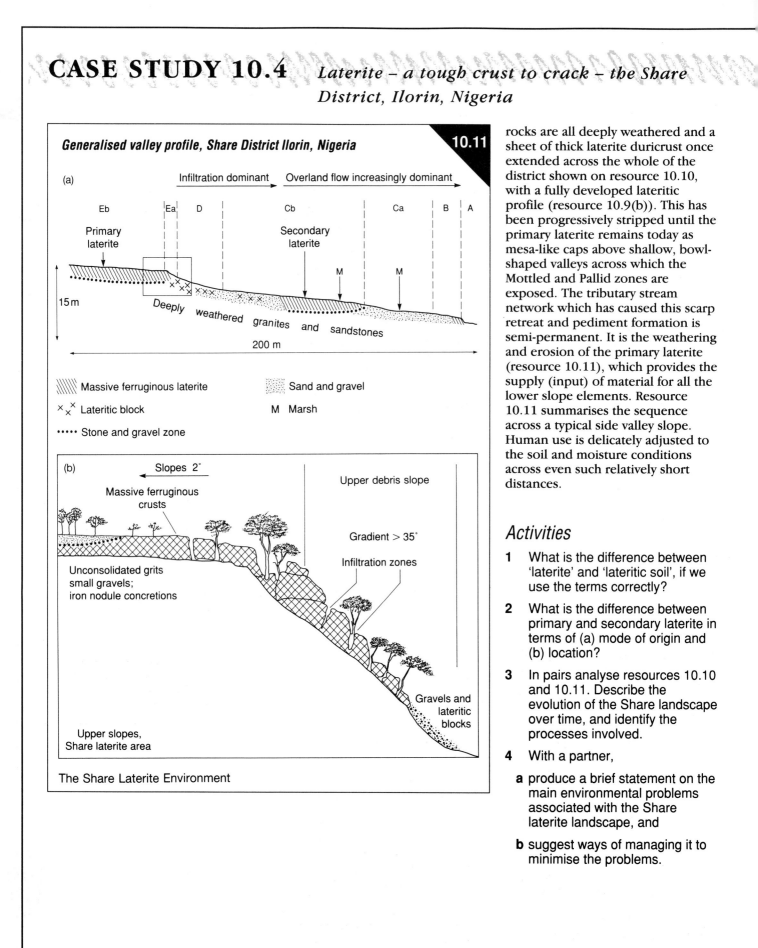

Generalised valley profile, Share District Ilorin, Nigeria 10.11

(a)

Infiltration dominant → | ← Overland flow increasingly dominant →

Eb   Ea | D   Cb   Ca   B | A

Primary laterite

Secondary laterite

M   M   M

15 m

Deeply weathered granites and sandstones

200 m

///// Massive ferruginous laterite

×ₓ× Lateritic block

••••• Stone and gravel zone

⣿ Sand and gravel

M Marsh

(b)

Slopes 2° ←

Massive ferruginous crusts

Upper debris slope

Gradient > 35°

Infiltration zones

Unconsolidated grits small gravels; iron nodule concretions

Gravels and lateritic blocks

Upper slopes, Share laterite area

The Share Laterite Environment

rocks are all deeply weathered and a sheet of thick laterite duricrust once extended across the whole of the district shown on resource 10.10, with a fully developed lateritic profile (resource 10.9(b)). This has been progressively stripped until the primary laterite remains today as mesa-like caps above shallow, bowl-shaped valleys across which the Mottled and Pallid zones are exposed. The tributary stream network which has caused this scarp retreat and pediment formation is semi-permanent. It is the weathering and erosion of the primary laterite (resource 10.11), which provides the supply (input) of material for all the lower slope elements. Resource 10.11 summarises the sequence across a typical side valley slope. Human use is delicately adjusted to the soil and moisture conditions across even such relatively short distances.

Activities

1 What is the difference between 'laterite' and 'lateritic soil', if we use the terms correctly?

2 What is the difference between primary and secondary laterite in terms of (a) mode of origin and (b) location?

3 In pairs analyse resources 10.10 and 10.11. Describe the evolution of the Share landscape over time, and identify the processes involved.

4 With a partner,

a produce a brief statement on the main environmental problems associated with the Share laterite landscape, and

b suggest ways of managing it to minimise the problems.

CASE STUDY 10.5 *Combatting soil erosion – are trees always the answer?*

Background

'All soils erode naturally. Rain washes them down slopes and they are blown away by wind. Changing the way in which land is used ... speeds up the natural pace of erosion.' (Resource 10.12.) As more soil is removed, so its yield and productivity fall. Yield is the short-term output while productivity refers to the longer-term capability of the soil to nourish vegetation. This latter ability is related to nutrient levels, water-holding ability, structural characteristics and stability. What is important to understand when studying the implications of soil erosion is that the relationship between productivity and soil loss in a locality is exponential not linear, at least in the initial stages. Thus, a small loss of soil will result in a proportionately greater decline in productivity. A second characteristic, with serious implications for many economically developing countries, is that the impact of erosion on productivity seems greater in the tropics. For example, 'farmers in the corn belt of the US may expect a decrease in yield of 100 kg/hectare for every 10 mm of soil lost. In Nigeria the same loss of soil caused an initial drop in yield of 5.8 tonnes/hectare'.

The most common remedy for soil erosion is to plant trees – the canopy protects the surface from sun, wind and rain; the roots hold the soil together; the litter enhances the organic input to the soil store. The data in this case study, from humid and semi-arid environments, asks us to question whether trees are always the best answer, especially as they are an expensive and long-term solution. All forms of erosion control cost money, and erosion is widespread. So, as this case study illustrates, it is important to select when and where to concentrate the effort. While the obvious answer may seem to be 'Where the erosion is most severe', this may be a less effective policy than attacking areas where erosion is just taking off.

Slope failure caused by heavy winter storms near Malaga, Spain, January 1990

Solutions to soil erosion

Clear a forest and erosion will strip off the soil. Plant a forest and you might save it: or so the theory goes. But theories of soil erosion owe more to myth than to hard science

The images of global dust bowls and future famine increase people's awareness of erosion but they also help to propagate a number of myths that have arisen from poor science. Failure to understand the real mechanisms of erosion may lead to the imposition of expensive, inadequate and sometimes fundamentally incorrect solutions.

Much of this confusion arises from the lack of good data from the areas where erosion is worst. Erosion varies even over short distances because of the variety of soils, vegetation and the slope of the ground. It also varies enormously through time because of seasonal patterns of rainfall and plant growth, the impact of storms of differing magnitudes and the varying rates at

which damaged soils recover. The rate of recovery depends partly on how quickly soils are broken down by weathering and on the rock over which they lie. Chalk and marl soils erode very quickly but are probably restored quickly too; other soils can take more than a century to recover. Added to these natural differences are the effects of human activity, which are almost infinitely varied.

A key area is how the covering of vegetation affects erosion. For decades, hydrologists have investigated the complex relationships between plant cover and runoff. Yet even in this case, when runoff is easy to measure and the processes are much simpler than

Key understandings

◆ Raindrops falling to the soil surface from vegetation may have as much erosional impact as direct rainfall.

◆ Planting trees may not always be the best way to combat soil erosion.

◆ Severely eroded landscapes may no longer be experiencing rapid erosion and may not be the most effective locations for erosion control projects.

Studies in both tropical Brazil and rural Bedfordshire, found that the kinetic energy of water dropping from the forest canopy and from the vegetation beneath is much greater than that of rain falling in the open. This holds true whatever the size of the storm. Other researchers have obtained similar results in the coniferous forests of New Zealand and the rainforests of Borneo. The studies showed, more precisely, that the water droplets falling from all types of plant coverings ranging from Brussels sprouts to fully grown trees, are all around 4 millimetres across (resource 10.13(a)). Given the relationship between cover and erosion, this implies that it is the lower layers of shrubs and herbs and the layer of litter that protects the soil rather than the tree canopy itself because drops falling from them have a lower velocity and less energy for erosion.

Part I: Studies in Brazil's rainforests

As part of the Royal Geographical Society's Maraca Project, a year-long study of Maraca Island on the northern edge of the Amazon Basin, a team of soil scientists and hydrologists investigated how much protection the under storey and litter give to the soil. They measured the changing levels of moisture in the soil, runoff from the surface and the amount of sediment produced from plots with different types of plant cover. Three control plots remained under virgin forest. Another three were cleared of trees, leaving the litter and understorey intact. In the third set they removed all the cover, the canopy, understorey and litter, and kept them clear throughout the experiment. In the other two plots, they let the vegetation grow more or less uninhibited.

The sites at Maraca showed that vegetation strongly influences the proportion of rainfall that runs off, although this depends on the size of

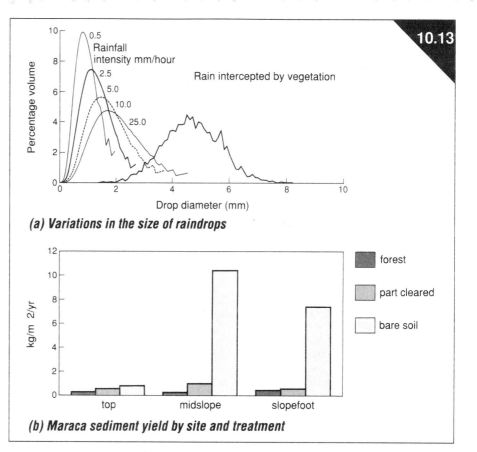

10.13

(a) Variations in the size of raindrops

(b) Maraca sediment yield by site and treatment

the storm. For very large storms, there is little difference in the amount of runoff from different plots. With smaller rains, between 50 and 80 per cent more water runs off bare plots than other plots. The evidence suggests strongly that the rate at which water infiltrates the soil is important too.

As expected, the bare plots at Maraca had the wettest soils because there were no plants to draw off the water (resource 10.13(b)). These plots also suffered the highest runoff both because they lacked plants and because the water did not infiltrate the soil very effectively. The bare plots also produced the most sediment because they lacked organic material to bind the soil. In fact, the degree of erosion was very high compared with other environments.

This is the kind of result that has led people to equate the loss of trees with the loss of soil – and to assume that they have to plant more trees to

avoid losing even more soil. But the results from the plots that were only partially cleared gave a different lesson. Although great trees had been removed, the runoff, erosion and losses of chemical nutrients were closer to those of virgin forest than from cleared areas. This seems to confirm findings from the National Institute for Amazonian Research that rates of erosion at a range of sites in Amazonia are lower than those recorded for Bedfordshire and the West Midlands.

As the experiences at Maraca show, it requires a great deal of human effort to keep land completely clear of vegetation in this prolific environment, with an annual rainfall of 2500 millimetres: nature will replenish the cover if left to its own devices. But in dry lands with less than 500 millimetres of rain a year, this is no longer true. Once vegetation is stripped from semi-arid and arid environments, it is extremely difficult to replace.

Part II: Studies in Spain

Recent calculations of the natural productivity of the dry areas of Spain suggest that the climate would not sustain such a rich vegetation as forest. So unless the climate has changed markedly in the past 10 000 years, these areas would have been extremely marginal for plants: they are the nearest thing to real deserts in mainland Europe. Despite this, the standard way of protecting the soil from further erosion is to plant trees. Although this works well in humid areas, usually on mountain slopes in the semi-arid lands, it may not be best for lowland areas that the already badly eroded, for two reasons. First, trees have great difficulty in re-establishing themselves where erosion is continuing, where water is in short supply and where, as a result of erosion, the soil is lacking in nutrients. In these conditions, the trees will even increase erosion by changing the size of raindrops, unless they have a good understorey. Secondly, even if trees do become established, they produce wood very slowly; long-term investment would be needed to ensure any meaningful economic returns.

A cheaper form of protection

Some recent experiments in Spain compared the protection given to the soil by trees, mattoral (a dense, shrubby vegetation about a metre high) and a partial covering of stones, under simulated rainfall of different intensities. Predictably, the almost unvegetated stony ground showed a large amount of erosion, though the stones certainly offer some protection. The low shrub, of species characteristic of the area between Malaga and Alicante, protects as well as a cover of trees (resource 10.12). The emerging message is that we should consider mattoral as a cheap and effective way to prevent erosion in lowland areas rather than doggedly planting trees. But the land must be protected from grazing.

There is one further paradox in the south of Spain: the amount of sediment carried in rivers or building up in reservoirs is enormously variable. Some of the landscapes that appear most barren produce the least sediment. In part, this anomaly must be the result of inaccurate measurement and infrequent observations. It is clear, however, that some of the most intensely eroded landscapes are no longer producing much sediment. The usual explanation is that the climate has changed, but there is little evidence for this over the past 6000 years.

It is more likely that some areas are so eroded that not much more erosion can take place. The process of gullying is responsible for most of the sediment, which is released as the network of natural drainage channels extends into new areas. Gullies form after nature or people strip off the vegetation, when the climate becomes drier and the vegetation sparser, or when rivers bite deeply as the land rises in response to changes in the Earth's crust. Recent research on erosion indicates that an area may become 'saturated' so that although the landscape is devastated, a kind of equilibrium sets in, resisting further change. Competition for space may prevent more gully heads from forming. At this point movement of soil downslope becomes more important than the growth of channels.

Attempts to manage erosion in these devastated areas are unlikely to help farmers. They should simply be left, protected from grazing animals. This will allow a semi-natural vegetation to grow back over the soil, protecting it from erosion as a result of water runoff and reducing the risk of flood damage. The most critical areas are those where erosion is just beginning: protection is very expensive, and it should be directed where it will do most good.

Key problems

At the core of the range of problems related to soil erosion is its relationship with vegetation, especially in the earliest stages of abandonment, whether by a slash-and-burn farmer, as part of a crop rotation that leaves land fallow, or as part of a policy of set-aside (taking the land out of farming). At this point, there is essentially a competition between vegetation cover and erosion: sometimes one wins, sometimes the other. If erosion can establish a hold, it causes more erosion through a positive feedback. Stripping off the cover exposes soils that cannot absorb so much water, so encouraging higher runoff and further erosion. The loss of cover also impoverishes the remaining soil, making it harder for plants to establish themselves. But if vegetation can establish itself, it protects the soil and encourages more vegetation by increasing the soil's capacity to hold water and providing organic binding agents. In semi-arid areas the plant cover also shades the ground, lowering temperatures and decreasing the amount of water lost by evaporation, and preventing crusts from forming on the surface of the soil. A hard crust encourages runoff and makes erosion worse.

(Source: adapted from J Thornes, 'Solutions to Soil Erosion', *New Scientist*, 3 June 1989, pp.45–49.)

Activities

1   The article on which this case study is based has the sub-title: 'Clear a forest and erosion will strip off the soil. Plant a forest and you might save it: or so the theory goes. But theories of soil erosion owe more to myth than to hard science'.

From the evidence presented, explain what the author means and why he selected this sub-title.

2   Why does the author suggest that it is more cost-effective and efficient to focus soil erosion on areas of incipient rather than advanced erosion? Is this true in all circumstances?

CHAPTER 11

Ecosystems at work

Introduction

An ecosystem is 'an ecological unit composed of living and non-living components interacting to produce a stable system.' Such a functional unit can be seen as operating at all scales, e.g. from an individual tree (resource 11.2) to a forest and from a sand-dune (resource 11.1) to a sand desert. Such environmental systems are open systems. In addition to energy and matter moving in circular paths within the boundaries of a system, energy and matter also cross into, move through and exit from the system. Further, there remain today, few if any ecosystems in which these movements and stores have not been influenced directly or indirectly, accidentally or intentionally by human activities. In many ecosystems, humans have become the **ecological dominants.**

Energy flowing through an ecosystem is directed, stored and used by the components of the system. Competition for access to this energy produces an organisation in which the living components exist as a mesh of inter-related and competing individuals, e.g. food chains, food webs. A fundamental question in ecology has been whether this ordered organisation arises from separate decision-making by the individual parts or as an expression of some communal benefit. The latter idea suggests that an ecosystem may be working towards some goal, such as 'stability', based on an optimum level of organisation and species diversity.

This 'steady state' model often expresses itself as the **climatic climax vegetation,** the process by which biological communities evolve through successional seral stages towards a stable condition. Succession generates species diversity and diversity reinforces stability. Disturbance will be followed by **seral succession** to the steady state once more. In recent years this model has been increasingly questioned. An alternative model proposes that ecosystems should be viewed as **non-equilibrium** systems which exhibit stability as a result of fluctuations in the mortality rhythms of individual species. In this model, disturbance plays a more central role. An example of this thinking is given in a 1978 report by the US Forestry Service:

'Diversity of species is viewed as a consequence of the dynamics of the individuals composing the community ... An unmanaged forest behaves as a non-equilibrium, aimless community that is a consequence of the behaviour of individualistic systems.

An unmanaged forest has no centralised information network and a decision mechanism to direct the mortality and behaviour of individuals. Thus there can be no goals such as achieving and maintaining stability. If there were such a goal, evolution and extinction could not have occurred as indicated by the fossil and genetic evidence for billions of years.'

Both models stress the dynamics of ecosystems. A key difference is the role of disturbance and the response of the ecosystem to it. This aspect of the way ecosystems work, change and survive is becoming increasingly significant as human impacts spread and intensify. This provides a central theme of the case studies. A second theme is the critical evaluation of several popular perceptions about ecosystems and human interactions with them.

11.1

Dunes on 90-mile beach, Victoria, Australia. Note the vegetation sequence across the dune

The first case study of an English woodland, focuses upon medium-term dynamics as the woodland matures and has to cope with disturbances. In conclusion it compares these trends with those of a tropical rainforest ecosystem. The second case study gives evidence from the forester's viewpoint of the beneficial impacts of logging upon a forest, questioning the popular opinion that logging is detrimental to the health of a forest ecosystem. The exercise which follows reviews the various human causes of forest disturbance and destruction. The third case study evaluates the perception that shifting cultivation sustains ecosystem equilibrium, presenting evidence that even such relatively low intensity disturbances ultimately cause changes. The final case study uses the Namibian desert, one of the driest, harshest environments in the world, to illustrate adaptability, resilience and opportunism in ecosystems.

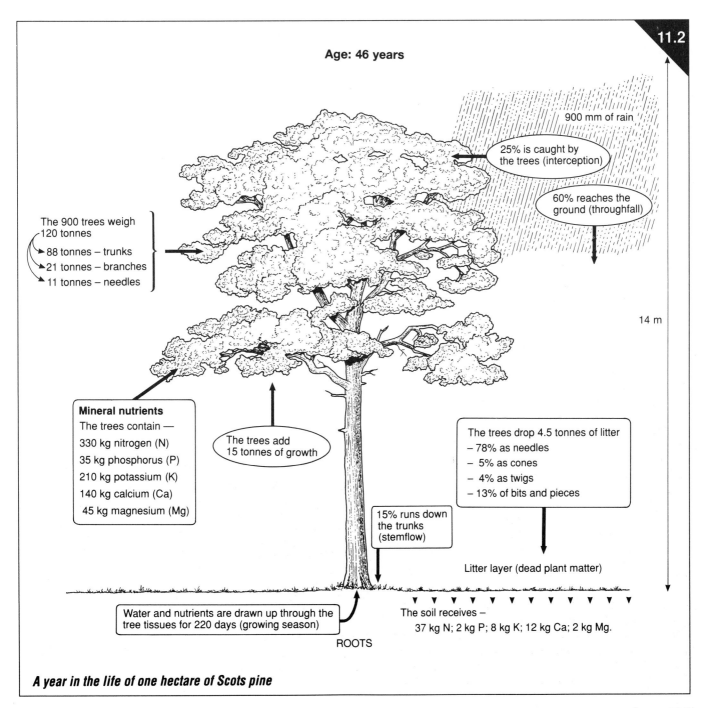

11.2

Age: 46 years

900 mm of rain

25% is caught by the trees (interception)

60% reaches the ground (throughfall)

14 m

The 900 trees weigh 120 tonnes
➤ 88 tonnes – trunks
➤ 21 tonnes – branches
➤ 11 tonnes – needles

Mineral nutrients
The trees contain —
330 kg nitrogen (N)
35 kg phosphorus (P)
210 kg potassium (K)
140 kg calcium (Ca)
45 kg magnesium (Mg)

The trees add 15 tonnes of growth

The trees drop 4.5 tonnes of litter
– 78% as needles
– 5% as cones
– 4% as twigs
– 13% of bits and pieces

15% runs down the trunks (stemflow)

Litter layer (dead plant matter)

Water and nutrients are drawn up through the tree tissues for 220 days (growing season)

ROOTS

The soil receives –
37 kg N; 2 kg P; 8 kg K; 12 kg Ca; 2 kg Mg.

A year in the life of one hectare of Scots pine

Background

Lady Park Wood (GR. 546145) is a small section of High Meadow Woods on the edge of the Forest of Dean. The 35 hectare stand of mixed native broadleaf trees was designated an unmanaged nature reserve in 1944. For centuries it had been managed as coppice woodland, and this had allowed the native mixture of beech, oak, ash, lime, elm, birch, maple and hazel to survive. Approximately 20 hectares was felled in 1943 and has since been left to regenerate. This case study focuses on the remaining 15 hectares, known as 'old growth' woodland, which has been largely untouched since 1902 and is dominated by trees which began their growth between 1800 and 1900.

The reserve lies on the north east flank of a spur of Carboniferous Limestone cut into by a wide meander of the River Wye (resource 11.3). Apart from a 30 m strip along the spur crest, the wood clads the slopes, varying in character across the several slope components (resource 11.4).

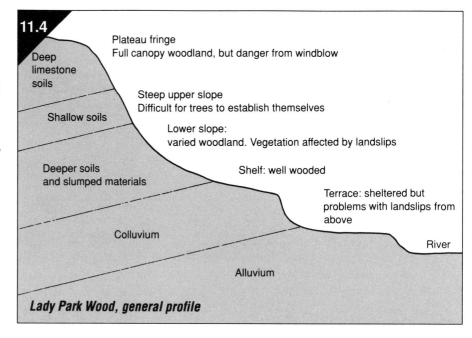

Plateau fringe
Full canopy woodland, but danger from windblow

Deep limestone soils

Shallow soils

Steep upper slope
Difficult for trees to establish themselves

Lower slope:
varied woodland. Vegetation affected by landslips

Deeper soils and slumped materials

Shelf: well wooded

Terrace: sheltered but problems with landslips from above

Colluvium

River

Alluvium

Lady Park Wood, general profile

The woodland dynamics

The 19th century management of the woodland kept oak and beech as the main canopy trees, with other tree species, e.g. ash, elm, lime, largely as coppiced under-wood. Although such management ceased almost a century ago, the age structure and balance of the old growth stands is still affected. For instance, oak and beech can live for up to 500 years on this type of site, but almost none are older than 180 years. Yet many features of natural deciduous woodland are found: this ancient woodland has never been completely cleared and there is a full range of tree and shrub species. Variations in species assemblages are closely adjusted to soil and slope characteristics. Thus, the stand has an almost natural structure.

Resource 11.5(b) shows that natural woodlands are constantly changing ecosystems. The outstanding difference over the 40 years is that tree density (number of trees per hectare) has almost halved, but basal

Lady Park Wood, Forest of Dean

Key understandings

◆ Distinct phases in the life of a woodland ecosystem can be identified, in terms of tree characteristics, species present and productivity.

◆ Woodland reacts sensitively to slope and soil characteristics.

◆ Woodland ecosystems tend to endure surges of relatively rapid change, separated by longer periods of slower changes. The surges may be triggered both by environmental and human factors.

woodland

Changes through time

Use the graph (A) and table (B) to illustrate an important key idea:
As woodlands mature, a process of natural thinning takes place. As the trees increase in size, so they decrease in number. Neither woodland has been thinned by humans. The changes take place because of **competition** (the strongest trees survive) and **natural disturbances** e.g. droughts, gales, disease.

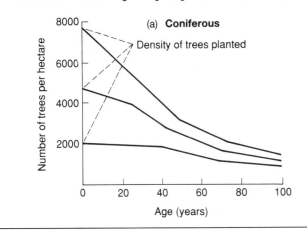

(a) Coniferous

11.5

(b) **Deciduous**

Changes in Lady Park Wood, Monmouth, 1945–1983
(Number of trees in a 35 hectare wood)

Species	1945	1955	1977	1983
Ash *	151	131	92	78
Beech	239	242	160	132
Elm	13	11	7	4
Lime	89	97	56	51
Maple *	36	29	10	6
Oak	58	56	37	36
Birch *	30	43	6	1
Total	616	509	368	298
Basal area of trees per hectare	20	25	32	9

* Pioneer species in this succession

1970s: Spread of Dutch Elm disease   1981–2: Severe gales

1976: Severe summer drought

The rate of diameter increase of the beech in the upslope stand in Lady Park Wood

11.6

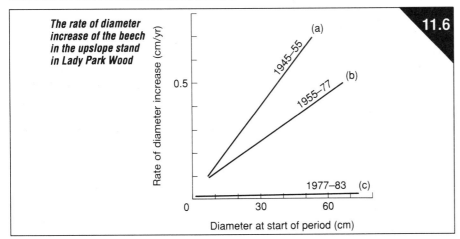

---

area (surface area taken up by tree species) has increased greatly. This is a fundamental feature of a maturing woodland: it becomes dominated by a smaller number of larger trees. Resource 11.5(a) shows that this may be true too, of single species coniferous plantations. Between 1945 and 1955, recruitment (appearance of young trees) and mortality (trees dying) were balanced. The recruits succeeded best on the margins of the stand where there is more light, while most deaths occurred among smaller trees and shrubs in the poorer light beneath the main canopy.

In the next phase, between 1955 and 1977, the increasing maturity was

illustrated by the absence of recruits but greater mortality as natural thinning took place through competition, e.g. of the 120 recruits of 1945–55, only nine remained alive in 1977. The result was fewer but larger trees.

The third phase, 1977–83, saw a marked deterioration in the health of the woodland, the chief signs being the appearance of gaps in the canopy, caused mainly by the death of beech trees. Thus, until 1977, Lady Park Wood appeared to be progressing through the orthodox successional stages towards climatic climax: tree species declined from sixteen to twelve, pioneer species were eliminated, subcanopy and

shrub layers became poorer, beech, ash, oak, lime increased their dominance and these main canopy trees decreased in number but increased in size. Basal areas of around 30 square metres/hectare and densities of approximately 400 individuals/hectare were typical of temperate deciduous woodlands. Mortality rates of canopy trees of 6 per cent per decade were normal.

Since 1977, however, mortality has accelerated to 4 per cent a year, and clearly the woodland is experiencing a phase of disturbance or 'stand disintegration'. As the introduction to this chapter has outlined (page 206), the traditional model of succession through seral stages to a steady state of climatic climax vegetation is being increasingly questioned. The alternative hypothesis, that ecosystems are subject to recurrent episodes of disturbance followed by longer periods of successional recovery, seems to be supported by the recent history of Lady Park Wood. Research identifies four agencies triggering the 'stand disintegration' phase:

1 Drought is a natural intermittent factor, and the 1976 drought 'was the most severe within the lifetime of the present stand'. It affected the beeches more

severely than the other main species, especially on the upper slope.

2 'The semi-natural disturbance of Dutch Elm disease, which was introduced to Britain by man, but spread naturally to Lady Park Wood.'

3 The instability of the steeper slopes causing loss of vegetation through landslips.

4 'Damaging gales have been a rare, but regular feature' causing windthrow, 'a natural factor, whose impact has probably been increased as a by-product of the drought and disease, and by the reduced shelter brought about by felling plantations to the west of the reserve.'

The impact of the disturbance can be seen by studying the growth pattern of beech, the main tree species (resource 11.6). Positive and vigorous growth rates 1945–77 are replaced by low growth and even shrinkage since 1977. Reviewing the situation in 1983, the researchers found that more beeches were dying and regeneration was poor. Since then there have been the severe droughts of 1989 and 1990, which are likely to prolong the 'stand disintegration' episode. The conclusion is that 'with the increased mortality and loss of vitality of both beech and elm, the trees which appear to be best placed to take advantage are ash and lime'. Neither are affected by drought and disease, and both germinate and regenerate readily. 'The prospect is therefore of a mixture in which ash and lime are balanced with beech. Oak is not regenerating.' This trend may be influenced by acid rain or other pollutants as there is concern over native hardwoods across southern England (resource 11.7).

(Source: adapted from: G F Peterken and E W Jones, 'Forty Years of Change in Lady Park Wood: The old-growth stands', *Journal of Ecology*, (75) 1987, pp.477–512.)

11.7

Greenpeace blames tree deaths on air pollution

Threequarters of the yew trees, half the oaks, and a third of beeches in southern England are sick or dying, probably from air pollution, the environmental group, Greenpeace, claims in a report published today.

The figures, based on a survey this summer by Mr Andrew Tickle, pre-empt the Forestry Commission's more widely based tree survey, to be published in the next couple of weeks.

The Greenpeace scientist's figures for oaks and beeches are slightly more cheerful than those published by the commission last year, which put Britain among the unhealthiest countries in Europe for broadleaved trees. It found the worst damage in the north and west.

The commission says oak and beech appear to have denser foliage, showing good health, in areas of the south and east which have the highest pollution levels, either because these areas are most favourable for tree growth or because pollutants like sulphate, nitrate and ammonia stimulate growth.

Dr John Innes, the scientist in charge of its surveys, says the links between pollution and tree damage are complex and difficult to evaluate. The commission is not expected to go much further in confirming the link in its new report.

Mr Tickle admits there is no clear proof that acid rain is responsible, but says the damage cannot be explained by weather or disease.

He quotes a recent House of Commons environment committee report on acid rain that the commission 'stands alone in its refusal to accept a nexus between air pollution and forest damage'.

His survey, based on the density of foliage on about 1100 trees, shows that 10 per cent of oak, 5 per cent of beech and 4 per cent of yew are healthy, while 53 per cent of oak, 39 per cent of beech and 74 per cent of yew are moderately or severely damaged.

(Source: John Ardill, *The Guardian*, 17 November 1988)

The mean percentage of moderately and severely damaged trees over sites surveyed in each county

	Beech	Oak	Yew
Avon	47	82	85
Dorset	29	37	89
Gloucester	49	53	74
Wiltshire	37	62	79
Berkshire	38	35	38
Hampshire	45	67	74
Buckingham	18	50	77
Surrey	50	33	55
Sussex	51	57	84
Kent	34	36	60

Activities

1 a Divide the period 1944–1983 into its main ecological phases.

b Summarise the main characteristics of each and suggest causes for these characteristics.

c Suggest how these trends illustrate the dynamics of woodland ecosystems.

2 The data of resource 11.8 (a)-(f), are for a similar period in the life of a tropical rainforest stand in Puerto Rico.

a Outline what these graphs tell us about the dynamics of tropical rainforests.

b Compare and contrast the changes and trends in the El Verde forest and Lady Park Wood.

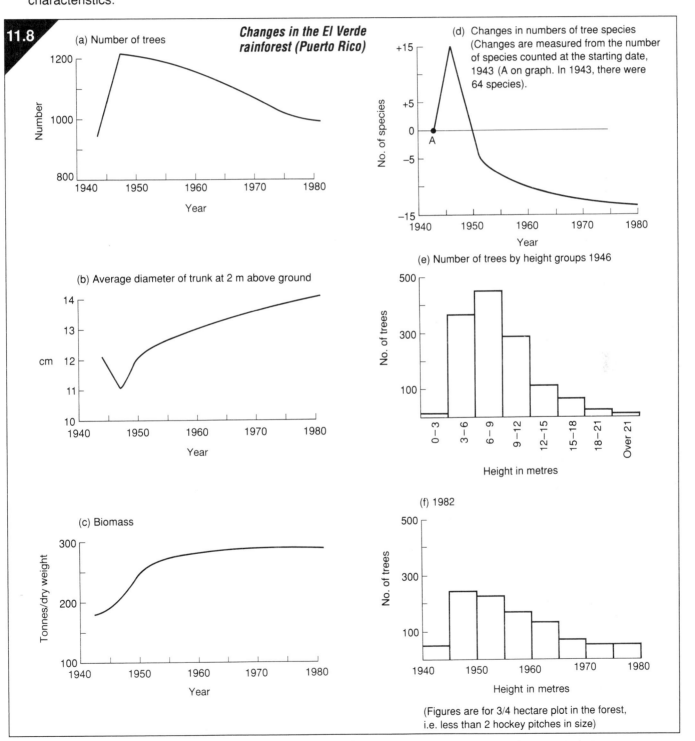

11.8

Changes in the El Verde rainforest (Puerto Rico)

(a) Number of trees

(b) Average diameter of trunk at 2 m above ground

(c) Biomass

(d) Changes in numbers of tree species (Changes are measured from the number of species counted at the starting date, 1943 (A on graph. In 1943, there were 64 species).

(e) Number of trees by height groups 1946

(f) 1982

(Figures are for 3/4 hectare plot in the forest, i.e. less than 2 hockey pitches in size)

Background

A tropical rainforest is garlanded with superlatives: it houses more species than any other ecosystem and so is earth's most valuable gene bank; it is the most productive terrestial ecosystem in terms of biomass output; it is the oldest major ecosystem, having survived climatic fluctuations for more than 1 million years by shrinking back to warm, moist 'refuges' during periods of global cooling, to advance again as climate ameliorated; it is the most constant ecosystem, with the smallest seasonal fluctuations of moisture and heat energy. These special qualities together with our growing understanding of the long-term implications of the accelerating deforestation have turned conservation of tropical rainforests into such a high profile crusade. Added impetus is given by the ethical issues surrounding the rainforests as homes for 'defenceless' societies and endangered species.

At least three-quarters of the massive forest clearance is caused by traditional shifting cultivators and new settlers seeking to grow subsistence and commercial crops and to rear animals. We must remember too, that most of the 70 or so countries which possess tropical rainforests are enduring population growth rates of more than 3 per cent and rank among the 'poorer' nations of the world (resource 11.9). Nevertheless, other 'culprits' receive much attention, e.g. governments with high-tech dam and reservoir schemes, rich plantation and ranch owners, international mining and logging companies.

There is no doubt that much deforestation has been wasteful and environmentally disastrous. There is truth too, in the concept that while the complex structure of rainforests, with its many highly specialised species, is stable when undisturbed, it rapidly becomes 'fragile' once disrupted, i.e. positive feedback takes over rapidly (resource 11.10) and gives rise to 'Hands off Rainforests' slogans and calls for National Parks and Biosphere Reserves, for example. Yet as pressures for space and resources mount relentlessly, it is inevitable that tropical rainforests must be used and some will be lost. This case study focuses upon one aspect: commercial logging. It uses research evidence from Australia to explore whether positive management can sustain the forest ecosystem while drawing on its resources. Note that the evidence presented is that of the Queensland Department of Forestry, which has a specific perspective.

Key understandings

◆ Tropical rainforests are complex ecosystems.

◆ That non-equilibrium created by recurring disturbances, rather than a steady-state condition in an ecosystem, may provide optimum species diversity and productivity.

◆ Management techniques should reflect and take into account natural structures and processes if sustained yield is to be the aim.

11.9

Time to face the facts about tropical forest destruction

Having recently returned from two countries listed by Friends of the Earth as major destroyers of tropical rain forest – Cameroon and Ivory Coast – I am disturbed at some aspects of the current campaign. Both countries are currently facing a dramatic decline in foreign exchange earnings due to the collapse in cocoa and coffee prices. Yet we are demanding that they stop exports of one of their more profitable lines – tropical timber. The campaign is based on far too narrow an information base to have a significant impact on the loss of Africa's rain forest.

Most African countries are doubling their populations every 20 years or less. To ignore this problem only weakens the impact of the campaign. It is in fact at the root of nearly all the forest destruction that is going on. In Brazil the need to open new land, build new roads and develop hydro-electric power is at least partly the result of population expansion. In Africa it is a much greater cause of forest destruction than the logging companies. We need a much more sympathetic approach to the countries of Africa which are in such a desperate position economically. Most of them are looking for investment from this country and there is no doubt that they would welcome investments in sustainable forestry. The Commonwealth Development Corporation would be extremely well placed to manage an initiative in this direction.

(Ronald Watts, Pen-y-cae, Swansea, *The Guardian*, 8 August 1989)

Fighting for the rainforest and their way of life: protestors in Sarawak, 1989

Key characteristics of the rainforest `11.11`

Natural forest	Under human impact
1 The oldest major ecosystem in the world	Young controlled ecosystem containing many introduced species
2 The most variegated and complex of the world's ecosystems	The more severe the human impact the simpler and more impoverished the ecosystem in terms of species numbers
3 The most productive land eco-system in terms of biomass produced/unit area/unit time	Reduction in biomass per unit area and often a reduction in productivity over time
4 High radiant energy inputs and fluxes throughout the year sustain high rates of chemical and biological reactions and cycling, emphasised by an absence of seasonality	A slowing down of chemical and bio-logical reactions and cycling. A tendency for more marked seasonality.
5 Rainfall and moisture availability not net radiation, are the controlling factors of plant growth.	Increased tendency for extremes of moisture availability: waterlogging/flood to desiccation. Reduced radiation energy absorbed by biota
6 Highly sophisticated life-form adaptations, and strong set of built-in balancing mechanisms	Increased susceptibility to hazards
7 Great stability of climax structure, i.e. HOMEOSTASIS, with dominance of NEGATIVE FEEDBACK	Reduced resilience and increased fragility, i.e. RHEXISTASIS, with increased tendency for POSITIVE FEEDBACK
8 A marked constancy of environmental conditions	Likelihood of increased fluctuations in environmental conditions.

Logging is good for the wood: the case put by the Queensland Department of Forestry

At least 70 per cent of the remaining rainforest in North Queensland is protected from logging activities, and less than 20 per cent has commercial potential. The Queensland Department of Forestry (QDF) has developed a management policy which attempts to accommodate ecological, aesthetic, ethical and economic values. It has accepted that extensive clear felling is undesirable, and has explored alternatives. It has rejected 'enrichment planting', in which commercially useful species are planted within existing forests, as research found that it was labour-intensive, costly, and to achieve commercially useful growth rates required 'massive canopy disturbance'. A second alternative has been plantations of native and non-native species of hardwoods, especially on deforested and degraded land. Results have been disappointing, e.g. animals and insects devoured young trees; growth rates were no better than in natural forests, and more expensive to achieve.

In contrast, research has shown that well-managed selective logging can sustain and, at times, enrich the forest. This involves a 40–50 year cycle of felling up to 20 per cent of the useful species trees. The QDF bases its current policy goals of **sustained yield** and **multiple use** on this method. It bases its case on the idea that periodic disturbance and a non-equilibrium or dynamic-equilibrium state produce a better forest ecosystem:

'It is a popular view that succession follows an inexorable path towards a forest dominated by more mature phase species, in which the greatest diversity of life forms and species is maintained. The corollary is that disturbances such as cyclical logging will lead to the extinction of mature phase species by continually deflecting the succession at any earlier stage ... Studies of Queensland rainforests ... suggest that the greatest diversity of species occurs only in a non-equilibrium state,' and 'the frequency and intensity of disturbance have been crucially important in determining the floristic composition of rainforest.'

The information below, an extract from the QDF 1984 Management Plan, summarises how the policy builds upon the natural dynamics of the rainforest ecosystem, i.e. the way it works. The following sections present evidence in answer to questions about the impact of logging. Remember – the evidence is about selective logging not clear felling.

Does logging make the forest less productive?

'Resource 11.12 shows the results from three types of 'growth and yield' research plots: (i) undisturbed virgin forest; (ii) selectively logged forest left to regenerate naturally; (iii) selectively logged forest where recovery has been assisted by 'treatment', i.e. management to ensure that light reaches young commercial species. Note the use of the standard measure for tree growth: DBH, or Diameter at Breast height = the diameter of the tree trunk, measured at chest height of an adult. From the graphs 'it is clear that logging results in improved diameter increment on the remaining stand, and the silvicultural treatment (woodland management) provides further improvement'. Resource 11.13 reviews the results in terms of volume and growth. Only trees of more than 40 cm DBH are given as this is the minimum size for commercial logging. In fact, few trees of less than 60 cm DBH are actually felled.

But what about damage to the remaining forest?

A major criticism of logging is that even where only a small number of trees are removed, there is extensive damage to the remaining forest. Figures from Amazonia and Malaysia have suggested that at least six out of every ten remaining trees of all ages are destroyed or significantly damaged. The Queensland research shows that such destructiveness need not occur (resource 11.14), although the figure of 42 per cent of the residual stand (commercial species remaining after logging) is still considerable. The figures are for commercial species, but researchers claim that 'the percentages of damaged and destroyed stems (trunks) remain the same even when non-commercial stems are included' and 'that 1.32 per cent of stems is lost for each tree felled per hectare'.

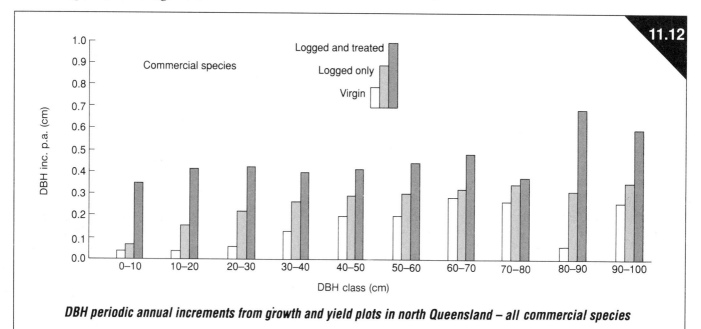

DBH periodic annual increments from growth and yield plots in north Queensland – all commercial species

But will the main canopy species regenerate after logging?

The intense competition for space and energy, and the poor dispersal and germination records of many canopy tree species make regrowth of these species variable (resource 11.15). Furthermore, the absence of certain species of sub-canopy trees could disrupt or deflect the succession. It has been suggested that logging makes these tendencies more likely. The QDF research does not support these suggestions, and concludes that 'the mosaic of logged and undisturbed patches resulting from selective logging suggests that the conditions for successful regeneration are assured'. They quote several case studies to support this conclusion:

(i) Warwick Forestry District: 'Sufficient regeneration of the later seral species is produced at a relatively early age about the margins of the canopy gaps to ensure adequate restocking with prime quality species'.

(ii) Millaa Millaa District, on a site cleared for grazing in 1937 and abandoned soon afterwards: 'Regrowth forest is capable of growing back within 40 years to the same basal area (surface area covered by tree trunks/hectare) as virgin rainforest. The stand lacks large individual trees ... The regrowth sites have a good representation of commercial species and the initial flush of pioneer species has degenerated and is being replaced by species characteristic of the mature rainforest'.

11.13

Annual growth rates of commercial species (cu.m/ha)

Plot type	Increment	Mortality	Recruits
1 Virgin forest	−0.6	2.3	0.5
2 Selectively logged	0.3	0.7	0.7
3 Selectively logged and treated	0.5	0.5	1.1

Increment = growth; *Mortality* = volume of trees dying;
Recruits = trees reaching the 40cm DBH category during the year

N.B. *Only trees of >40cm DBH are included*

1 High mortality in the virgin plots is made up by the ingrowth of recruits, thus the figures are 'consistent with the classic concept of a virgin rainforest, where growth is balanced by death and decay'.

2 Logged plots show lower mortality, indicating that selective logging harvests trunks which would otherwise die naturally. Overall production rates of the commercial species are 75% greater than in virgin forest.

3 The treated plots show the lowest mortality, and highest ingrowth of recruits. Production is three times that of virgin plots.

Conclusion: 'Selectively logged and, particularly, silviculturally treated stands are well structured, productive forests, with the potential for good production in the future'.

11.14

Impact of selective logging
(commercial species >20cm DBH)

Commercial trunks	Virgin sites	Re-cut sites
Number of trunks/hectare	156	128
Number of trunks logged/hectare	17	14
Volume logged (cubic m/ha)	63	34
Condition of remaining trunks		
Destroyed (%)	12.7	5.3
Damaged (%)	20.7	24.7
Severely damaged (%)	8.6	14.5
Little or no damage (%)	58.0	55.5

Change in species numbers **11.15**

	Unlogged plot	Heavily logged plot	Normally logged plot	Normally logged plot
No. of species before logging	104	76	88	83
15 years later:				
Number of species	96	62	80	76
Species gained	2	6	2	2
Species lost	10	21	10	7

But do all the species survive after logging?

It is often claimed that the secondary rainforest which regenerates after logging never regains the full species diversity of primary forest, and the more extensive the area logged the greater the chances of species depletion. Thus, the following conclusion from studies on three selectively logged and one unlogged plot each approximately 0.3 ha should be treated cautiously: 'The logged plots exhibit virtually no change directly as a result of logging in the proportions of different species ... There is no evidence that logging systematically and permanently removes any species from the stand.' Resource 11.15 indicates that species numbers do fall, but the researchers claim that there are similar reductions in the species numbers on the unlogged plot, reflecting the natural forest dynamics of the ecosystem (see the case study about Lady Park Wood on page 207). The QDF regard the 50 year logging cycle as giving sufficient time for the species range to recover and be sustained.

But will logging increase runoff and erosion?

As logging temporarily opens up the forest canopy and exposes parts of the land surface, potential environmental impacts include increased surface runoff, soil compaction, erosion and stream sedimentation, especially on hilly catchments (resource 11.16). For example, logging tracks lay bare at least 6 per cent of the surface area, and can expose 20 per cent. In contrast, it is claimed that undisturbed forest acts as a sponge and a protective blanket. Studies in Amazonia, for example, have shown many streams to be remarkably clear and to be transporting low sediment and solute loads.

The QDF evidence confirms that logging does influence runoff and sedimentation. Suspended sediment loads doubled in the years immediately following logging

disturbance, but then declined steadily. However, two interesting findings are that overland flow (surface runoff) is common in undisturbed forest and that there are significant differences from slope crest to slope foot. Resource 11.17 shows water movement from three storms during April 1977 (after the main monsoon) in Wyvuri catchment near Babinda, the location of case study 8.6, which illustrates the

intensity of tropical rainfall. The results show that:

'during post-monsoonal storms, overland flow is the dominant process on the upper slope site, but is restricted to the intensity peaks of the storm on the lower slope sites, with subsurface flow becoming much more important'. In the more intense storms of the monsoon period, overland flow is dominant

Deforestation on steep slopes: Daintree River, North Queensland

Runoff response in undisturbed forest, Wyvuri

	Storms		
	1	2	3
Total rainfall (mm)	51.3	41.3	121.6
Storm duration (hours)	6.0	4.5	12.0
Max. 6 min. rainfall (mm)	5.3	6.6	4.3
Max. 60 min. rainfall (mm)	16.5	17.8	20.7
Runoff (litres):–			
Lower slope site A			
Surface	283	464	1030
0.25m depth	336	265	526
0.5m depth	66	47	90
Lower slope site B			
Surface	13	43	38
0.25m depth	75	9	57
0.5m depth	No data	3	25
Upper slope site			
Surface	508	812	1229
0.25m depth	48	30	64
0.5m depth	Little	Little	Little

across all parts of the slope. All the local soils are permeable in the top 0.2 m zone, with lower horizons having lower infiltration capacities. Thus, in heavy storms, a perched water table develops, leading to saturation of the upper zone and hence to surface runoff.

As a result of these findings, the QDF makes two basic **management proposals**:

1 To protect the critical lower slopes and stream banks: 'The retention of undisturbed streamside buffer strips whose prime function is to prevent harvesting operations creating soil disturbance in the streambed or along the immediate banks. In the intense rainfall, even small catchment areas can produce large discharges, and any streambed disturbance can contribute large quantities of sediment to downstream areas. The frequency of stream rises ensures that disturbed areas have little chance to revegetate before the next storm and remain active sources of sediment for long periods.'

2 To minimise the area laid bare by logging tracks: 'Management of the track network is potentially the greatest influence on water movement through the forest, and appropriate location and drainage is important. Planning reduces the area of bare soil and drainage reduces water velocity on the bare surfaces ... Reduction of water velocity is vital where there are deeply weathered, loosely consolidated subsoil horizons.' Exposure of these horizons can 'cause spectacular on-site erosion'.

(Source: 'Rainforest Research in North Queensland: A position paper', *Queensland Department of Forestry*, Queensland 1983).

Activities

1 You have been asked to speak in a debate on the motion: 'We must learn to use and to conserve tropical rainforests'. Use the materials of this case study to write a 5-minute speech supporting this motion.

2 Use resources 11.18 and 11.19 as the basis for a brief report on (a) the causes and impacts of deforestation on the environment and upon the people, and (b) government role and responses to this destruction.

11.18 **Ivory Coast's forests fall victim to the cash crop**

Lieutenant Dangui Anga of the Ivory Coast police stationed his men on the edge of the forest under cover of darkness. At first light a three-pronged assault began as the police surrounded the sleepy bush villages and arrested the inhabitants. Operation Knuckleduster was a model manoeuvre, but this was not a military exercise. The assailants, members of Ivory Coast's Forestry Commission, had been sent to clear the area of illegal occupants.

The Upper Sassandra reserve, which covers 400 square miles in the west of Ivory Coast, is a protected forest area, but during Operation Knuckleduster it was found, as in other supposedly sacrosanct forest areas, that much of the land had been cleared of trees and made into farmland by clandestine planters.

Twenty years ago there were 70 000 square miles of primary forests, but large-scale commercial logging, slash-and-burn farming, scavenging for fuel-wood and an intensive cash-crop drive have reduced it to 4000 square miles. To stop this plunder the government has threatened to ban the export of tropical timber, still the country's third-biggest foreign exchange earner, as soon as its strained finances can bear the loss.

But deforestation is continuing at an annual rate of 1200 square miles, and replanting amounts to only 18 square miles.

Soundele Konan, head of Sodefor, the Ivorian agency responsible for forestry development, nevertheless says: 'There is no point in preserving the forests just for the sake of preserving them. They must be useful.' This was the policy of the 1970s, when Ivory Coast was dubbed 'Africa's economic miracle' and reaped huge windfalls from high-priced cocoa and coffee, grown mainly by smallholders in cleared forest land.

The large European logging companies operating throughout West Africa insist that they cannot be blamed for forest depletion. They claim that less than 10 per cent of the wood available is potentially marketable, as European buyers want only a handful of the 100 or so species in Ivorian forests. But independent experts point out that for every cubic yard of wood felled intentionally by the loggers, a further five are destroyed in the process.

The same experts believe that the main culprits are the smallscale cash-croppers, who for the past 25 years have been encouraged by the Ivorian and other governments to make the forest their own. Would-be planters follow the tracks cut by loggers through the forest, pick their patch, and then hack or burn down trees to cultivate cash crops.

Bush fires are another constant problem in Ivory Coast. Until recently they were contained in the savannah areas by a dense belt of humid forest, but that natural fire-break has disintegrated as the trees have thinned out, often with disastrous consequences. During the 1983 dry season more than 46 000 square miles of forest, savannah and plantations were destroyed by fire.

The Ivorian government has now adopted a number of measures, apart from the threat of a timber export ban, to try and save the remaining forests. The latest plan is to allocate plots of land to agricultural workers who will then be responsible for policing the forests. The object of the exercise, says a government official, 'is to turn the poacher into gamekeeper'. However, the environmental damage done by deforestation is all but irreparable. Scientists say the weather has become increasingly dry over the past 20 years, and this year's rainy season is six weeks late.

Meanwhile, foreign logging companies have already started pulling out of Ivory Coast and are heading for other countries on the continent where the pickings are, for the time being at least, richer.

(Source: Gerald Bourke, *The Independent*, 13 July 1987)

CASE STUDY 11.2 *Can tropical rainforests withstand logging activities?*

Forest War

Troops clear the Thai hills

High up in the province of Kampaeng Phet, in the dusty little marketplace of Klong Samakkee, Thai soldiers have thrown a barricade across the only road leading into the bare hills. Farm families living above the barrier have been ordered to leave. Residents of Klong Samakkee will be the next to go. By early summer the entire area down to the broad valley of the Mae Ping River will be cleared. By one estimate, 20 000 people are affected. Those with no place to go will be resettled by the government. Most of the evacuees are hill people of the Hmong and Yao tribes who have no Thai citizenship. Their offence is that they are farmers who have squatted on government forestlands and tilled them the old-fashioned way: they slash and burn.

The army swung into action after the Bangkok government finally came to grips with the fact that more than two decades of slash-and-burn farming, combined with illegal logging and improved agricultural techniques, has wiped out some of Thailand's most valuable stands of teak and sandalwood – and the remainder is going fast. A report made public last month by the UN Economic and Social Commission for Asia and the Pacific concluded that between 1961 and 1985, Thailand lost nearly half of its timberlands. In the mountains of Kampaeng Phet province, hundreds of square miles of watershed were stripped of trees. As a result, irrigation ditches are in danger of silting up, and the plains below are vulnerable to flooding. 'The forests are like a sponge,' says the UN report's author, West German Geographer Ulrich Scholz. 'They retain water in the wet season, and they deliver water in the dry season. It is a very fragilely balanced ecology.'

The evacuation of Klong Samakkee has its origins in the destruction of provincial timberlands, which began with the building of a strategic road in 1963. Learning that virgin forest had become accessible, hill tribespeople in search of farmland migrated from hundreds of miles away. The first who squatted in the area were welcomed by road builders nervous about attacks from Communist insurgents then roaming the region. 'They let us in as a buffer,' recalls Kaw Yoon, one of the early settlers. 'Now they don't want us anymore.' Kaw Yoon will be moved because he cleared and tilled eight acres of land, and when the soil became exhausted four years later, he slashed and burned another eight acres nearby. Along with others among his fellows, Kaw Yoon will be given land in government-funded 'agricultural villages' in neighbouring Tak province.

The evacuation drive is run by Lieut. General Ruamsak Chaicomintr, the Third Army region commander who helped lead a successful campaign to rid parts of Thailand's north of opium-poppy cultivation. 'The hill people are destroying forests not only up here,' he says, 'but also in the central plains and even down south. We have to stop them.' That will take some doing. Many now being told to leave Klong Samakkee were among those settled nearby on 32 000 acres a decade ago. After five years, most had taken to the hills again.

Slash-and-burn farming is part of a broader problem created by unscrupulous logging companies and land-hungry Thai peasants from rice-rich lowland areas. 'Thailand has had an agricultural revolution,' says Scholz, who points out that lowland farmers are growing not only more rice but also such cash crops as tapioca, maize and sugarcane. At the same time, the population has doubled, land use has tripled, and pressure has grown on the government to open up new areas for agriculture. 'People want to improve their lives,' says Scholz. 'Thus the main cause of deforestation in Thailand is agricultural expansionism.' If that is the case, resettling the hill people will be merely a temporary solution.

(Source: Lloyd Garrison, *Time,* March 17, 1986.)

CASE STUDY 11.3   *Shifting agriculture and tropical rainforest ecosystems – the Bismarck Range, Papua New Guinea*

Background

It is often argued that traditional societies live 'in harmony with the rainforest' and hence do not destroy its natural equilibrium. Hunters and collectors adapt to the natural rhythms of the forest. Shifting cultivators occupy small plots for a year or two, then move on, allowing vegetation and soils to recover for 15–20 years. Such a concept may be true for small populations at low densities, where villages with their halo of secondary forest are widely separated by extensive spreads of primary forest which will give a supply of seed to sustain species diversity. As populations increase, however, more land is used, existing land is used more intensively and stands of primary forest decrease (resource 11.20).

Under such pressures, positive feedback may take over, causing permanent changes to the ecosystem. This case study, from the rugged Bismarck Range, Papua New Guinea, illustrates firstly the optimistic view of the sensitive way traditional societies utilise their rainforest environment, and secondly, the reality of long-term ecosystem deterioration which can result. It is an excellent example of the process of **ecological**

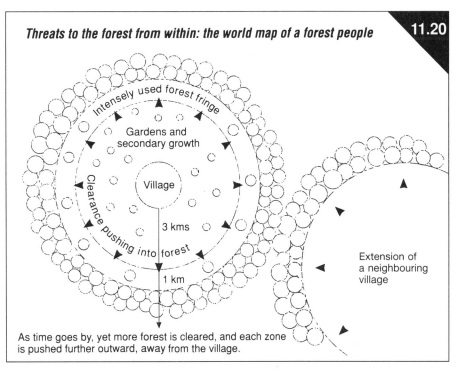

Threats to the forest from within: the world map of a forest people   11.20

Intensely used forest fringe

Gardens and secondary growth

Village

Clearance pushing into forest

3 kms

1 km

Extension of a neighbouring village

As time goes by, yet more forest is cleared, and each zone is pushed further outward, away from the village.

retrogression whereby an ecosystem becomes less diverse and less productive over time, even if succession is no longer deflected by human activities.

The Maring horticultural system, Papua New Guinea

'Maring horticulture is of the sort called 'swiddening'; 'bush-fallowing' or 'slash-and-burn'. Each year a gardening pair will clear-cut one or more gardens in the secondary forest. These are seldom more than an acre in extent. After clearing the underbrush, felling and pollarding the trees and making fences from some of the logs, the slash is burned. Burning not only disposes of the litter but also liberates the nutrients in the cut vegetation making them available to the crop about to be planted. Since the stratum of fertile soil under Maring forests is seldom more than two inches in depth and easily depleted, the nutrients freed by burning are highly beneficial to the growth of garden plants.

When the burning is completed a great variety of cultigens – banana, taros, sweet potatoes, yams and many more – are interplanted in the same garden in what appears to be, but is not, helter-skelter fashion. The Maring gardener is expert at taking advantage of micro-environmental variations and there is a reason for each plant to be where it is.

Weeding is selective. Herbaceous species are removed, but arboreal species are allowed to remain. After 14 to 28 months, depending upon the altitude and other factors, the regenerating trees have made harvesting so difficult that the gardeners abandon whatever crops remain to their pigs. The pigs, in their quest for tubers, soften and aerate the soil and thin the regenerating seedlings. Secondary forest then takes over completely and the site remains fallow until a canopy has formed on trees 12 inches or more in diameter and until the ground becomes soft again. This takes 8 to 40 years, depending upon the altitude ...

Key understandings

◆ If the shifting agriculture cycle is repeated too often, the regenerating ecosystem may be deflected from a forest to a grassland succession.

◆ Ecological retrogression is the process whereby an ecosystem becomes less diverse and less productive.

◆ Beyond a certain intensity of use, positive feedback may cause permanent changes to an ecosystem.

The Maring derive perhaps 99 per cent of their diet directly from their own gardens and from their pigs. Thus, these slash and burn gardens must be highly productive. In fact, only 0.15 to 0.2 acres need to be put into production each year to feed an adult, and about as much for a grown pig ... Energy return for energy input is high, approaching 20:1. On this index alone, Maring horticulture compares very well with 'more sophisticated' agriculture practised elsewhere in the world ... In some localities population densities exceed 200 persons/square mile of arable area. Yet this horticulture does not seem to do serious damage to the ability of the climax to return to sites from which it has been removed.'

(Source: R A Rappaport, 'Forests and Man', *The Ecologist*, 6(7), August–September 1976, pp.240–246.)

The study from which the above extract is taken concludes that the system involves sensitive and rapid information (feedback) to the Maring and so the essential circular structure of the rainforest ecosystem is sustained, i.e. the Maring react to environmental messages, and they realise that their survival depends upon the maintenance not the mere exploitation of the ecosystem.

Recent research has shown that even the Maring bring about fundamental ecosystem changes, particularly as their population grows. The landscape of their homeland across the wet ridges of the Bismarck Range (where rainfall is more than 3000 mm) is today a mosaic of forest remnants, secondary regrowth, subsistence gardens and anthropogenic grasslands. Under repeated 'swidden' cultivation there is steady deterioration in soil productivity. At first the fallow periods see the rapid re-establishment of tree species, but through time the fallows become dominated by grasses and slower fertility build-up. This causes the Maring to move their occupance from the valley floors and lower slopes to the middle and upper ridge flanks. Abandoned areas are unlikely to return to woodland, but continue to deteriorate until short-grass species dominate. This process, known as ecological retrogression, is identified by reduced biomass and species diversity. The grassland soils have lower nutrient status, e.g. less organic matter, nitrogen etc.

Resource 11.21 summarises the results from six sites in the Kompiai district. Sites 1 and 2 are currently occupied, while distance from the present village and length of time from abandonment increase through Sites 3–6.

The climatic climax vegetation of the Bismarck Mountains is tropical rainforest. Mean annual rainfall exceeds 3000 mm and there is no marked dry season. Yet today, the vegetation cover is tropical grassland, known as Alang-Alang, over extensive upland areas of the interior.

Vegetation Mosaic in the Maring Territory, Kompiai District, Papua New Guinea　　11.21

Survey Site	Alt. (m)	Slope (°)	Biomass (kg/100m)	Species (No.)	Vegetation		
1	1820	25	135 000	48	4 year secondary forest fallow	Forest	} } CURRENTLY
2	1770	15	68 000	38	Recently burned 4 yr forest fallow	Forest/grass incipient imperata	} USED } AREA }
3	1770	30	70 000	21	Tall grassland: IMPERATA association		Increasing distance from currently used areas
4	1690	30	48 000	33	Tall/short grassland mixture	} } } CAPILLIPEDIUM	
5	1660	30	58 000	28		} association	
6	1550	30	46 000	21	Short grassland: THEMEDA association		

Six sites were studies in the Kompiai district, i.e. the territory of the Maring people.
Three main grassland types are identified:
Imperata　Found in small patches near to secondary forest and subsistence gardens.
Capillepedium }　Found in extensive tracts far from forest or cultivated land. Productivity of themeda is lower than
Themeda　　　}　capillipedium.
Note: Soils under imperata are physically and in terms of nutrients, superior to soils under themeda.

11.22 *Negative impacts of deforestation in the rainforest of Nigeria*

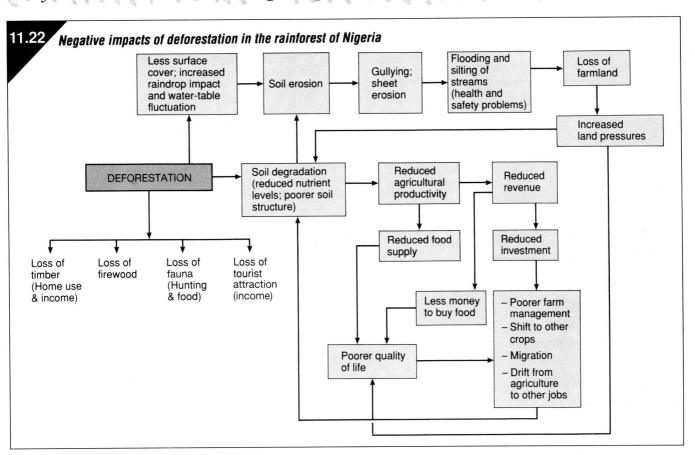

Activities

1 Define the term 'ecological retrogression'.

2 In what ways does the information above (resource 11.21) illustrate ecological retrogression? (Use graphs to support your answer.)

3 **Decision making exercise:** controlling the impacts of deforestation.

The rainforest belt of Nigeria is densely populated, deforestation is severe, and scientists forecast that by the year 2000 there may be no primary rainforest outside protected reserves. Resource 11.22 is a flow diagram tracking the progress of positive feedback observed in some districts following deforestation. Note that there are two main, interlinked pathways: impacts upon the environment and upon the people.

In groups:

a Follow the pathways carefully and familiarise yourselves with the structure and sequence of the downward cycle.

b As a government conservation and planning group, you are asked to make recommendations about how to break down this cycle in a district, i.e. to replace positive feedback by negative feedback, to restore a balance and increase productivity of the ecosystem.

Note:

• It is impractical to simply clear the population out of the district and hope that the forest will regenerate. The district must remain settled and used, so the best you can propose is selective reforestation.

• Where would you apply your management inputs and what inputs of energy and material would you recommend – money, technology, fertiliser, plantations, drainage, education etc?

• All inputs and management policies cost money and so you need to consider where results per unit of money spent will be most effective.

• Consider and evaluate a number of options, e.g. inputs may be made at various 'boxes' on the flow diagram. List the costs and benefits of each and how they would pass on through the system.

• Remember – forests are important ecologically and to the people of the district economically.

• Are there any *general principles* about environmental management which emerge from your discussion?

Background

Arid environments experience permanent moisture budget deficits. Except for brief episodes, potential and actual evapotranspiration exceed inputs from rainfall and groundwater flow, and environmental conditions tend towards extremes of temperature and moisture availability. Deserts are harsh environments. Vegetation generally covers less than 20 per cent of the surface and species ranges are narrow. Yet desert ecosystems are surprisingly varied and resilient ecosystems. All living organisms exhibit high levels of adaptation to the severe conditions of diurnal temperature range, long spells of aridity, brief episodes of flood etc. (resources 11.23 and 11.24). This case study illustrates the remarkable adaptability of desert ecosystems by using one of the hottest, driest environments in the world – the Namib Desert of southwestern Africa. Note particularly how some species cope with moisture deficiency by dormancy, others adapt to live on minimal water intake, others respond rapidly to moisture inputs and some adopt nocturnal habits. Note also that within the desert, there are sub-environments, each of which plays a part in the functioning of the whole.

11.23

Adaptations to desert ecosystems

Animals
1. Increasing water intake
2. Direct water intake from atmosphere
3. Efficient use of water in metabolism
4. Reduction of water loss
5. Impermeable covering
6. Behaviour designed to reduce water loss

Plants
1. Deep, spreading roots
2. Water storage tissues
3. Reduction in leaf transpiration.
4. Deciduous habit and/or very small leaves.
5. Photosynthetic stems.
6. Photosynthetic modifications.
7. Tolerance of tissues to reduced water content.
8. Increased ability to extract soil water.
9. Synchronisation of growth with periods of favourable precipitation.

Key understandings

- Adaptations of plants and animal species to extremes: moisture deficit; sudden moisture supply; temperature variation.

- Concepts of dormancy, rapid response, opportunism, ephemeralism, rhythms in ecosystem functioning.

- Character and inter-connectivity of small-scale habitats in ecosystem functioning.

The Namib environment

The Namib Desert, stretching some 2080 km along the southwest coast of Africa, is an environment of extreme aridity (with mean annual rainfall of less than 20 mm), where a sequence of rainless years may be broken by intense storms. One such episode occurred from January to March 1976 over one section of the desert, during which 118 mm of rain fell (the highest since 1934). The ecological impact was measured and compared with conditions prior to the rains.

The area for which data was collected lies at the intersection of three of the main environments of the Namib Desert; gravel plains; an E-W riverine strip supported by groundwater beneath the dry Kuiseb River bed; and an expanse of active linear dunes running N – S (24°N, 15°E). This case study focuses upon the last environment, which itself consists of three habitats (resource 11.25).

11.24

Creosote bush: small leaves, broad spread to give shade and hence keep surface cooler and so reduce evaporation; spacing of plants; wide-spreading roots

ecosystems – the Namib Desert, Namibia

The main moisture source is the recurrent fog which rolls inland from the cold Benguela Current offshore. There are high diurnal ranges of temperature and humidity, with intense insolation through much of the day as average cloud and fog cover decreases from 41 per cent at 0800 to 18 per cent at 1400 hours (resource 11.26). Temperature measurements across a sand dune on two December (summer) days showed that at 0800 hours, with the fog still present, the dune surface was 16°C. by 0900 hours, the fog had lifted and the temperatures soared to 60°C by midday. The winds shift seasonally and play an important role in (a) sculpting the dunes, (b) transporting dried grass detritus on to the dunes, thereby providing an important source of food, and (c) influencing temperatures. The interaction of insolation, fog and wind creates highly distinctive micro climates and specialised habitats across the dunes, with a complex patchwork of vegetation cover (resource 11.27).

Overall, surface cover is low, **biomass is small** and, in turn, material and protein status is poor. This last characteristic is a strong limiting factor in many desert regions, for even when there is plant litter, microbial decomposition is slow because of the absence of moisture. Nitrogen, phosphorus and calcium amounts are all low.

In the extreme Namibian environment, **species range is narrow** and **associations simple.** Only two perennial dune species – one coarse grass and one succulent – are able to survive the long dry spells on fog moisture alone. Other grasses are ephemeral, requiring rain episodes to germinate, after which some cover may remain for two years before dying away, illustrating the water-holding properties of loose sands. The coarse, stony valleys between the dunes support a higher degree of cover and provide the main source of wind-blown grass detritus for the dune habitats.

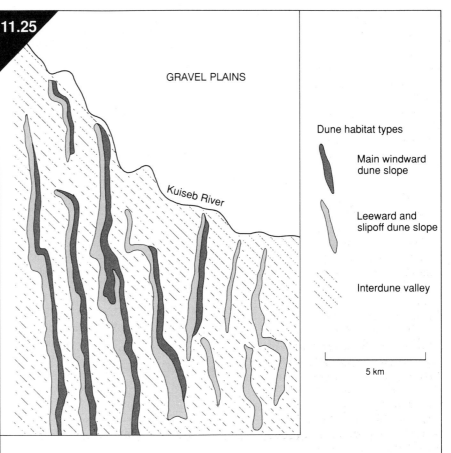

11.25

GRAVEL PLAINS

Kuiseb River

Dune habitat types

Main windward dune slope

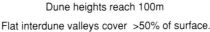

Leeward and slipoff dune slope

Interdune valley

5 km

Dune heights reach 100m

Flat interdune valleys cover >50% of surface.

Namib dune landscape

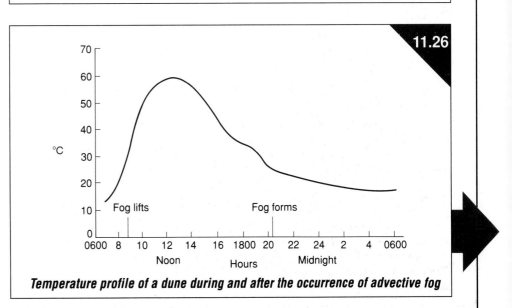

11.26

Temperature profile of a dune during and after the occurrence of advective fog

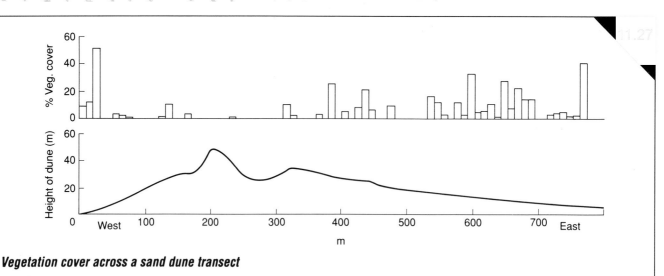

Vegetation cover across a sand dune transect

Life in the Namib

The resident fauna is similarly restricted, being dominated by insects, beetles, lizards and snakes, enriched by more mobile heat-tolerant visitors such as antelope (oryx, gemsbok), hare and bustards. In these severe habitats both residents and visitors exhibit considerable *opportunism* and *flexibility* in their feeding habits: if they are to survive they must take advantage of what is available. (Note the contrast with the varied riches of the rainforests where many inhabitants occupy very narrow niches with highly specific food requirements.) One result is that surprisingly complex food webs may evolve in desert habitats (resource 11.28). Two outstanding characteristics of flora and fauna in arid environments are their abilities (a) to endure severe moisture deficiency and extreme heat, and (b) to respond rapidly to an amelioration of moisture and temperature conditions. For instance beetles, snakes and lizards burrow into the cooler, moister sand, many are nocturnal, and all have physiologies which minimise inputs and outputs of water. One type of beetle basks in an inverted position on dune crests as the fog rolls in from the ocean so that water droplets forming on its body run

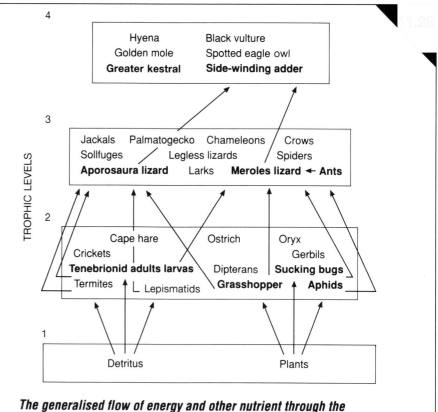

The generalised flow of energy and other nutrient through the animals of the dune ecosystem. Only one major food web, ending with the side-winding adder, is indicated in heavy type.

into its mouth, and so achieves its entire moisture need; a lizard absorbs dew directly from its body surface. The vigorous response to the input of water to the system is illustrated clearly in resource 11.29(a) – (d). Following the rain, the plant biomass increased ninefold, the detritus biomass sevenfold and the animal biomass sixfold.

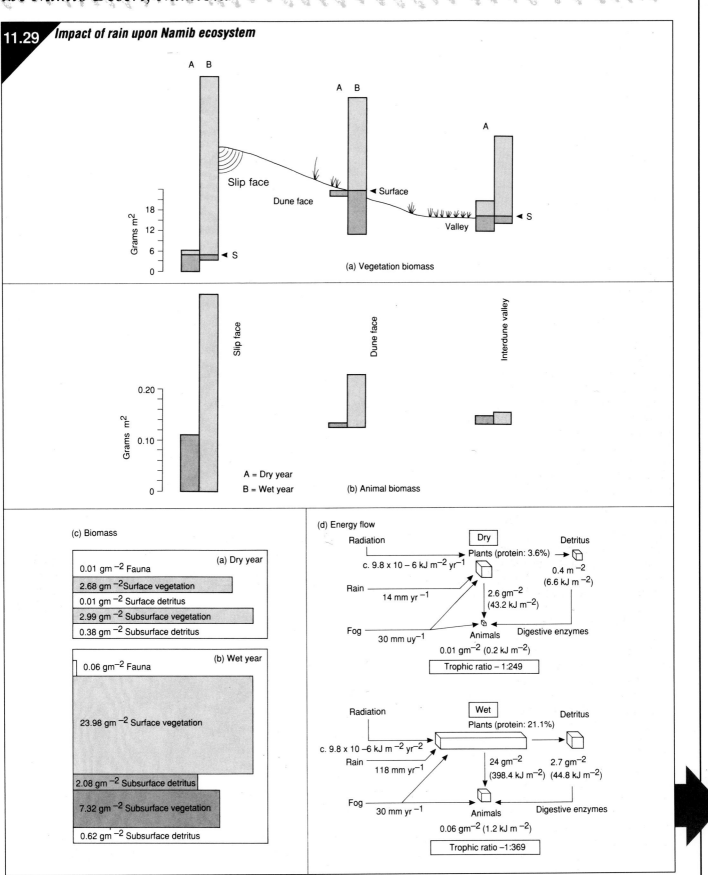

11.29 *Impact of rain upon Namib ecosystem*

Slip face

Dune face

Surface

Valley

A B

A B

A

S

S

S

Grams m² 18 12 6 0

(a) Vegetation biomass

Slip face

Dune face

Interdune valley

Grams m² 0.20 0.10 0

A = Dry year
B = Wet year

(b) Animal biomass

(c) Biomass

(a) Dry year

0.01 gm⁻² Fauna
2.68 gm⁻² Surface vegetation
0.01 gm⁻² Surface detritus
2.99 gm⁻² Subsurface vegetation
0.38 gm⁻² Subsurface detritus

(b) Wet year

0.06 gm⁻² Fauna
23.98 gm⁻² Surface vegetation
2.08 gm⁻² Subsurface detritus
7.32 gm⁻² Subsurface vegetation
0.62 gm⁻² Subsurface detritus

(d) Energy flow

Dry

Radiation

Plants (protein: 3.6%)

Detritus

c. 9.8 x 10 – 6 kJ m⁻² yr⁻¹

0.4 m⁻²
(6.6 kJ m⁻²)

Rain

14 mm yr⁻¹

2.6 gm⁻²
(43.2 kJ m⁻²)

Fog

30 mm uy⁻¹

Animals

Digestive enzymes

0.01 gm⁻² (0.2 kJ m⁻²)

Trophic ratio – 1:249

Wet

Radiation

Plants (protein: 21.1%)

Detritus

c. 9.8 x 10 –6 kJ m⁻² yr⁻²

Rain

118 mm yr⁻¹

24 gm⁻²
(398.4 kJ m⁻²)

2.7 gm⁻²
(44.8 kJ m⁻²)

Fog

30 mm yr⁻¹

Animals

Digestive enzymes

0.06 gm⁻² (1.2 kJ m⁻²)

Trophic ratio –1:369

CASE STUDY 11.4 *Survival and response in desert ecosystems – the Namib Desert, Namibia*

Each of the three habitats of the dune environment responds in a distinctive way. The bulk of the rain-induced vegetation consists of ephemeral grasses, with vigorous root development. In terms of total biomass the dune slope, which occupies approximately 40 per cent of the surface area, dominates. The slipoff slope, which is much steeper (approximately 32°) and covers less than 10 per cent of the surface area is the most dynamic landform element, and is regularly fed by sand from the dune crest. Its remarkable response to the rain episode in terms of bulk per unit area is achieved mainly by the accumulation of grass detritus blown from the dune slope and interdune valley. Much is buried, remains available as food and this is an important faunal habitat. The interdune valley is the most stable of the habitats with the smallest differences between dry and wet periods, and is a major source of grass detritus to the dune slope and slipoff slope.

(Source: M K Seely, and G M Louw, 'First approximations of the effects of rainfall on the ecology and energetics of a Namib Desert dune ecosystem', *Journal of Arid Environments*, 3, 1980, pp.25–54.)

Activities

1 What is meant by the term 'opportunism' and why is it so important in this ecosystem? Give examples.

2 List examples of the ways plants and animals adapt (a) to survive periods of severe moisture and (b) to make the most of what moisture is available.

3 How many trophic levels are there in this ecosystem? Give an example of a food chain.

4 Summarise the non-living and living component characteristics of each of the three dune zones. Explain the differences and illustrate how the three zones are interconnected.

5 Using resource 11.29

  a put into table format the contrasts in this ecosystem between dry and wet periods,

  b describe and explain differences in response in the three dune zones.

6 Resource 11.30 gives details of rainfall and biomass relationships in the Rajasthan Desert of India. Use the information to:

  a illustrate these plant growth/rainfall relationships

  b assess the influence of factors other than rainfall on biomass production.

7 As a group discuss: How does the information from Namibia and Rajasthan exemplify the key understandings about ecosystems given on page 220?

11.30

Biomass of ephemeral plants, Ajmer, Rajasthan, India
August 1972–January 1973 (grams/m) (26°N; 74°E)

Month	Site I Shoot	Site I Root	Site II Shoot	Site II Root	Site III Shoot	Site III Root	Site IV Shoot	Site IV Root
August	45	11	36	16	27	16	20	6
September	50	12	108	23	51	21	17	6
October	36	13	126	42	32	18	15	6
November	31	10	116	38	22	14	9	4
December	21	8	21	12	14	8	8	4
January	17	8	18	13	15	8	7	3

Site I Sandy area, always exposed to sun
II Sandy area shaded for most of the day
III Sloping, well drained sandy area
IV Gravelly areas
} Gravel 6% sand 71%
Clays & Silts 23%

Climate: Annual rainfall c. 250mm, arriving from the July-September monsoon. Daily temperature max >22°C; coolest month December.

Rhythm: The ephemeral plants complete their life-cycle in 1.5–2.0 months, peaking in September-October when soil moisture is at its maximum, dying away by end January, to persist as seeds until the next monsoon.

Variation: Biomass variation is related to topography, soil permeability and fertility, species characteristics and grazing pressure, eg note the effect of the poor moisture and water-holding capacities of the gravelly soils.

CHAPTER 12

Use, abuse and conservation

Introduction

The photographs in resources 12.1 and 12.2 were taken on the same day in July 1989. The locations lie only 15 km apart in North Island, New Zealand, and represent extremes of human interactions with and responses to environmental processes. Resource 12.1 lies within Urewera National Park, where the climatic climax ecosystem of temperate rainforest is sustained by the strong conservation policies of the Park managers. In resource 12.2 the forest has been cleared, originally for lumber, and followed by the creation of a grassland ecosystem managed for the rearing of sheep, cattle and goats. It is currently enduring rapid erosion.

The two scenes would seem to represent the 'good' and the 'bad' sides of human impact upon the environment. However, reality is rarely so clear-cut. For example, the priority given to conservation within Urewera National Park means a denial of many traditional rights and usages of the local Maori communities, and access of any sort is restricted. Outside the Park the farmers have worked hard to create a productive grassland from the fractured environment abandoned by the loggers. Until the early 1980s they

seemed to have succeeded in sustaining a stabilised environment and a viable economy. Yet in 1989 this environment seemed to be disintegrating. The flow-chart in resource 12.3 summarises the sequence of events leading to the triggering of this latest surge of change.

The story told by the flow-chart lights up several fundamental signals about how environmental systems work and hence how humans should manage environmental resources:

1 Surges of accelerated environmental change are commonly triggered by the coming together or the rapid succession of several influential factors rather than the operation of a single factor.
2 Natural ecosystems develop built-in resistances to change through negative feedback mechanisms which operate to dampen down disturbances. This is particularly so when the ecosystem is mature and near to the optimum for the set of local environmental conditions, e.g. the rainforests of the hills of north-west North Island, New Zealand.
3 Periodic disturbance is part of the normal functioning of many ecosystems, with the natural resistances and resilience working to absorb the disturbance. Indeed, disturbance may enhance the quality and strength of the ecosystem. The 1989 storm, for example, blew down many over-mature trees in the Urewera forests, creating canopy gaps into which young vigorous trees can grow.
4 Human occupance frequently produces less varied, less mature and more sensitive environments, with reduced resilience and resistance to disturbance. There is a greater likelihood of positive feedback triggering accelerated and progressive change. This seems to be occurring across the farming landscape of resource 12.2: the weakened grass cover cannot absorb the impact of an extreme storm event on these steep slopes, and once the surface cover is broken, even normal rains can produce sheetwash, gullying, and slope failure.

Forest in Urewera National Park, New Zealand

Eroded landscape outside Urewera National Park, New Zealand

12.4

12.5

Young coniferous plantation North Island, New Zealand

Mixed wood planting North Island, New Zealand

5 Human occupance should be based on a thorough understanding of and response to natural environmental processes. By working from a basis of natural processes and rhythms, resilience and strength to absorb disturbance can be retained and the productivity of the environment maintained. In resource management terms this is a strategy of **sustained yield**. In the eroding districts of North Island, the most obvious answer is to plant quick-growing conifers to stabilise the slopes (resource 12.4) and to remove all grazing animals, especially goats, from denuded areas. In the longer term, however, a form of agroforestry may be a more effective answer to ensure farmers a more productive livelihood (resource 12.5). The exposed ridges remain under semi-natural woodland; the slopes are planted at low densities with native species, which allow enough light through to energise a grass sward for grazing while protecting the slope from storms.

The case studies in this concluding chapter take up this crucial issue of searching for strategies which allow use of environmental resources while conserving the quality and productivity of environments. A second theme is that of **interconnectivity** both within and between environmental systems at all scales.

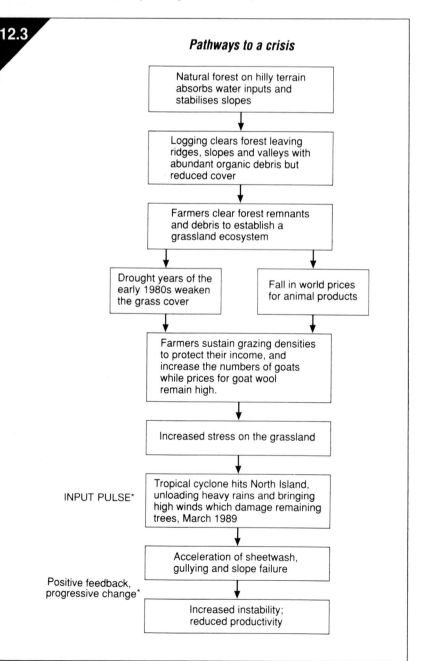

12.3

Pathways to a crisis

Natural forest on hilly terrain absorbs water inputs and stabilises slopes

↓

Logging clears forest leaving ridges, slopes and valleys with abundant organic debris but reduced cover

↓

Farmers clear forest remnants and debris to establish a grassland ecosystem

↓

Drought years of the early 1980s weaken the grass cover

Fall in world prices for animal products

↓

Farmers sustain grazing densities to protect their income, and increase the numbers of goats while prices for goat wool remain high.

↓

Increased stress on the grassland

↓

INPUT PULSE*

Tropical cyclone hits North Island, unloading heavy rains and bringing high winds which damage remaining trees, March 1989

↓

Positive feedback, progressive change*

Acceleration of sheetwash, gullying and slope failure

↓

Increased instability; reduced productivity

CASE STUDY 12.1 *Valuing mangroves and coral reefs – Australia*

Background

Mangroves are the characteristic forest and swamp ecosystems of tropical and sub-tropical intertidal regions, covering approximately 240 000 square kilometres. Twice each day the tides rise and fall across the mangrove zone and plants and living organisms have adapted to this rhythm. The warm, moist conditions make mangroves extremely productive. These highly distinctive wetlands are dominated by trees and bushes with raised root systems (resource 12.6) and are home for more than 2000 species. Sixty of these types of bush and tree are found only in the mangrove environment. There is a zonation of vegetation associated with the degree of immersion. Species have differing competitive power

Mangroves, Port Douglas, Queensland

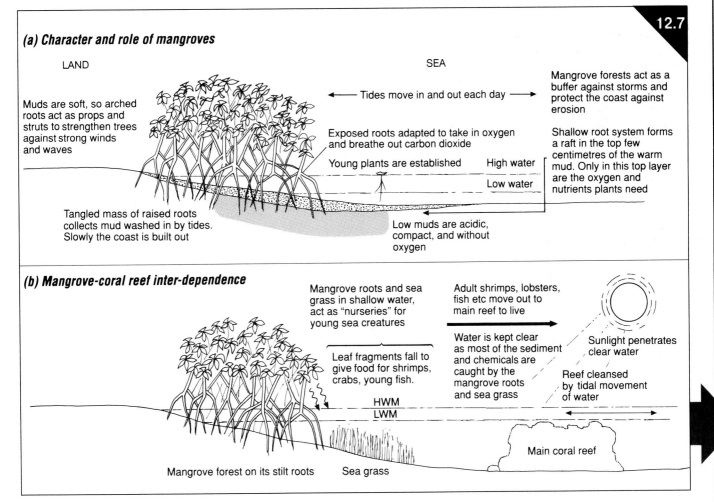

(a) Character and role of mangroves

LAND

SEA

Muds are soft, so arched roots act as props and struts to strengthen trees against strong winds and waves

Tides move in and out each day

Exposed roots adapted to take in oxygen and breathe out carbon dioxide

Young plants are established — High water

Low water

Tangled mass of raised roots collects mud washed in by tides. Slowly the coast is built out

Low muds are acidic, compact, and without oxygen

Mangrove forests act as a buffer against storms and protect the coast against erosion

Shallow root system forms a raft in the top few centimetres of the warm mud. Only in this top layer are the oxygen and nutrients plants need

(b) Mangrove-coral reef inter-dependence

Mangrove roots and sea grass in shallow water, act as "nurseries" for young sea creatures

Adult shrimps, lobsters, fish etc move out to main reef to live

Water is kept clear as most of the sediment and chemicals are caught by the mangrove roots and sea grass

Leaf fragments fall to give food for shrimps, crabs, young fish.

Sunlight penetrates clear water

Reef cleansed by tidal movement of water

HWM
LWM

Main coral reef

Mangrove forest on its stilt roots

Sea grass

according to their tolerances of salinity, moving mud, and changing sea level. The plants are salt-tolerant but as they are not true marine plants, they cannot stand extreme salinity. Thus, mangroves flourish best along the muddy shores of estuaries and deltas where rivers bring fresh water. In addition, plants have evolved strategies for extracting some of the salt from the water, e.g. special glands which collect salt. Their ability to react and adapt to diurnal, monthly and seasonal rhythms of environmental conditions make mangroves resilient ecosystems, and they play an important role in the functioning of coastal marine environments (resource 12.7).

> Mangrove ecosystems constitute a reservoir, refuge, feeding ground and nursery for many useful and unusual plants and animals. Through the export of decomposable organic matter (mostly in the form of plant detritus) into adjacent coastal waters, mangroves provide an important nutrient input and primary energy source for many tropical estuaries.
>
> (Source: Mercer and Hamilton, *Nature and Resources*, XX(2), April–June, 1984, 28)

12.8

A closer look at the animals inside those stony cups

When zoologists talk about coral, they generally mean the reef-building stony corals, Scleractina, found all over the world including the Caribbean Sea.

Corals are tiny animals closely related to sea anemones and jelly fish, consisting of a large stomach topped by tentacles. These waving arms waft food into a pharynx. Armed with sting cells the tentacles poison the prey, which is then swept towards the mouth by either the tentacles or by microscopic hair-like cilia which poke through an outer coating of mucus.

Corals make lime from a thin layer of cells, to build up a hard skeleton. The protected polyps emerge periodically from their horny cups to capture food particles. The reefs are the accumulated limestone remains of dead corals with the living corals found on top.

Buried fossil reefs located on cotintinental shelves are valuable sources of petroleum and more recently the reefs have become targets for mining prospectors. Some corals contain small amounts of metals such as zinc, and copper which they extract from the surrounding sea.

Essential to formation of the hard skeleton are thousands of single celled algae or zooxanthellae. The algae obtain nutrients, probably phosphorus and nitrates, and in return their photosynthesis aids the coral in depositing its layer of calcium carbonate. So corals do not form skeletons in the dark. Coral growth is very slow, the fastest adding skeleton at a rate of a few centimetres each year.

The corals favour warm, well-lit tropical waters to construct massive reefs whose architecture can vary enormously. Massive coral sculptures can reach three metres in height, enormous in proportion to the thin layer of living tissue on the base of the coral with which it is in contact.

(Source: *New Scientist*, 5 November 1981)

Mangroves act as effective protection against storm wave impacts along low-lying coasts. The dense root network collects sediment and thereby slowly advances the shoreline. The first part of this case study is an authentic appeal to the Australian government from an ecologist living in North Queensland, stressing the need to conserve this important ecosystem and protect it from proposals for large scale tourism developments.

The second part illustrates the concept of interconnectivity between ecosystems by outlining the relationships between mangroves and coral reefs. It shows that what happens to Queensland's mangrove

fringe has implications for the health of Australia's Great Barrier Reef. A reef is a massive limestone structure built by tiny marine organisms called polyps (resource 12.8). The polyps thrive in clear, shallow waters with optimal temperatures around 18 °C. While fine sediment is steadily absorbed into the limestone structure, the polyps are light-sensitive and turbidity levels must remain low. Despite their immense size and complexity, coral reef ecosystems are more sensitive to disturbance and less resilient than mangroves.

> ## Key understandings
>
> ◆ Ecosystems vary in their resilience and sensitivity to disturbance.
>
> ◆ Mangroves play an important role in maintaining coastal environments.
>
> ◆ Coral reefs are sensitive and threatened environments.
>
> ◆ There is an interconnectivity between ecosystems and the need for management policies to reflect this interconnectivity.
>
> ◆ Development should be balanced with the need to sustain natural processes.
>
> ◆ There are different meanings of the term 'value'.

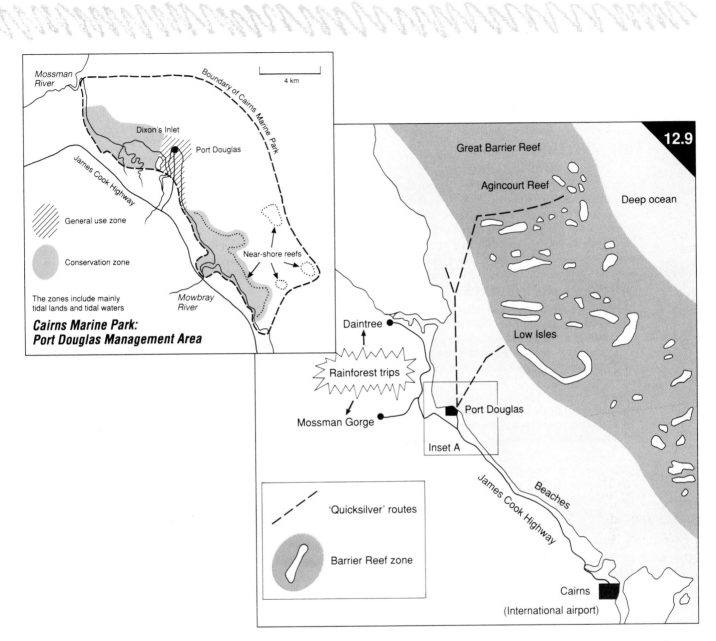

Cairns Marine Park:
Port Douglas Management Area

Mossman
River

Boundary of Cairns Marine Park

4 km

Dixon's Inlet

Port Douglas

James Cook Highway

General use zone

Conservation zone

The zones include mainly
tidal lands and tidal waters

Mowbray
River

Near-shore reefs

Great Barrier Reef

Agincourt Reef

Deep ocean

Low Isles

Daintree

Rainforest trips

Mossman Gorge

Port Douglas

Inset A

'Quicksilver' routes

Barrier Reef zone

Beaches

James Cook Highway

Cairns
(International airport)

Part I: Making a case for the mangroves of Port Douglas, Queensland, Australia.

Port Douglas is a small resort north of Cairns, along the south shore of Dickson's Inlet estuary (resource 12.9). In common with much of the Queensland coast, it is undergoing a tourism 'explosion'. For example, Cairns airport is being expanded to take the largest jet aircraft, and international tourism companies such as Mirage-Sheraton are developing or submitting planning proposals for massive resort and marina complexes. These facilities hug the coastal fringe, especially estuaries which provide shelter for marinas. It is, therefore, the mangroves which are at greatest risk.

The Australian government is aware that the impacts of tourism growth are becoming a national issue. Consequently, during 1988 a government committee was preparing a report on 'the environmental impact of tourist developments, particularly in coastal regions and national heritage areas', and invited submissions from the public. The following material is the response of Stephen Raaymakers, a biologist living in Port Douglas

(resource 12.10). His concern may, at first, seem odd, as this coast lies within the Cairns Marine Park and so should be protected (resource 12.9). However, as the map shows, the Port Douglas estuary is zoned for 'general use', yet it is along such estuaries that mangroves are at their best. The 'protected' zone does not contain the finest mangrove ecosystems. Note particularly how Raaymakers assesses 'value'; what he tells us about the functioning of the mangrove ecosystem; how mangrove clearance will be a disadvantage not only for the coastal environment but also, in the longer term, for tourism itself.

Response from Stephen Raaymakers

Introduction

Traditionally in Australia mangrove areas have been perceived as 'swampy wastelands'. This is directly attributable to their unsuitability for 'productive' land-uses such as farming and to the fact that they are generally inhospitable to humans. As a result they have been subjected to extensive clearing and filling.

Such a naive attitude would have been excusable thirty years ago, but certainly not today when the immense values of mangroves have been clearly and definitely identified.

Tourism in North Queensland is overwhelmingly dependent on the coastal and marine environments as major drawcards, and mangrove areas have suffered heavily with scant regard for their inherent value.

Values of mangroves

1 Mangroves are of immense value to conservation:
   a They provide irreplaceable habitat for a whole host of native wildlife, some of which are highly specialised to the unique mangrove environment and cannot survive elsewhere.
   b Mangroves provide important en-route habitat for several species of migratory birds.
   c The mangrove tree species represent a highly specialised assemblage of plants worthy of conservation in themselves.
2 Mangroves are of special interest to science:
   a The specialist adaptations of the mangrove tree species are of immense biological interest.
   b The complex ecological relationships within the mangrove community are still ill-understood.
   c They represent a potential source of valuable medicinal, chemical and other products and uses for mankind, such as a gene pool for developing new types of salt-tolerant plants.
3 Mangroves are absolutely vital to the sustenance of the marine system:
   a They are the link between the terrestrial and marine systems, acting as a buffer zone.
   b They are a major source of primary productivity in the marine system. Dead leaves dropping into the water in large quantities decay and provide essential nutrients for marine life. They are at the base of the food chain.
   c Their complex root systems provide substrate for attachment of marine life, which in turn provide food for higher levels in the food chain, and are also a vital refuge for numerous juvenile marine species.
4 Mangroves are an integral part of a stable coastline:
   a They act as sediment traps, preventing mud and silt from being washed out to sea. Mangrove clearing will allow this sediment to be carried offshore. This has drastic implications for the Great Barrier Reef as corals die under high sediment loads, and will affect the valuable tourist industry which sells clear, blue tropical waters.
   b They act as irreplaceable natural shock absorbers for the coastline during cyclones and storm surges, and as a vital refuge for small ships and boats during cyclones.
5 Mangroves are the basis of several significant commercial industries (they are important to the economy as well as the environment):
   a They provide habitat, breeding, nursery and/or refuge grounds for many marine species, including the commercially important mud crab, barramundi (a large game fish) and several species of prawn. Their role at the base of the food chain means that they also ultimately support many of the offshore fisheries. The majority of Australian fisheries production, especially prawns, is exported. Removal of mangroves will destroy this valuable source of foreign exchange.
   b They are also vital to many economically significant recreational fisheries.
6 Mangroves offer a considerable resource for tourism itself.
   a Bird and nature-watching groups from Europe and North America are showing increasing interest in Australia. Australian tropical mangroves contain over 250 species of birdlife and are excellent nature viewing areas.

c The Australian tourist industry is linked with the seafood industry, to which mangroves are absolutely vital.

7 Mangroves act as a natural control for mosquitoes.

There is normally no mosquito breeding in healthy mangroves. However, when mangroves are impacted extremely favourable mosquito breeding conditions are created, causing much discomfort for local residents, tourists

Impact on mangroves

Many mangrove areas in North Queensland are currently experiencing detrimental impact. Much of this impact is a direct effect of tourist development. Impact on mangroves occurs in two ways, it is either direct, such as blatant bulldozing, clearing and filling, or indirect such as some type of river or coastal engineering works which alters terrestrial freshwater runoff, tidal flow or sediment deposition, that may in turn impact on mangroves in adjacent areas. Both types of impact are rampant in North Queensland.

Port Douglas

Some of the richest Australian mangrove forest has been totally destroyed on the south bank of Dickson's Inlet, Port Douglas. Part of this is being used by the Douglas Shire Council as a garbage dump, and another area as a sewerage treatment plant. Both of these facilities will be in greater demand as the tourist industry expands.

A large part of the destruction is the direct result of a major tourist development – the Mirage resort, marina and golf course. This destruction is expanding into the small remaining patches of mangrove on the south bank of Dickson Inlet, with plans by Mirage to purchase, clear and fill for development areas of Crown land designated Reserve 113 (64Ha) and Reserve 177 (90Ha) (see resource 12.11).

A presently healthy area of mangrove remains on the north bank of Dickson's Inlet. However, this may slowly deteriorate by indirect impact as it is directly adjacent to the Mirage Marina, which has undoubtedly altered the tidal flow and sediment deposition patterns of the inlet.

Lavish development on mangrove reserves

Mirage Chief Executive, John Tabart informed the meeting that the proposed extensions to the Mirage Resort would involve a new nine hole extension to the existing Mirage golf course together with a golf school and attendant facilities.

In addition, 200 golf villas and associated private marina facilities will be built.

All of this is proposed for the area known as Reserve 113.

Around the perimeter of R113, except for that area where the private marina facilities are located, a wide band of mangroves will be retained together with some stands of mangroves within the proposed development site itself.

Mr Tabart advised the meeting that the fishermen's basin and maintenance area would not be under Mirage tenure but would be operated and managed by others – possibly the Council or the Fishermen's Association.

Provided it is able to acquire and develop this land, Qintex has offered to give $3m in the form of community facilities for Port Douglas.

It is the intention of Qintex to construct these facilities on the Town Reserve which is presently used as the town tip.

(continued)

Qintex has confirmed that its offer to provide $3m worth of sporting and community facilities for Port Douglas is conditional upon it acquiring 90 hectares of waterfront land to expand the existing Mirage Resort.

This was disclosed by Mirage Resort's Chief Executive, John Tabart at a public meeting attended by 300 local residents held in Port Douglas last Saturday.

It became evident early in the meeting that the issue which interested the residents most was the expansion plans for the Resort; and particularly the impact of this development on the mangroves covering much of the land Qintex is seeking to acquire.

According to local member for Barron River and Minister for Mines and Energy, Martin Tenni, plans have been drawn up by the Lands Department to subdivide and sell off much of the land Qintex is seeking to acquire.

He said it is therefore up to the people of Port Douglas to decide whether they want to accept what is being offered by Qintex or take their chances with some other form of development on the areas.

Among the major additional matters disclosed were:
* Quintex proposes to conduct an environmental impact study of the area it seeks to acquire.
* Not all the mangroves in Reserve 113 will be destroyed. Qintex intends to retain a large bank fringe of mangroves bordering the Inlet along with some stands of mangroves within the proposed development site itself.
* Qintex proposes to rehabilitate an area of mangroves equivalent to the area which will be destroyed by its development.
* The proposed development will not proceed until Qintex fulfills its offer to the people of Port Douglas concerning the construction of sporting and community facilities.

The whole of Reserve 113 is an inter-tidal wetland and is currently about 80 per cent mangrove forest.

Two types of mangrove dominate the vegetation – a smaller lighter green variety on the higher ground, commonly called yellow mangrove and the taller dark green, stilt rooted mangroves which dominate the waters edge and the more frequently inundated areas.

In Queensland, mangroves are protected under Section 71 of the Queensland Fisheries Act 1976–1984. Under the terms of this legislation, it is an offence to cut, lop, burn, remove or otherwise destroy or damage any marine plant.

Application may be made for exemption from the terms of Section 71 and this may be granted in the form of a permit issued by the Minister for Primary Industries.

However, both the letter and the spirit of the law is often ignored in Queensland so that mangroves are frequently damaged or destroyed with neither permission nor retribution.

At first sight the $6 million package of sporting facilities and other community benefits being offered to residents of Port Douglas appears almost too good to be true.

However, perhaps in this case it's appropriate to look the gift horse in the mouth.

The press release quotes Mirage Chief Executive John Tabart as saying that although it is their intention to develop the area with a vast array of luxury facilities, 'the great majority of mangroves lining Dickson Inlet will not be touched in the redevelopment.'

While not questioning Mr Tabart's integrity one is entitled to ask what engineering or construction technologies exist which would enable the type and scope of facilities proposed by Mirage to be constructed on an area largely covered by mangrove forests but yet leaving the great majority of the mangroves intact.

(Source (all extracts): *Port Douglas Gazette*, 24 November 1988)

Part II: Will the Great Barrier Reef stay healthy?

Australia's Great Barrier Reef is the world's largest coral ecosystem (resource 12.12). It has special status as a Marine Park (11 800 square kilometres) and as a World Heritage Site. The Marine Park Authority (GBRMPA) 'is committed to minimising regulation of, and interference in, human activities. It aims to protect the natural qualities of the reef while providing for reasonable use of the reef's resources ... and recognises that any use of the reef or associated areas should not threaten the reef's essential ecological characteristics and processes' (GBRMPA, July 1988). In other words, it has a policy of sustained yield based upon a balance between conservation and development.

The key problem is that the park operates as a closed system, having jurisdiction only within its boundaries. Yet much of the pressure upon the Reef is generated outside the Park. One of the main reasons for the tourism explosion along the Queensland coast is its proximity to the Barrier Reef. More resorts and more marinas mean more private and commercial boats, more companies wanting to run excursions to the reef (resource 12.13). The GBRMPA thus comes under enormous commercial pressure to grant tourism permits. An Authority report of April 1988 stated: 'When the initial Zoning Plan for the Cairns Section was developed in 1982, the section's only fixed structure was the Green Island underwater observatory. There were no large catamarans, helicopters or hovercrafts. No operations involved permanently moored pontoons or floating hotels. All these types of facilities are now operating in the Marine Park. Organised tourism on reefs close to Cairns has increased by 30 per cent per annum over the last three years. In the Cairns section in 1985–86, there were 52 tourism program permits issued; in 1987–88 this had increased to 185 permits.

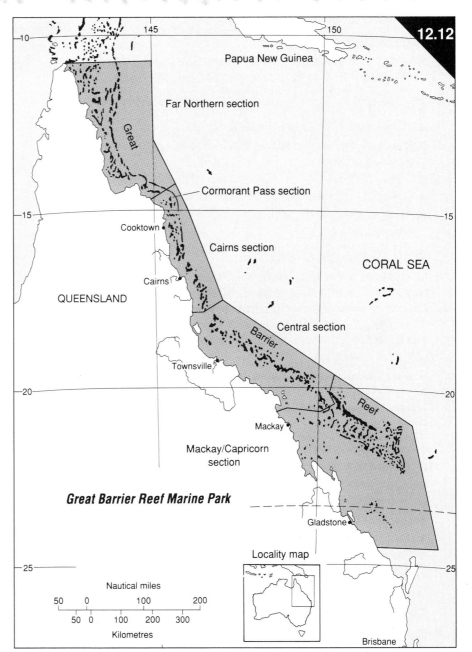

Great Barrier Reef Marine Park

Coral reefs are sensitive ecosystems and ecologists are concerned about the effects of this increased activity: more powered craft mean emissions and water disturbance, increasing water toxicity and turbidity; more divers mean more water disturbance, coral damage by contact and souvenir hunting; increased commercial and sport fishing; bigger resorts mean more sewage effluent into the ocean.

A further threat comes from the clearance of coastal mangroves, which reduces food supply for certain reef feeders (resource 12.7(b)). Loss of mangroves also means increased volumes of sediment reaching the ocean, as the roots no longer intercept the river sediment in the estuaries. This sediment load is already increasing as a result of inland forest clearance across the river catchments. Again water turbidity is increased and the sediment itself may smother the polyps.

Why Agincourt Reef?

Agincourt Reef is the only ribbon reef on the very outer edge of the Great Barrier Reef to be visited by day cruises.
It offers

- Excellent year round visibility
- Ideal swimming and snorkelling areas
- Spectacular scuba diving on one of the reef's most acclaimed sites
- Over 1000 species of multi-coloured tropical reef fish
- Over 200 varieties of spectacular and colourful corals
- An abundance of giant clams, anemones and other marine life

Why Wavepiercers?

Quicksilver is the first marine tourism operator to use these modern 37-metre Wavepiercers (52kph), and feature spacious air-conditioned passenger-cabin areas and fully licensed bar. The revolutionary Wavepiercer's torpedo shaped hulls actually pierce the waves, providing the smoothest possible ride in all weather conditions.

Fare $85   Departs 10.00 am daily

Your fare includes:

- Morning and afternoon teas on board
- Informative reef presentation by marine biologists
- Lavish tropical smorgasboard lunch with seafood
- All snorkelling equipment provided
- Qualified snorkelling adviser on hand
- Underwater observatory coral viewing
- Coral viewing cruises in semi-submersible

Plus, of course, our friendly Quicksilver Crew who will help you to make the most of your day with us.

Optional extras

Guided snorkelling tours with marine biologist
Certificate and introductory scuba dives
Spectacular scenic helicopter flights (must be pre-booked)
Underwater camera hire

'Our first visit to Agincourt Reef was one of the most exciting experiences of our lives. We hope your day at the reef is just as memorable.'

Jim and Jo Wallace

Finally, there is one major natural threat to the health of the Barrier Reef. The Crown of Thorns starfish may owe its recent population explosion to changes created by human activities. Since the 1960s this predatory starfish which eats the coral polyps has devastated sections of the reef but although scientists now believe that damaged reef areas are likely to recover, they are uncertain as to the cause of the increase in numbers. A GBRMBA report of 1985 sets out the alternatives (resource 12.14).

Activity

Group discussion: From resource 12.10 and from the information given in the local newspaper articles (resource 12.11) decide whether conservation and development can work together in this environment, and if not, which should be given priority. (N.B. In the extracts, 'Mirage' is the resort company; 'Qintex' is the developer; 'Reserve 113' is a section of mangrove reserve. The reports are an outcome of a public meeting.)

Guidelines:

- What is the 'value' of the mangroves?
- What is the 'value' of development?
- What will be the environmental and economic impacts of clearance and development?
- List the 'costs' and 'benefits' over various timescales.

Population explosions

Like many other sea creatures, female crown of thorns release millions of eggs each year but usually only a very small proportion survive to become mature starfish. If conditions change to allow more larvae to settle on coral reefs and to allow more of the larvae that settle on a reef to survive, this can lead to what ecologists term a 'population explosion' on that reef.

It is not known what causes population explosions in the crown of thorns. Some scientists believe that the discovery of crown of thorns spines in old reef sediments indicates that population explosions have occurred from time to time in the past before humans became a factor in reef ecology. However, other scientists believe that the spines occurring in sediments are from normal populations of crown of thorns starfish.

Some evidence suggests that extra heavy rainfall during the monsoonal season, which causes a run-off of extra nutrients into the coastal waters adjacent to the Reef, may have a role to play. The nutrient enriched waters lead to an increase in phytoplankton (algae) upon which the starfish larvae feed. This could enhance survival of the larvae and lead to a subsequent marked increase in the numbers settling on reefs. Extra heavy rainfall following droughts may have allowed phytoplankton blooms and therefore greater survival of crown of thorns larvae on rare occasions in the past. These events may be occurring more frequently in recent times because of increasing land clearing for urban and industrial expansion, forestry and agricultural activities. These developments generally cause an increase in water and sediment runoff during heavy rains. However, why an increase in phytoplankton should favour just the crown of thorns larvae and not some of the many other larval forms which also feed on it is not yet clear. Since an adult crown of thorns can release 10 to 30 million eggs, a 1 per cent increase in survival rate of the young starfish could mean as many as 300 000 more adult starfish from each adult female. This, in turn, could trigger a population explosion.

Others believe that increased human activities such as shell collecting and reef fishing have caused a decline in natural predators which would normally keep the starfish numbers in check irrespective of the numbers of larvae that settle on reefs. Some scientists who have adopted this theory maintain that the population explosions of crown of thorns could result in catastrophic damage to coral reef communities.

Some scientists maintain that the crown of thorns population explosions observed in recent years are natural phenomena that have occurred repeatedly in the past and that the predator has a role in maintaining high species diversity on reefs. By eating away the living corals on the surface of a reef, particularly fast growing species like staghorn corals, the crown of thorns creates space for young corals and other sedentary reef animals to become established. In other words these starfish may 'prune' the reef corals and indirectly allow different coral species to successfully compete for the limited available space. These theories and others have their adherents, but there are inadequate observations to satisfactorily resolve these alternatives.

(Source: Marine Parks pamphlet, (Great Barrier Reef Marine Park Authority and Queensland National Parks and Wildlife Service)).

CASE STUDY 12.2   *Carbon dioxide and the global*

Background

A report on polar research published in September 1989, included this finding: Between 1976 and 1986 there was a 30 per cent thinning of the Arctic ice cap. In 1976 it had been up to 6.5 m thick, but by 1986 it was less than 5 m thick. Furthermore, the effects would be cumulative: less ice → more water → more heat absorbed → more warming → less ice, and so on.

The report identified 'the greenhouse effect' as the main process behind this thinning. The greenhouse effect is the general term given to the global warming caused by the increase of carbon dioxide (CO_2) in the atmosphere (resource 12.15). The build-up of atmospheric carbon dioxide has been known for a long time, but only since the mid-1970s have the medium and long-term implications for the functioning of the global system become apparent. The graphs of resource 12.16 vividly sum up the relationships between human activity and environmental change. Furthermore, one of the main arguments for reducing the destruction of tropical rainforests is the large volumes of carbon dioxide released by the burning associated with the clearance. This is a classic example of the interconnectivity and openness of systems (in this case at a global scale) linking atmosphere, lithosphere, hydrosphere and biosphere.

There is no doubt that atmospheric carbon dioxide is increasing, that there is global warming, and that atmospheric processes seem to be producing extreme events with increased frequency (Chapter 7), e.g. the droughts of the USA in 1988 and the UK in 1989; the Alaskan cold snap in the winter of 1988–89; the exceptional rains of the southern half of Australia in the winter of 1989; Hurricane 'Gilbert' of 1988 was the most powerful of the twentieth century (case study 8.2 and resource 12.17). However, there is less agreement among scientists

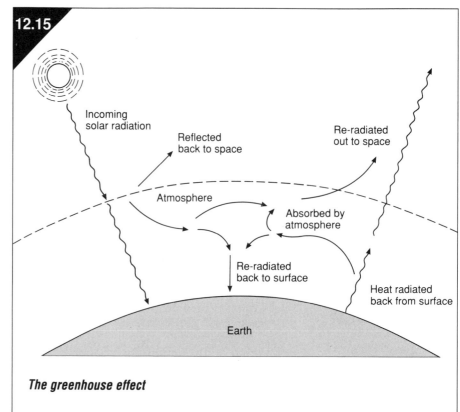

12.15

Incoming solar radiation

Reflected back to space

Re-radiated out to space

Atmosphere

Absorbed by atmosphere

Re-radiated back to surface

Heat radiated back from surface

Earth

The greenhouse effect

Key understandings

◆ Carbon dioxide is a vital element in the functioning of environmental systems. Changes in its location and availability will, therefore, affect their structure and functions.

◆ Increased atmospheric carbon dioxide is an important factor in current global warming.

◆ Environmental changes will be greater in higher latitudes.

◆ The main components of the global system (atmosphere–litho-sphere–hydrosphere–biosphere) are interlinked. Therefore, changes in the stores, processes and pathways of one will have a knock-on effect through the others and by feedback, to the original source.

◆ Human activity is the prime cause of increased atmospheric carbon dioxide. Therefore, changes in the way humans use resources are the only way to prevent further build-up (resource 12.18).

about (a) the strength of the relationship between increased carbon dioxide and global warming (i.e. other factors are influential), (b) the effects the extra carbon dioxide will have (e.g. estimates of the rise in global temperatures by the middle of the twenty first century range from 1˚C to 5˚C), (c) the 'winners' and 'losers' in the global climatic shifts (resource 12.18).

The case study outlines some of the environmental impacts projected at a major World Wildlife Fund conference held in October 1988, and so reflects the forecasts of that time. Projections and forecasts change constantly, and one of the more accessible sources for updating your information is the weekly *New Scientist* magazine.

How increased carbon dioxide may change our world

The greenhouse effect is no longer controversial, although estimates of how hot the world will become vary considerably. Most climatologists believe that the overall rise in temperature will be about 3°C in the next 50 years – with a small increase in the tropics and a much larger increase towards the poles. An increase of 3°C will make the world warmer than it has been for 100 000 years – warming at a rate the Earth has probably never experienced before.

The speed of the change could leave many species stranded – left behind in an unsuitable environment as the conditions they have evolved to live in alter faster than they can. Extinctions are inevitable as plants and animals fail to track their shifting habitats, or adapt too slowly to the new conditions.

Changes have begun already. Even an increase of 1°C can produce profound ecological change. Perhaps more important from a biological point of view, the increase will vary from place to place. Estimates range from an increase of 1°C at the equator to as much as 12°C at the poles. Other, equally damaging changes will accompany the rise in temperature. Sea level will rise both because water expands as it heats up and because the polar ice will begin to melt. In many parts of the world, storms will be more frequent and more ferocious; heat waves will be longer and hotter and droughts protracted. Elsewhere, rains will be more severe.

Ecologists do not wholly understand what controls the distribution of species. Many factors, including climate, food supply and an ability to compete with other species, are involved – and all these factors affect each other in a complex web of interactions. The change in climate, and all the associated changes, can act on any part of the web and still

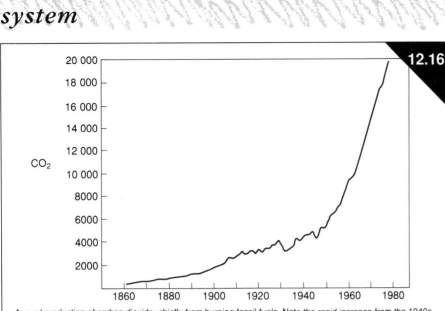

Annual production of carbon dioxide, chiefly from burning fossil fuels. Note the rapid increase from the 1940s.

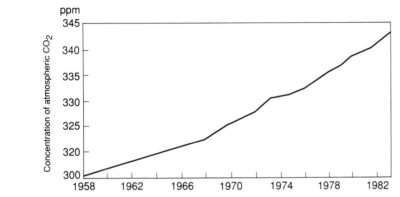

Measurements in Hawaii show the build-up of carbon dioxide in the air

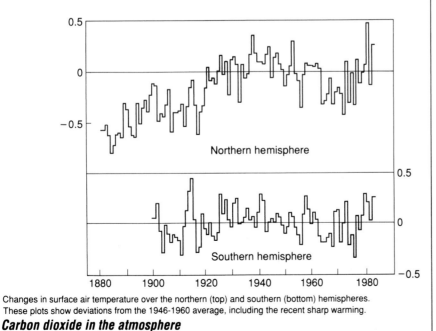

Changes in surface air temperature over the northern (top) and southern (bottom) hemispheres. These plots show deviations from the 1946-1960 average, including the recent sharp warming.

Carbon dioxide in the atmosphere

12.17

Greenhouse effect powers hurricanes, say scientists

Hurricane Hugo is a harbinger of the intense storms that can be expected more often in the future as a result of the greenhouse effect and global warming, say American researchers.

Higher ocean and air temperatures will feed extra energy into the hurricanes, increasing their wind speeds by up to 25 per cent, according to computer models.

'We can say with some confidence that the frequency of category four and category five hurricanes (the most severe) will increase, but we can't say by how much,' said Mr Richard Anthes, a meteorologist who heads the university consortium that operates the National Centre for Atmospheric Research in Boulder, Colorado.

The most intense hurricane ever observed over the Atlantic Ocean occurred last September: Hurricane Gilbert, with its wind speeds of more than 200 mph. But neither Gilbert nor Hugo can be definitely linked to global warming.

Mr Jay Hobgood, an Ohio atmospheric scientist whose models are used to project hurricane strenghts, said: 'It's difficult to take something as complex as a hurricane and attribute changes to a single cause like warmer temperatures, simply because the atmosphere is such a complex mixture and there are so many physical processes going on.'

The link to global warming occurs because heat is the engine that drives hurricanes. Strong sunlight heats both air and water near the equator, causing a greater evaporation of moisture from the ocean. The warm, moist air expands and rises, creating a ring of storms around the equator.

As the moist air rises, it cools, causing its moisture to condense into clouds. But that condensation releases a huge amount of heat stored in the gaseous water, accelerating the heating and rising of the air.

This condensation and heat release is the 'kicker' that starts vast amounts of air climbing upwards, drawing in ever larger quantities of moist air from the ocean surface.

Eventually, the earth's rotation causes the fast-moving air masses to spin an anti-clockwise direction in the northern hemisphere or clockwise in the southern.

Hurricanes typically take between five and six days to form, developing wind speeds that range from 75 mph (the official minimum) to more that 200 mph. The storms continue as long as they can draw warm moist air from the ocean. Hurricanes peter out when they pass over cold water or land.

Climatologists predict global warming – caused by the accumulation of carbon dioxide and other gases which trap the earth's heat like a greenhouse – will cause ocean and air temperatures to increase. A warmer ocean causes more water to evaporate and warmer air can hold more water vapour. Both factors would increase the strength of hurricanes.

(Source: Thomas Maugh, *The Guardian*, 21 September 1989)

---

place stress on the ecosystem and individuals in it. The most direct effect is physiological. 'Warm-blooded' animals control their body temperatures and have mechanisms to cool themselves, such as panting and sweating. 'Cold-blooded' animals can control their temperature by changing their behaviour, by sheltering in the shade or moving about only in the cooler parts of the day. But even with behavioural adjustments there are limits.

Adult animals and mature plants are much hardier than the younger stages. If the young do not survive, the population will not replace its older generation as it dies.

Moreover, stress, such as too hot a temperature or a lack of water, often interferes with reproduction. Some plants will not flower or set seed if it is too hot and dry; some will not flower if it is too wet – both conditions that will occur in some places as the greenhouse effect takes hold. Many animals do not breed at all if their offspring are likely to be born into a hostile world.

Effects on migrations

Migratory species may be some of the first to disappear. Although designed to travel long distances to find the conditions they need at particular times of the year, they time their journeys to fit in with food supplies along the route. In the US, shorebirds such as sanderling and plovers spend the winter in South America and travel north to breed in the Arctic in summer. They must arrive in the north and hatch their young just as the arctic insects undergo their summer population explosion, providing the young with ample food. The adults must also feed on the journey, however, and every year they stop in Delaware Bay to eat the eggs of horseshoe crabs. The crabs arrive and lay their eggs at the same time each year. If these events get out of phase, the effects on the migrants would be catastrophic.

Effects of timing changes

The loss of synchrony might be one of the more important aspects of the changing climate and how it affects the ecosystem. Another example is the timing of ice melt each year, an event that has important implications for both aquatic and terrestrial organisms. Normally, snow and ice melt over a period of several weeks. The acidic meltwater drains through the soil, which neutralises it before it runs off into lakes and rivers. In a warmer climate the melt would be earlier and faster; the meltwater would run over the soil and into the rivers, introducing a pulse of acid water, at a time when many animals are at their most vulnerable stage – eggs or fish fry, for example. Mortality of many species would be much heavier. Another effect of an early melt is that less water is available in the following months, and with a warmer summer, water is likely to be short. More seedlings will die. The pools and shallow lakes of the taiga and tundra – home to large populations of waterbirds – will become seasonal.

Changes in vegetation zones

Although the individual species will respond in many different ways, we will begin to see some broad trends. Most evident will be the changes in the belts of vegetation that encircle the world. The most dramatic changes will be in the northern hemisphere, where the greatest mass of land and most continuous belts of vegetation are. Moreover, if the arctic ice melts, the climatic equator will shift north, pushing the vegetation belts towards the North Pole.

Tropical forests will show little overall change. The temperature will rise only a little, perhaps 1°C. To either side of the equatorial belt, most types of vegetation will begin to move towards the poles. As mixed deciduous forests move north they will squeeze the northern boreal forests up into the far north, in turn squeezing the tundra into remote refuges in the high Arctic. According to Ian Woodward, of the University of Cambridge, this trend has already begun. In the past 100 years, the average summer temperature in North America has increased by about 2°C. Deciduous species of trees have become more prominent in both mixed forests and in boreal forests. The spread of the boreal forest into the tundra will be faster, he suggests, and he predicts that the tundra will shrink visibly in the next decade.

In some regions the vegetation will move uphill as well as shifting north and south. As a general rule, moving up 500 metres is equivalent climatically to moving 250 kilometres north. But as the treeline moves upwards, the new forests will drive alpine vegetation and its associated fauna to the highest altitudes, perhaps displacing it altogether.

Effects in cold environments

Biological diversity varies hugely in the different 'life zones' of the world. Tropical forests are the richest in species yet the loss of fewer species in other zones may have greater consequences. The Arctic Ocean is more vital to the functioning of the biosphere than a count of species would suggest. It is also the region that will suffer most and soonest.

Vera Alexander, director of the Institute of Marine Science at the University of Alaska, Fairbanks, suggests that if the calculations of the climatologists are right, many of the most familiar animals of the Arctic – such as polar bears and walruses – will disappear. The Arctic Ocean would become less productive and, more significantly, the changes in the Arctic would have repercussions through all the oceans. Changes in the cold waters of the Arctic will alter the pattern of circulation in the world ocean, disrupting currents, food supplies for species that make up some of the world's richest fisheries, and the climate of other parts of the world (resource 12.19).

Areas covered by sea ice might be exposed to the greatest increase in temperatures – and more in winter than in summer. If the ice melts in summer, winter temperatures might not be low enough for it to refreeze. An increase of 5°C in the next 50 years will melt even the permanent Arctic ice. The loss of ice would also speed up the warming of the ocean because it would reduce the albedo – the reflectance – of the water, which would absorb more heat.

Seasonal sea ice is a vital part of the Arctic ecosystem. The algae that grow on its underside form the base of the food chain that ultimately supports vast numbers of seabirds, fish and seals. The ice also serves as a platform from which seals search for food and on which they breed. The spotted seal breeds only at the edge of the ice. Harp seals, ringed seals, ribbon and bearded seals all live in association with the ice.

The first signs of a biological response to global warming in the Arctic might be an invasion of more southerly species. True Arctic species will be pushed farther north, but there is a limit to how far they can go.

As the sea ice disappears from the north coast of Alaska, Arctic species will retreat to strongholds in the Canadian high Arctic and Svalbard. If warming continues, however, these refuges may also disappear.

To the south of the Arctic Ocean, the great expanses of tundra will shrink, almost to nothing according to some ecologists, pushed to the edge of the ocean by advancing boreal forests. The tundra is both at risk and a risk. Below the top few centimetres of vegetation lies an enormous depth of permanently frozen peat – a vast store of organic material. If the ice melts, the peat will begin to decompose and release enormous quantities of carbon to the atmosphere, enhancing the greenhouse effect. About 14 per cent of the Earth's organic carbon is tied up in the frozen peat beneath the tundra. If the ice melts, the structure of the tundra will also begin to break up, with severe erosion and collapse of the soil.

What happens to the permafrost depends largely on what happens to the layer of vegetation – mosses, sedges, grasses and small hardy shrubs – that blankets it. This layer protects the frozen ground in the short, hot Arctic summer, preventing it from melting.

Effects upon temperate forests

The great forested zones of North America and Eurasia will change much more slowly. Trees generally live a long time and most will stick out deteriorating conditions at the southern boundaries of their ranges for several decades. These old surviving forests will differ from

today's in one vital element: they will not be renewing themselves. In the new climate, seeds might not germinate or seedlings might fail to establish themselves. Eventually, the old trees will succumb to storms, forest fires or pests – and there will be no young ones to take their place. We may see signs of such changes in 20 to 60 years, depending on the types of trees.

The survival of the species of trees that make up the forests depends on how well they disperse their seeds. A tree that drops its seeds to the forest floor to lie dormant until a gap appears in the forest canopy will probably not be able to track the moving climate. Trees with light, windblown seeds or seeds carried by animals stand a better chance of covering the necessary distances.

Effects in the tropics

In the tropics, the change in the pattern of rainfall will have more effect than the rise in temperature. The lack of a dry season, or a dry season that is longer than usual, can produce strong responses in plants and animals. In the forest of La Selva in Costa Rica, there is usually no dry season. After a few weeks without rain, young seedlings begin to wilt and die. On the island of Barro Colorado, in the Panama Canal, however, several important fruit trees flower only if there is a dry season. In 1970, when there was no dry season, fruit-eating animals went hungry.

Like tropical forests, tropical waters are rich in species. Although the change in temperature in the tropics

12.18

Winners and losers – carbon dioxide as a fertiliser

Carbon dioxide is one of the raw materials of photosynthesis, the process by which green plants convert carbon dioxide, water and mineral nutrients into organic compounds using the energy from sunlight. However, many plants, including most of those grown as crops in temperate regions, waste between a quarter and half of the carbon they fix in a process called photo-respiration. The loss increases at higher temperatures.

Some scientists point out that an increase in the concentration of carbon dioxide in the atmosphere will increase the efficiency of photosynthesis in these plants, and improve the yields of crops in warmer parts of the world. Experiments in glasshouses show that extra carbon dioxide has a fertilising effect. Indeed, commercial growers of indoor crops, such as tomatoes, cucumbers and lettuces, have added carbon dioxide to the

atmosphere of their glasshouses for many years, with good effect.

Researchers at the Institute of Horticultural Research at Littlehampton, in Sussex, found that trebling the atmospheric concentration of carbon dioxide can increase the rate of photosynthesis of a tomato leaf by 50 per cent. Researchers in the US have experimented with many crop plants in a 'phytotron', a chamber for growing plants in controlled conditions. Increasing the concentration of carbon dioxide to 1000 parts per million produced higher yielding wheat, bigger sugar beets – and radishes that were big enough to eat in half the usual time. What happens in a greenhouse, however, will not necesarily happen in the field.

However, plants fertilised with carbon dioxide might be bigger and grow faster, but they are less nutritious. Caterpillars that eat plants grown under these conditions have

to eat more to achieve their normal rate of growth. If this is a general effect, pests will become a bigger threat to crops.

Another factor that offsets the advantages of the fertilising effect is that a higher concentration of carbon dioxide in the atmosphere interferes with the process of transpiration. In normal circumstances, a plant loses water as it takes in carbon dioxide through the pores, or stomata, in its leaves. The more open the stomata, the more water is lost. Many trees now have fewer stomata than they did when the concentration of carbon dioxide was lower. This is a response to the increasing concentration of carbon dioxide. In addition, when the concentration of carbon dioxide is high, the stomata partially close – so reducing the loss of water. In the presence of so much carbon dioxide, the rate of photosynthesis will not suffer but the plants become more efficient in their use of water.

(Source: *New Scientist*, 12 November 1988, page 39)

12.19

Salmon fishing fleet, Cordova, Alaska. Will they have a future as planet earth warms?

will be small, other factors will disturb the equilibrium of the ecosystem. Coral reefs grow only in warm tropical and subtropical waters. Two-thirds of the species of fish in these waters live around reefs. The reefs are threatened more by the rise in sea level than the change in temperature. Corals grow actively only near the surface of the water and most do not grow fast enough to keep up with the rising waters. Antler corals do grow quickly, but break easily in storms. Storms are likely to worsen in the area where coral reefs are.

Key issue

The question for both conservationists and politicians is: is the world bound to become a different place? Even if governments take steps to prevent global warming, some change is still probably inevitable. According to Michael Soule, president of the Soviet for Conservation Biology, a rise of 2°C is inevitable in the next 30 to 50 years, so conservationists must plan their strategy now. Plans to preserve wildlife and whole ecosystems will have to be on a

totally different scale to anything done before.

(Source: adapted from Stephanie Pain, 'No escape from the global greenhouse', *New Scientist*, 12 November 1988)

Activities

1   Produce a set of labelled maps illustrating the shifts in distribution of climatic zones and ecosystems projected in the case study. Include a map indicating implications for human occupance in the different zones.

2   Select one of the environments and detail the knock-on effect through the system of climatic change (Note: begin with the climatic change itself).

3   List the major uncertainties in the projections.

4   The build-up of atmospheric carbon dioxide depends upon firstly the sources of the gas and the rate of release from each source, and secondly the sinks,

other than the atmosphere, into which carbon dioxide can be absorbed (stored). **In a group** identify these sources and sinks. Allocate them among group members and carry out a search to find out for each:

a the main characteristics, and

b ways in which humans can influence the release in the case of a source and the absorption in the case of a sink.

Pool your findings and produce a brief report, wall display or computer information/data file reviewing the issue.

5   This case study has not explored the issue of 'ozone holes' in the atmosphere. There is no doubt that human activities are influencing the character of the ozone layer and that such changes will affect the functioning of global systems. Research this topic and suggest how it relates to the greenhouse effect, and what are the implications of this relationship: will it dampen down or accentuate global warming?

CASE STUDY 12.3 *Options for conservation*

Background

As humans extend their occupance and influence at increasing density and level of impact, the question of conserving ecosystems and species – including more vulnerable groups of homo sapiens – becomes ever more urgent. This is especially so if we accept the environmental changes envisaged in the preceding case study. The article which formed the basis of that case study concluded that 'plans to preserve wildlife and whole ecosystems will have to be on a totally different scale to anything done before. The traditional way ... is to create a reserve, but reserves are 'man-locked' refuges – islands trapped in a sea of artificial landscape. Reserves will not help in a changing climate, so the species in the reserve will have to move out to find the conditions they need. Outside its borders, the migrating species will face a hostile landscape.'

Despite this somewhat pessimistic scenario, the most common conservation strategy throughout the world is the designation and management of protected reserves. Simply drawing a line round an area and giving conservation values priority may not be enough. For example, the area may not be fully representative of the valued environment, e.g. some rainforest reserves contain mainly secondary growth; it may not be large enough for species to survive and regenerate, e.g. a single family group of mountain gorillas needs a territory of up to 350 square kilometres; it may be hemmed in by settled areas and inadequately managed and 'policed', e.g. elephant poaching in the East African game parks. Nevertheless, parks and reserves now have a lengthening history, and experience is allowing more sensitive strategies to be applied.

This case study illustrates three such promising strategies. Firstly, the United Nations Environmental Programme (UNEP) as part of the World Conservation Strategy, has launched its World Biosphere Reserve project, whose goal is to encourage the establishment of large scale reserves in all major world biomes. Such reserves are to be organised on the zoning principle; that is an identified core area will be given improved protection by a surrounding buffer or transition zone. Secondly, local communities will become involved in the establishment and running of conservation areas. The aim of this is to combine development and conservation. Thirdly, 'conservation corridors' will be established to link remnants of ecosystems and different ecosystems. This should help to sustain genetic diversity and allow movement between reserves, thereby improving chances of survival as environmental conditions fluctuate.

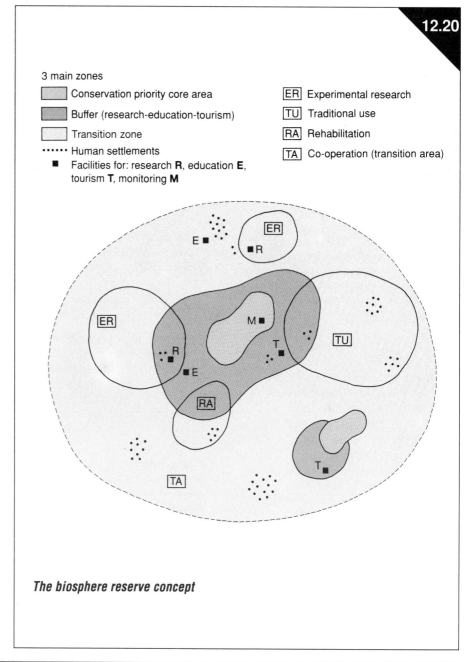

12.20

3 main zones

▨ Conservation priority core area
▨ Buffer (research-education-tourism)
☐ Transition zone
····· Human settlements
■ Facilities for: research **R**, education **E**, tourism **T**, monitoring **M**

ER Experimental research
TU Traditional use
RA Rehabilitation
TA Co-operation (transition area)

The biosphere reserve concept

Part I: The Biosphere Reserve concept

The UNEP has identified 14 major world biomes and is in discussion with individual governments with the aim of achieving biosphere reserves in all of these biomes. Individual reserves will vary according to the interaction of a complex set of political, economic, social, geographic and ecological variables. Yet the principle is straightforward (resource 12.20 on page 242):

1 Identify an extensive area in which a valued environmental system remains intact or in a restorable condition;

2 Persuade a government or neighbouring governments to give protected status;

3 Establish a management policy based upon a set of zones, at the heart of which is a core where conservation values are given highest priority. This precious core is protected by a buffer zone in which controlled access and development are permitted. As distance from the core increases, so development values are given increasing priority.

Part II: Power to the people – the Annapurna Conservation Area Project, Nepal

Extensive deforestation of the steep Himalayan slopes in Nepal has caused accelerated runoff and erosion. The effects are being felt well beyond the Nepalese border as the flood surges and sediment load move down the Ganges and become contributory factors in the recurrent disastrous Bangladesh floods of the Ganges delta. Since the 1970s the Nepalese government has reacted by the encouragement of community reforestation schemes, where the local people make the decisions and run the projects.

From such schemes has emerged the ambitious Annapurna Conservation Area Project (ACAP) (see resource 2.21). This has four distinctive qualities:

1 Large scale (1000 square miles) and large population involved (40 000 people).

2 It is managed by the local communities and assisted by the King Mahendra Trust, in the belief that conservation will only work if it involves and benefits local people.

3 It is organised on the zoning principle: In 1985, a director of the World Wildlife Fund and the director of Nepal's King Mahendra Trust for Nature Conservation 'sat down with a map of Nepal ... and drew a circle around the Annapurna Range. This was to be the approximate boundary of the Annapurna park. Then they drew a smaller circle within the first one. Within a year this 310 square mile area was established as the core of the Annapurna project, including the villages of Ghandruk and Chomrong and the area called the Sanctuary'.

The Special Management Zone (resource 12.21 overleaf) contains the main trail into the Sanctuary, a bowl of undulating meadows with panoramic views to the great mountain peaks. It is the focus of trekking tourist activity and is especially vulnerable to tourist pressure and deforestation, hence the need for sensitive management. In 1977, for example, there were only two teahouse-lodges along the trail beyond the village of Chomrong, but by 1987 there were 24.

4 Part of its funding comes direct from the booming tourist trade. Each tourist entering the ACAP is charged a fee of 200 rupees (approx. $8US) and this money goes direct to the local communities operating the project. In 1988 more than 25 000 trekkers entered this magnificent mountain area. The rest of the finance comes from the World Wildlife Fund and other private donors, until the park and the people eventually become self-supporting.

Resource 12.20 sums up the ambitious plan and the well-developed zoning system which provides the framework in which the local people are to work out their policies. ACAP is a broadly based scheme involving much education and training for the local people. As the chairman of Chomrong's village council says: 'We now have nurseries to grow wood for fuel and a kerosene depot so that we can prohibit the use of firewood in and around the Sanctuary. ACAP is helping us train guards, repair and clean trails, build latrines, and use electricity, not wood, for cooking and lighting wherever possible.'[2]

Part III: The potential of conservation corridors

Even in countries as vast as the USA and Australia, heightened environmental consciousness is revealing how little of 'the wilderness' remains. There are, of course, large stretches of this wilderness already under protected status, such as Denali, N.P., Alaska;

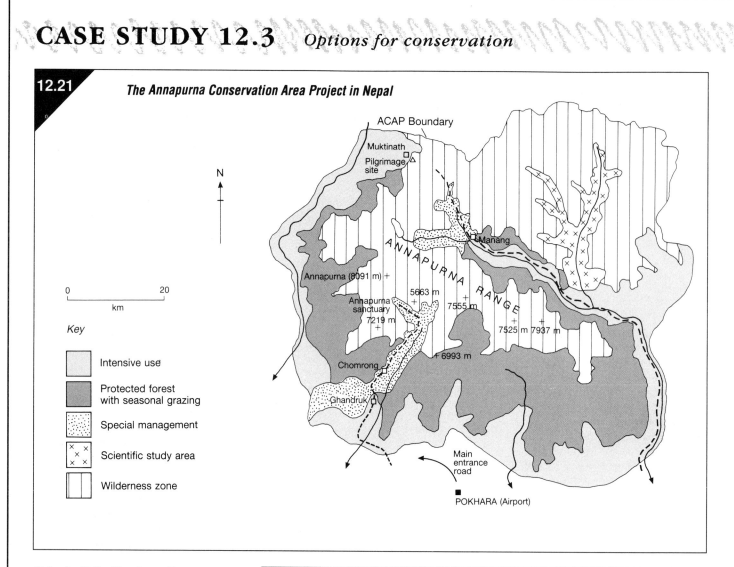

12.21

The Annapurna Conservation Area Project in Nepal

N

0 ___ 20
km

Key

Intensive use

Protected forest with seasonal grazing

Special management

Scientific study area

Wilderness zone

ACAP Boundary

Muktinath

Pilgrimage site

Manang

Annapurna (8091 m) +

5663 m +

+ 7555 m

Annapurna sanctuary 7219 m +

+ 7525 m + 7937 m

+ 6993 m

Chomrong

Ghandruk

Main entrance road

POKHARA (Airport)

Kakadu N.P., Northern Territory, Australia. However, equally precious and certainly more accessible remnants are found within settled and developed areas. The problem is their fragmentation and the key to their survival may be to link them together. In the USA a network of 'greenways' is being introduced, while the Australian version is the 'conservation corridor'.

This case study sets out the potential of such corridors by analysis of the wheat belt of Western Australia (resource 12.22). This area of 140 000 square kilometres was originally covered by a mosaic of eucalypt woodland and heath, and has been largely cleared since 1830.

The wheatbelt of Western Australia provides a good illustration of the changes that follow development. An examination of the history of land

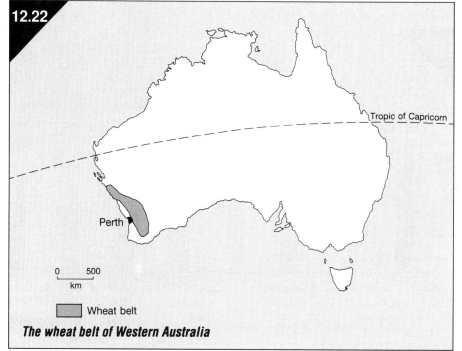

12.22

Tropic of Capricorn

Perth

0 ___ 500
km

Wheat belt

The wheat belt of Western Australia

clearance and the effects it has had on the plants and animals of the region highlights several conservation issues – in particular, how to manage what remains of the native vegetation. All over the region are patches – remnants –of native vegetation. Some are isolated but others are linked by narrow strips, or corridors, of native vegetation along roads and rivers.

One of the most important questions in conservation is whether these remnants and corridors function as a continuous network of habitat or whether they are merely islands in a sea of farmland. A network might sustain more species than a disjointed series of pocket handkerchief reserves. Where patches are connected, animals can move from one to another. In effect, the corridors extend the area of suitable habitat. Free movement of animals results in a greater exchange of genes across the region and so lessens the chances of extinction. But if animals happen by a series of chance misfortunes to become extinct in one part of their range, others of their kind can recolonise the area by travelling along the connecting corridors. Only now are ecologists beginning to gather evidence to suggest that corridors do have the desired effect.

Habitat loss

During the rush of development, neither government nor settlers gave much thought to conservation. Some patches of native vegetation survived, however, set aside by the government not as reserves for conservation but for water catchment, town sites, camping areas or roads. During the 1960s and 1970s, the government designated many of these patches as conservation reserves, and now there are 639 such reserves scattered through the wheatbelt. This rearguard attempt at conservation has provided a large number of mostly very small reserves, many of which are of little value in terms of conservation. At present these

reserves account for 6.7 per cent of the wheatbelt, but most of the land is in three large reserves. If these are not included, only 2.4 per cent of the wheatbelt is given over to conservation. Moreover, these reserves are not representative of the original vegetation of the region because settlers were very selective about the land they cleared. Early settlers chose woodland areas because they thought that woodland was an indicator of soils with good potential for agriculture. The result is that woodland is poorly represented in the reserves. Before clearance woodlands covered more than 41 000 square kilometres but only a little over 1000 square kilometres now remains.

The extensive clearance of native vegetation has also left thousands of privately owned remnants scattered across the wheatbelt. These remnants, like those designated as reserves, are of various shapes and sizes and are isolated to different degrees. These privately owned remnants, together with those owned by the state, now constitute the natural heritage of the region. Species of animals that depend on native vegetation for their survival must be conserved in this scattered collection of remnants. There is nowhere else for them to go.

Forty-six species of native mammal lived in the wheatbelt before European settlers arrived. Thirteen of these species have disappeared from the region and nine of those thirteen are extinct on the Australian mainland. Fewer than half of the species are regarded as common in the wheatbelt now. That habitat destruction is the main cause of this decline is shown by a comparison with the mammal fauna of Tasmania, which still has large areas of native vegetation. Thirty of the 34 species of terrestrial mammals present in Tasmania at the time when Europeans settled there are still common.

Once an area is isolated, the rate of extinction of the animal species within it depends on the size of the

remnant, the variety of plants growing in it, how isolated it is and what lived in it before it was cut off. Survival also depends on the changes imposed on the remnant – not all uncleared areas are untouched – and the lifespans of the surviving species.

Several of the most important species of trees are present in remnants only as mature individuals, with no regeneration or young individuals. Without replanting and efforts to encourage regeneration, such as excluding stock and controlling weeds, trees could disappear altogether in the next century.

Danger from introduced species

While native species have disappeared, other species have moved into the area. Settlers introduced exotic vegetation both deliberately for agriculture and accidentally as weeds. The invasion of weeds into remnants of native vegetation is a problem particularly with some types of woodland. The change from woodlands to an open plain of annual grasses and cereals and provision of watering points for stock created an attractive habitat for species such as the galah. This pink-and-grey cockatoo has become one of the most abundant and widespread species in the wheatbelt. Galahs nest in holes in trees, so competing with other hole nesters, such as Carnaby's cockatoo. Galahs also damage the trees by stripping bark from the trunks, in some cases ringbarking the tree, and they eat cereal crops. In some areas galahs are a significant cause of tree death, which is a serious problem in an area where the native woodlands are not regenerating themselves.

Diversity and carrying capacity

One aim of conservation is to preserve representative populations of those species that lived in the area before development. To maintain the original diversity of species, management must be at several levels – from the individual patches of native vegetation to the district and regional levels. It is essential to maintain viable populations of species at several places to ensure against extinction if disaster wipes out the population in one particular reserve.

Analysis of the changes in the abundance and distribution of species of the wheatbelt shows that the remaining reserves can probably maintain only a limited proportion of the original fauna. Indeed, the management of remnant vegetation for conservation poses enormous problems. Scientists at the CSIRO Division of Wildlife and Ecology in Western Australia are studying the role of these remnants in conservation. In particular, we need to know how the flora and fauna have reacted to the fragmentation of the landscape and how they respond to natural factors, such as droughts, and human-induced effects, such as patterns of burning and grazing. As well as trying to understand how to conserve existing remnant areas we also need to find ways to restore native vegetation in cleared or damaged areas.

The Western Australian Department of Conservation and Land Management is responsible for managing the reserves in the wheatbelt. Like most conservation agencies in the world, it has limited resources. In addition, there are the

thousands of privately owned remnants to take into account. Plants and animals do not discriminate on the basis of ownership and if conservation is to have a chance of success, management cannot stop at legal boundaries. This is also true because of the interdependence between remnants of native vegetation and the surrounding farmland.

Community conservation

Ideally, conservation should be a community responsibility with the conservation agency acting as a consultant. In a country like Australia, with large areas to manage and a small, sparsely distributed population, it is particularly important to involve the community in management. Without their help conservation will fail.

Local communities can help in preparing the inventory of their local reserves and remnants and then to monitor and manage them. Progress is already being made with large programmes of tree planting, initiated by organisations such as Greening Australia. Farmers are also taking action by forming local soil conservation groups and by recognising the aesthetic and economic value of retaining native vegetation on their farms.

(Source: adapted from 'Corridors for Conservation', by D Saunders and R Hobbs, *New Scientist*, 28 January 1989, pp.63–68.)

Activities

1 Group discussion

a For the three conservation strategies of this case study, make two lists:

(i) The characteristics of the strategies which improve the chances and quality of environmental conservation;

(ii) The problems which are likely to occur in the setting up and operating of the strategies.

Note: The strategies may be applied together in a single project.

b Suggest ways in which the problems can be overcome.

2 Suggestion for coursework

Find information on an area which has certain environmental and conservation problems or where policies are already operating. Produce an assessment for your area in the framework of the strategies outlined in this case study. You might ask questions such as: could the environmental problem be solved by these strategies?; do existing policies include these strategies?

Final food for thought
If humans are, indeed, 'stewards of planet earth,' then should we not make sure that creatures such as these **always** have a place that is 'theirs' and not 'ours'?

12.23

Caribou at home, Denali National Park, Alaska

Index

Acknowledgements

Photographs

The publishers are grateful to the following for permission to reproduce the following photographs:

Colorific/Heikki Sarviaho: p.19, p.159, /ESA: p.160
Cunard: p.105;
Harris Corporation: p.162;
Chris Johns/*The Seattle Times* (*The Guardian*): p.14;
Leader Photos/Nigel Dickinson: p. 211;
Les Morris: p. 41;
NOAA: p.163;
Oxford Scientific Films/James M Robinson: p.13; Richard Packwood: p. 21;
Max Pemberton: p. 29;
George Peterken: p. 206;
Robert Prosser: p. 8, p. 21, p. 22, p. 27, p. 56, p. 58, p. 64, p. 83, p. 91, p. 92, p. 93 p.96, p. 112, p. 123, , p.126, p.131, p.137, p.139, p.142, p.151, p.175, p.190, p.191, p.197, p. 201, p. 204, p. 215, p. 220, p. 225, p. 226, p. 227, p. 241, p. 246;
Science Photo Library/David Parker: p. 16; Dr Fred Espenak: p.163;
R J Small: p.121;
Swift Picture Library/Mike Read: p. 110;
University of Dundee: p.198;
USSR Photo Library: p. 154.

Artwork and tables

The following resources are based on material taken from the following sources:

Chapter 1

1.1: *The Sunday Times*, 8 May 1983;
1.14: *Bulletin of Volcanic Eruptions*, December 1984;
1.3: *Bulletin of Volcanic Eruptions*, Nos. 20 and 21, 1982;
1.4: *Earthquake Information Bulletin*, 12 (4), July–Aug 1980;
1.14: *Bulletin of Volcanic Eruptions*, December 1984;
1.17: C R Allen, *Conference on the Geologic Problems of the San Andreas Fault System*, Stanford University, 1968;
1.18: US Geological Survey, *Earthquake Information Bulletin*, Vol 6, No 5, 1974;
1.19: *The Guardian*, 9 December 1988;
1.21: *Geographical Magazine*, March 1989.

Chapter 2

2.9: adapted from A J Gerrard, *Rocks and Landforms*, Unwin Hyman 1988;
2.14, 2.15, 2.17: Clayton, 1966;
2.16: M Pemberton, 'Shakeholes: a morphometric field project for sixth-form geographers', *Geography*, 65 (3), 1980;
2.20: G E Wilford and J R D Wall, *Journal of Tropical Geography*, Vol 21, 1965;
2.23: R H Kesel, Slope runuff and denudation in the Rupununi savanna, Guyana, *Journal of Tropical Geography*, 44, June 1977;
2.24, 2.26: B H Adlam, A J Gerrard, L Morris, 'Accelerated erosion near Aix-en-Provence, Southern France, *University of Birmingham Department of Geography*, Working Paper 25, 1983;
2.27, 2.28: L Morris and A J Gerrard, 'Mass movement forms and processes on Bredon Hill', *University of Birmingham Department of Geography*, 1974;
2.29, 2.31: B D Fahy and T H Lefebre, 'The freeze-thaw weathering regime at a section of the Niagara escarpment on the Bruce Peninsula, Canada', *Earth Surface Processes and Landforms*, 13 (4), June 1988.

Chapter 3

3.1: Chorley, Schumm and Sugden, *Geomorphology*, Methuen, 1985;
3.5, 3.10: *CCSTWS Annual Report*, 1987;
3.6: *CCSTWS Quarterly Bulletin*, 1988
3.11: *New Scientist*, 15 January 1987
3.12: G Brook et al, *Exercises in Physical Geography*, Contemporary Publishing Co, 1988
3.13: P J Godfrey in R H Platt (ed), *Cities on the Beach*, University of Chicago Research Paper, No 224, 1987;
3.16, 3.18: *Scientific American*, 257 (1), 1987;
3.17: R H Platt, 'Cities on the Beach', University of Chicago Research Paper, No 224, 1987;
3.22: R Kirby, 'Sedimentological implications of building the Cardiff-Weston barrage in the Severn Estuary', *Proceedings of the USSHER Society*, 7(1), 1988.

Chapter 4

4.2: Chorley, Schumm and Sugden, *Geomorphology*, Methuen, 1985;
4.5, 4.6, 4.7: J Rose, 'Contemporary river landforms and sediments an an area of equatorial rainforest, Gulong Mulu National Park, Sarawak, *Transactions of the Institute of British Geographers*, 9 (3), 1984;
4.29, 4.30, 4.31: A D Knighton, 'River adjustment to changes in sediment load: the effects of tin mining on the Ringarooma River, Tasmania, 1875–1984', *Earth Surface Processes and Landforms*, 14(4), June 1989
4.32: Lake Biwa Research Institute, Otsu, Japan;

4.33: G E Petts, 'Water management: the case of Lake Biwa, Japan', *Geographical Journal*, 154 (3), November 1988

Chapter 5

5.1: J Gribbin, 'The end of the ice ages', *New Scientist*, 17 June 1989
5.2: Chorley, Schumm and Sugden, *Geomorphology*, Methuen, 1985;
5.5: Skinner and Porter, *Physical Geology*, Wiley, 1987;
5.9, 5.11: M F Meier and E F Roots, 'Glaciers as a water resource', *Nature and Resources*, July–Sept 1982;
5.13, 5.14: F B Wood, 'Global Alpine Glacier Trends, 1960–1980, *Arctic and Alpine Research*, 20(4), 1988;
5.17, 5.18: L S Govorukha, 'The present state of ice cap islands in the Soviet Arctic', *Polar Geography and Geology*, 12(4), Oct–Dec 1988;
5.21, 5.22: A P. Voloshina, 'Some results of glacier mass balance research on the glaciers of the polar Urals', *Polar Geography and Geology*, 12, July–Sept 1988;
5.23: W K Hamblin, *The earth's dynamic systems*, Burgess, 1982;
5.39: R Muir Wood, 'Decay in the Karakorum', *New Scientist*, 26 March 1981.

Chapter 6

6.28: *New Scientist*, 18 February 1988
6.30: *Soviet Weekly*, 20 May 1989

Chapter 7

7.3: *The Guardian*, 1 September 1989;
7.5: *The Sunday Times*, 12 February 1989
7.6: *The Sunday Times*
7.7: *The Guardian*, 27 February 1990

Chapter 8

8.11: K U Sirinanda, *Journal of Tropical Geography*, 49, December 1979;
8.12: N Singh, 'On the duration of the rainy season over different parts of India', *Theoretical and Applied Climatology*, 37, 1986;
8.14, 8.15: I Subbaramayya et al, 'Variations in the onset of the summer monsoon over India, *Meteorological Magazine*, 116, 1987;
8.17: D B Frost, 'Diurnal precipitation patterns at Guatemala City, 1930–1969', *Singapore Journal of Tropical Geography*, 3(1), 1982;
8.18: S K Sharma, 'Diurnal variation of rainfall at Nandi Airport, Fiji', *Weather*, 38(8), 1983;
8.19: H Riehl, *Climate and weather in the tropics*, Academic Press, 1979;
8.20: *Tables of temperature, relative humidity and precipitation of the World Meterological Office*, HMSO, 1966, and Climatology Division of the Meteorological Department, Bangkok, 1980;
8.21: A Henderson-Sellers and P J Robinson, *Contemporary Climatology*, Longman 1986;
8.22: M Bonell and D A Gilmour, 'Variations in short-term rainfall intensity in relation to synoptic climatological aspects of the humid tropical N E Queensland coast', *Singapore Journal of Tropical Geography*, 1(2), December 1980;
8.24, 8.25: M Bonnell and D A Gilmour, 'Six minute rainfall data for an exceptionally heavy tropical rainstorm', *Weather*, 34(4), April 1979.

Chapter 9

9.1, 9.2: *The Guardian*, March 16, 1989
9.6, 9.7, 9.8: D G Tout, 'The variability of days of air frost in Great Britain 1957–83', *Weather*, 42(9), September 1987;
9.9: R M Murray, 'A quarter of a century of weather in the Isle of Skye', *Weather*, 41 (3), March 1986;
9.10, 9.11: G R Bigg, 'Micrometeorology of a moorland lake', *Weather*, 46(7), June 1988;
9.12, 9.13, 9.14: C M Haggett, 'Thunderstorms over North-west London – 8 May 1988', *Weather*, 43(7), July 1988.

Chapter 10

10.4, 10.5: E M Bridges, 'Glacial landscapes and soils in Southern Germany, *Swansea Geographer*, 11, 1973;
10.13: J Thornes, 'Solutions to soil erosion', *New Scientist*, 3 June 1989;

Chapter 11

11.5: K Reynolds and A Pearce, *Forestry*, 59 (1), 1986;
11.6: G F Peterken and E W Jones, 'Forty years of change in Lady Park Wood: the old growth stands', *Journal of Ecology*, 75, 1987;
11.12, 11.13, 11.14, 11.15, 11.17: 'Rainforest Research in North Queensland: a position paper', *Queensland Department of Forestry*, 1983;
11.20: *Disappearing Rainforests*, Batsford, 1987
11.22: J D C Onyemelukwe, 'Transformation of the Nigerian forest ecosystems: a statement of knowledge assessment of their socio-economic effects', *Geojournal*, 3(6), 1979;
11.21: H Y Manner and H Lang, 'A quantative analysis of the induced grasslands of the Bismarck Mountains', *Singapore Journal of Tropical Geography*, 2 (1), June 1981;
11.30: B M Sharma, 'Plant biomass in the semi-arid zone of India', *Journal of Arid Environments, 5, 1982*.

Chapter 12

12.15, 2.16: J Gribbin (ed), *The Breathing Planet*, Blackwell;
12.20: *Nature and Resources*, XXII (3), July–September, 1986.